Interior Landscape Design

DEDICATION

To my wife, Lora; my son, Daniel; and my daughter, Alison.

For the past two years, my ability to be a husband and father to them was compromised by my commitment to prepare this book. Without their patience and understanding, I could not have put forth the effort this project needed to complete it.

To the memory of Everett Conklin, one of the great pioneers of the interior landscape industry, who helped establish legitimacy to this field, and whose warmth, openness, and talent helped forge my interest in it.

Interior Landscape Design

by Nelson Hammer, ASLA

Design and Illustrations by Mel Green

Library of Congress Cataloging-in-Publication Data

Hammer, Nelson
Interior landscape design / Nelson Hammer: design and illustrations by Mel Green.
p. cm.
Includes index.
ISBN 0-07-025861-9
1. Interior Landscaping. 2. House plants in interior decoration.
1.Title.
SB419.25.H37 1991
747'.98—dc20 91-42888
CIP

First published in the United States of America
in 1991 by
McGraw-Hill Architectural & Scientific Publications, Inc.
11 West 19th Street, New York, NY 10011

1234567890 HAL/HAL 9765432

ISBN 0-07-025861-9

The editor of this book was Joel Stein. The design and illustrations were by Mel Green Graphic Design. This book was set in ITC Berkeley Old Style and Frutiger. It was created electronically by Mel Green Design using Aldus Pagemaker 4.01 and Adobe Illustrator 3.01 on the Apple® Macintosh.™

Printed and bound by Arcata Graphics / Halliday.

TABLE OF CONTENTS

ACKNOWLEDGMENTS

A great number of people and companies assisted me in the production of this book by providing information, photographs, illustrations, advice, or moral support. I would like to thank the following for their specific contributions to Interior Landscape Design:

Neil Berman, MD, my friend and neighbor, whose knowledge of computers and his eagerness to share that knowledge with me helped me to maximize the use of my computer system and make the task of producing this book that much easier; another friend and neighbor, Ron Raphael, and his son Brian, for the use of their computer system to do things my computer couldn't; Walter Rosenfeld, CSI, for his help in preparing the chapter on specifications, and more importantly, for helping to show me how to go about getting a book published, and Fred Briese of Rentokil Tropical Plants, for his assistance in reviewing and refining the Master Interior Plant List, Appendix C.

John Cuoco and Anne Robinson of Omni-Lite, and Christos Mpelkas, formerly of GTE Sylvania, for reviewing material on plant growth lighting; the Associated Landscape Contractors of America, particularly Executive Director Debra Dennis, for the use of a number of slides of award-winning projects and for their support in general; Mary Beth Hennigan of The Carrier Corporation, for information on the history of air-conditioning; Wrenda Goodwyn of the Grand Cypress Resort, Inc.; Polly McCarthy of Westin Hotels & Resorts; Robert Shay of GTE Sylvania; General Electric, Inc.; Bruce Keller of Kalwall/Structures Unlimited; Chuck Whiting of Opryland, USA; Troy Moss and Stanley Kozak of the Isabella Stewart Gardner Museum; Colvin Randall of Longwood Gardens, Inc.; Peter Cummin, ASLA, John Haederle, ASLA, and Wally Palladino of the Charrette Corporation, for information on reprographic techniques and terminology.

I wish to also thank the following professionals and companies in the design and interior landscape construction community:

Landscape Architectural Firms: Dan Kiley of the Office of Dan Kiley; Edward Durrell Stone, Jr., ASLA, Gary Derck, ASLA and John Miller, ASLA of Edward Durrell Stone, Jr., and Associates, Inc.; Peter Wells, ASLA of the Berkshire Design Group; Alfonso Muray of Muray Arquitectos; and M. Paul Friedberg, ASLA, Rick Parisi, ASLA and Klio Miniotakis of M. Paul Friedberg & Partners.

Architectural Firms: Earl R. Flansburgh, FAIA and the staff of Earl R. Flansburgh + Associates, Inc.; Mark Zarrillo of The Architects Collaborative, Inc.; and Alice Stevens of John Portman & Associates.

Interior Landscape Contractors: McRae Anderson of McCaren Designs, Inc.; Michael Baron and Elizabeth Hess of Interior Landscapes International Corporation; Gary Mangum of Creative Plantings, Inc.; Roger Cheever and Meg Conant of City Gardens; Bruce Crowle of Decora, Inc.; Barbara Mank and Jill McIntyre of Greenspace, Inc.; John Mini and Richard Butchko of John Mini Indoor Landscapes, Inc.; Tim Morris of Interior Plant Specialists, Inc.; Richard Ott of Botany Center; Linda Schmude-Lewis of the Plantworks, Inc.; Gerry Leider, Terry Anderson, Steve Swihart, and Bob Specht of Rentokil Tropical Plants, Inc.; Tata White of mr. greenjeans; and Lydia Paneri of Associated Plantscapers, Inc.

A special thanks to Leonard Kersch of Garden Milieu, Inc., for the use of his previously published material on plant growth lighting and his assistance in preparing computer simulations of daylighting.

For assistance in the preparation of information on irrigation, I would like to thank Rain Bird International; Ken Brock of The Toro Company; Jim Wearin of Wade Rain, the Micro-Irrigation Division of Wade Mfg. Co.; Richard Lakutis; Larry Kellem; and Stuart Snyder of Aqua Trends, Inc. for permission to reprint information on Aqua Trends' Precision Micro-Irrigation System.

Nurserymen: Dave Fell of Kraft Gardens; Jerry Soowal of East Marsh Nurseries; and Joe and Phil Cialone of Tropical Ornamentals.

Suppliers: Nature Preserved of America; Barbara Helfman of Topsiders; Architectural Supplements, and the M.H. Stallman Company, Inc..

Finally, I would like to thank Mel Green of Mel Green Graphic Design, my partner in the production of this book, who put forth a Promethean effort to create all the illustrations and a high quality book design within strict time limitations.

PREFACE

Just about anyone who is employed can recall a person, event, or experience which ultimately resulted in their decision to enter their "chosen profession". I have my own story, which is unique, convoluted, and frankly, boring. The impetus for my becoming a landscape architect is not relevant to this discussion, but the foundation of my interest in interior landscape design is both pertinent and illuminating.

While working at the Office of Dan Kiley in 1969 in my first job out of college, I learned of one of the firm's more publicized built projects, the garden of the Ford Foundation Building on 42nd Street in New York City. Other than the fact that it was an indoor garden, I was completely unfamiliar with its design.

While visiting the Big Apple in March 1970, my curiosity got the better of me, and I took the opportunity to visit and photograph the garden. I learned that it is generally considered to be the first large-scale, permanent, commercial use of plants indoors in the United States (that is, a space for human occupation into which plants are introduced, as opposed to a space for botanical or horticultural use such as a conservatory or botanical garden). For me, however, it was much more than just an indoor garden; the quiet beauty of the atrium struck me as a delightful and incredibly serene environment amid the bustle and dirty slush of a late winter's day in New York. My academic training as a landscape architect had not prepared me for a professional assessment as to why the garden "worked". The plant materials were largely unfamiliar to me, since my college horticulture courses and professional experience thereafter had dealt exclusively with northern temperate specimens. I was oblivious to the problems entailed in trying to keep the plants of this space irrigated and free from insects, disease, and dust; of growing plants in a root-constricted environment; and of getting mature trees into a building whose largest opening might be 6 ft 0 in x 8 ft 0 in (1.8 x 2.4 m). But it apparently dawned on me that the use of plants within an enclosed, environmentally controlled volume was a subdiscipline of landscape architecture that I wished to learn more about.

I was sufficiently intrigued by this first visit there that I mark the date of March 1970 as the beginning of my interest in the field of interior landscaping. This fascination was naturally accompanied by a compelling desire to become more knowledgeable in the subject. Unfortunately, the references available in 1970 to learn more about this discipline were nonexistent. There were few books or magazines on the subject; nor were there any courses to take, at either the baccalaureate or even the adult education level.

Without a source of information, my ability to become more conversant with the field was frustrated until 1974, when the firm with whom I was employed at the time, The Architects Collaborative (TAC), was hired to design a hotel in the Middle East. The client had requested that a large interior garden be the focal point of the lobby. After volunteering to design the lobby garden, and immediately realizing that I didn't have the slightest clue as to how to proceed with the work, I convinced the firm to hire Everett Conklin, the interior landscape contractor who installed and originally maintained the Ford Foundation garden, as a consultant. With ample and able assistance from Everett, we successfully completed the design work, although for reasons beyond our control the lobby planting as we had conceived it was never implemented.

I continued my quest to learn more about interior landscaping by accepting the responsibility to do all the interior landscape design needed for the buildings which TAC was designing. After all, now that I had one project under my belt I was, of course, an "expert"! Unfortunately, this "expert" soon realized that the more I learned, the more I didn't know (to a great extent, I feel the same way today). My sources of information remained quite limited; namely, only the minds of those few real experts in the business—the interior landscape contractors and foliage growers who were in practice at that time. I found that after a brief apprenticeship with Everett Conklin, I had unwittingly enrolled myself in the University of Trial & Error (UT&E), the only school one could attend to learn about interior landscaping.

Now, more than 20 years after the opening of the Ford Foundation Building and its beautiful garden, I find that UT&E is still the only program of its kind despite the vast popularity which the field of interior landscaping has achieved in the intervening time. There are now several excellent books and two national magazines devoted to the field. But most of the books and both magazines are intended mainly for the benefit of the interior landscape contractor—the person or firm responsible for purchasing, installing and maintaining the plants and related accessories within a building. Several courses are available throughout the country at the associate degree, continuing education, or adult education level (including one I have taught) which deal with interior landscaping in general but only touch on the design aspects. One still cannot apply to college and say to the registrar, "I wish to become an interior landscape designer. Where do I sign?" Except, of course, at UT&E.

Interior landscaping has become the fastest growing field of ornamental horticulture, chiefly by virtue of our primal appreciation of things natural. In September 1989, the National Aeronautics and Space Administration published a study of the beneficial physiological effects of plants on indoor air quality which may (*will*, we in the business all pray) open the door to a vastly increased demand for interior plants based on the *need* for plants rather than just the *desire* for them.

With all this activity, however, the ability to become an interior landscape designer strictly by taking academic programs to attain a minimum proficiency level sufficient to serve as an apprentice to a practicing professional does not yet exist. The best graduates of UT&E are currently interior landscape contractors who have acquired design skills, or design professionals (chiefly landscape architects, but also architects and interior designers) who have become conversant with the environmental requirements of interior plants.

This book is intended to assist either faction—the interior landscape contractor with an interest in design, or the design professional with an interest in interior plants—in achieving a passing grade in UT&E's course in interior landscape design.

Nelson R. Hammer, ASLA
Needham, MA

Fig. 1-1.
The garden of the Ford Foundation Building was the first permanent, large scale interior landscape installed in a commercial building in the United States.

CHAPTER ONE

SOME BRIEF HISTORICAL MILESTONES

From the time of my first exposure to landscape architecture as a design discipline, I have always looked it as an upstart, a "johnny-come-lately" compared to the stately, age-old profession of architecture. The term "landscape architecture" was coined only in the mid-nineteenth century by Frederick Law Olmsted in his design for New York City's Central Park, and historical references to the landscape architecture as a profession barely trace back before the time of Andre Le Notre, the master "gardener" of the Palace of Versailles.

Interior landscape design, however, is newer still; for the technological achievements necessary for interior landscape design to exist as a design discipline were not yet in place in the seventeenth century, when the Versailles gardens were the epitome of Renaissance garden design. If landscape architecture is a flower whose bud has opened within the past 150 years, interior landscape design is still a seed just breaking through the soil.

It is that new a profession. As recently as 1967, when the Ford Foundation garden was installed in New York City (Fig. 1-1), the team of professionals responsible for the design, installation, and maintenance of this landmark project had virtually no prior, documented experience on which to draw to determine the appropriate environmental parameters needed to keep plants alive in this (or any) building. And while the strides taken since 1967 have been enormous, much of the work now being executed throughout the country and the world still has a similar ring of experimentation to it. With a design discipline only 25 or so years old, it is hardly surprising.

What has happened, seemingly so all of a sudden, that indoor plants have become ubiquitous after being ignored for hundreds of years? The answer lies in a series of technological milestones which were achieved over a span of centuries. We will see that in spite of the relative youth of the discipline as we know it today, the innovations necessary for its success were begun before the birth of Christ.

Of interior landscape design's kindred design arts, architecture has been around for virtually as long as recorded history; as has (perhaps arguably) interior design, whose beginnings are considered by some to be 20,000 years ago, marked by the cave murals at Altamira, Spain and Lascaux, France. It is interesting to note that Olmsted's first use of the term landscape architecture was just about the same time that interior landscape design was first made feasible because of a series of technical innovations which we shall discuss in detail.

Interior landscape design: the art and science of arranging and placing living interior plants and related accessories within enclosed and environmentally controlled structures for the purpose of creating aesthetic appeal.

If we were to define interior landscape design as the art and science of arranging and placing living interior plants and related accessories within enclosed and environmentally controlled structures for the purpose of creating aesthetic appeal, we might well begin our trip backward in time with the famed nineteenth-century glasshouses of western Europe. But the forces behind the flourishing of the glasshouses bear examination.

That examination will begin with the first decorative use of plants out of doors, the practice we will call landscaping (more specifically "ornamental horticulture"), as differentiated from agriculture, the production of plants for sustenance. It is actually the divergence between exterior and interior landscaping that provides the relevance of this historical review. Key factors will be identified which over the years have enabled plants to thrive indoors, and we will focus our attention on the factors which differentiate between interior and exterior landscaping:

1. CONTAINERIZATION: A notable distinction between interior and exterior landscaping is the requirement for interior plants to be containerized. Exterior ornamental plants are root pruned during nursery cultivation to make them more readily transportable, but their roots are normally not restricted once they are transplanted. The vast majority of plants cultivated for interior use are, however, kept in their containers, or are at the very least root-constricted, for their usable life.

2. IRRIGATION: Interior plants are totally dependent on artificial means for irrigation. Although exterior plants are often watered with a boost from some sort of irrigation system, rainfall provides for the watering needs of most outdoor plants in non-arid climates.

3. LIGHT AND GLAZING: Many plants which thrive out of doors simply cannot withstand the lower light levels available to plants in indoor spaces. Other plants which can tolerate lower light availability may not be able to tolerate drastic alterations in the spectral energy caused by the use of even clear glass, or of certain types of tinted or reflective glazing, or of electric lighting.

4. TEMPERATURE: Interior plants are placed in spaces also occupied by people, people who want to be comfortable without wearing too much clothing. With interior spaces controlled to within a temperature range of perhaps 65° to 80°F (18.3 to 26.7°C), the palette of plants available to the interior landscape designer is limited to

tropical and subtropical species which thrive in that temperature range and also tolerate the other noted limitations.

5. HUMIDITY: The heating, ventilating, and air-conditioning (HVAC) systems of most modern buildings do not have special provisions for maintaining particular humidity requirements, with the result that many buildings will have humidities in the 10 to 20 percent range during the heating or air-conditioning season, as opposed to normal humidities for the outside air of that climate which may be 20, 40, or even 60 percent higher. Some plants which can tolerate other limitations cannot survive the drier humidity normally found indoors.

6. LACK OF DORMANCY: While temperate plants are widely known to go into dormancy during their fall and winter "hibernation", most people do not realize that subtropical and even tropical plants must have a dormant period as well. Dormancy for temperate plants is popularly noted by temperature fluctuation, but significant changes in light intensity and duration from season to season also affect the dormancy of not only temperate but subtropical and tropical plants as well. Only some tropical, equatorial plants are not subject to the fluctuations of either temperature or light availability. Interior plants, particularly those growing solely under electric lighting, may not experience seasonal changes in either light or temperature sufficient to trigger a dormant period. Interior plants must either be able to tolerate growth conditions all year long, or force themselves into dormancy without the benefit of temperature and light fluctuations, and must experience dormancy without dropping their leaves.

7. MAINTENANCE: Many exterior plants require no maintenance after establishment. Once their roots have taken hold, not even watering, except normal rainfall, may be necessary. Dirt and minor insect problems are often literally washed away by wind and rain. Many exterior species have been cultivated specifically to grow slowly so that not even pruning is necessary for years at a time. *All interior plants must receive maintenance.* Those plants given totally automated irrigation systems still must be checked for disease and insect damage and groomed on a regular basis to look their best.

8. WATERPROOFING: Because interior plants are placed within environments which are maintained more meticulously than the outdoors, and because leakage from the soil can damage interior finishings, the containers in which plants are displayed must be waterproofed lest water stains or damage mar the interior environment.

Fig. 1-2.
Re-creation of a wall painting from the tomb of Rekh-mi-Re at Thebes, circa 1450 B.C. The trees, carried in rope slings, were probably balled with woven Date Palm Fiber.

Fig. 1-3.
An artist's interpretation of the Hanging Gardens of Babylon. Although out of doors, it exhibited many traits later required of interior landscaping: containerization, waterproofing, and irrigation. (Courtesy of American Museum of Photography)

CONTAINERIZATION

The process of containerizing plants has an ancient heritage, with evidence that plants were grown in containers for more than 4,000 years. Both the Chinese and Middle Eastern civilizations have documented the use of potted plants through their art or recorded history before the advent of the Christian Era. The Minoan Culture of Crete was known to have used pottery some 4,000 years ago, but it was used at first for storage. Earthenware for growing plants was noted in tomb paintings in Egypt (Fig. 1-2), but more substantive evidence of the use of pottery by the Greeks for this purpose was discovered in 1936 near the Temple of Hephaistos in the Athenian Agora, where fragments of flower pots were discovered. It appears that they were used to root tree cuttings planted near the temple as early as the third century B.C. Greek women were known to have planted seeds of lettuce, fennel, wheat, or barley in pots for the festival of Adonis.

Containerized plants were also used in the most renowned example of ornamental horticulture of biblical times, the Hanging Gardens of Babylon (Fig. 1-3). The famed gardens offer an historical oddity in that detailed accounts of it exist despite the extraordinary fact that no trace of the Hanging Gardens has ever been found. This paradox is explained by the many historians who have separately documented its extent. The splendor of the gardens was apparently such that its description was passed down from generation to generation, and although some of the specifics of certain historians' accounts may differ, the similarities are enough to conclude that the Hanging Gardens of Babylon not only existed but were truly a Wonder of the World.

A Babylonian Priest named Berossus described the Hanging Gardens about 200 B.C., while the Greek historians Strabo and Diodorus both documented the Gardens in the first century A.D. The gardens are attributed to Nebuchadnezzar, who began his reign of Babylonia in 605 B.C. He created them near the present-day city of Baghdad, Iraq, for a

Persian wife who longed for the tree-covered mountains of her homeland. Strabos' and Diodorus' accounts both indicate that the gardens covered approximately 3 or 4 acres and were terraced. The placement of plants in the gardens was either in pots or planting beds placed on each terrace floor. In some cases, supporting brick columns were left hollow and filled with earth to provide for root growth.

IRRIGATION AND WATERPROOFING

The Hanging Gardens of Babylon were a precursor to the interior landscape not only in the use of containerized plants but also in the use of irrigation and waterproofing. One important historical difference in the accounts was with regard to the method of watering the plantings. While Diodorus claimed that "engines" drove the water up from the Euphrates River to the levels of the garden, Berossus and Strabo claimed it was slaves who supplied the power. The main garden on the uppermost terrace was waterproofed by a covering of reeds dabbed with asphalt, on top of which was placed a double layer of tiles or bricks set in mortar, over which were placed large sheets of lead.

Fig. 1-4.
The Roman atrium was an early example of the use of plants within an enclosed space. (Courtesy of the Viking Press)

Plants in an "Enclosed" Space

The architecture of ancient Rome was another major step in the evolution of interior landscaping. The Hellenistic architectural style favored the creation of almost windowless homes configured about an "enclosed" (i.e., surrounded, as opposed to being covered) interior court, or atrium (Fig. 1-4). The atrium was the entrance to the home, and since guests were greeted there, it was often beautifully decorated with plants, possible because the atrium was completely open to let in light and let out smoke.

Two cities displaying Hellenistic architecture were Pompeii and Herculaneum, whose ruins have been frozen in time as the result of Vesuvius' eruption on August 25, 79 A.D. The two cities have revealed much about the culture of the Rome of 2,000 years ago, confirming the use of plants within enclosed, if not climate-controlled, architectural spaces.

GLASS

Although the Egyptians are credited with the invention of glass, their resourcefulness did not lend itself to the use of glass for letting light in and keeping cold out of their homes. Pottery, beads, and goblets were the principal artifacts made of glass which date back to Egypt. Once again, it was the Romans to whom we can credit another technical achievement, for it appears they were the first to use glass for window glazing. Early Roman homes used a type of mica (lapis specularis) in thin, smooth sheets to let in light and keep out the elements. Evidence of the use of glass for windows was found in the ruins of Pompeii. Roman windows were thick, uneven, and dark (in fact, too dark to be suitable for plants), but glazing technology had come into existence.

Glass for windows was all but forgotten after the fall of Rome as the need (or desire) for light in homes was replaced by the need for defense. Homes became fortifications in the Dark Ages, and windows were replaced by narrow slits suitable only for observation or using weapons. Window glazing re-emerged first in churches, and then not for light but for decoration, as stained glass became a factor in church architecture. Documentation exists of an English abbott searching for foreign workers to glaze an abbey in 674 A.D.

Medieval glass was not much improved over the rudimentary Roman glass. It was made by blowing a globe, cutting it, and then spinning it into a disk perhaps 50 to 60 in (127.0 to 152.4 cm) in diameter, from which small panes were cut. The center of the disk had a series of thick circular ridges or rings called "roundels", and were prized for their decorative qualities. The popularity of glazed windows continued to grow in Europe, and created an odd milestone in England, where in 1696 the English Parliament passed the Window Tax, which stated, in effect, that citizens who wished to have light and air in their homes, must pay a tax for it. If unwilling or unable to pay, a citizen must brick up the windows and suffer the consequences of no sunlight or air. Illness and fever became rampant as the English discovered the precursor to "Sick Building Syndrome", which we shall discuss at length elsewhere in this volume. Incredibly, the Window Tax was not repealed until 1851. Needless to say, the popularity of windows did not grow significantly in England during the years of the Window Tax.

Meanwhile, the Renaissance generated renewed interest in flora. The Age of Discovery brought exotic plants, particularly fruits and other edibles, to Europe from distant lands. Botanical gardens became a reality (first in Padua, Italy in 1525; then Pisa, 1544; Leipzig, 1580; and Leyden, 1587) as the influx of heretofore unknown plants became available to western Europe and the wealthy and scholarly sought to nurture and propagate them. Oranges are believed to have been introduced to Europe toward the end of the thirteenth century, and were grown in Europe by the end of the fifteenth century. They remained quite rare, and as a result were highly prized by the wealthy.

Fig. 1-5. More mindful of its architectural style than its function as an environment for plant growth, this facility at Kassel, Germany was typical of the early eighteenth century orangery. (Courtesy of Rizzoli International Publications)

The climate of Western Europe required that orange trees be protected during the winter, since they were introduced from milder climates. The first structures designed to protect orange trees from winter cold ("orangeries") were developed in Stuttgart in 1626, where temporary buildings were erected in the fall and dismantled in the spring. They consisted of all-wood construction, including wood shutters to let in light and air. The practice of dismantling and re-erecting the structures became quite costly because all the joints had to be sealed to keep the buildings warm enough. It must be remembered that the trees were growing in the ground, and it was easier to build the structure around the tree than move the tree into the structure.

The culture of orange trees in Western Europe continued in popularity at the turn of the eighteenth century. Orangeries became permanent structures as the plants were grown in tubs rather than directly planted in the ground, enabling the potted plants to be moved into protective environments more readily. The prevalent architectural style of the time was Baroque, and the first permanent orangeries were quite elaborate examples of Baroque architecture, such as the orangery at Kassel, Germany (1701–1710) (Fig. 1-5). The Kassel orangery was an ornate stone building whose facade remained typically Baroque. No attempt was made to increase the transparency of the walls or roof to improve the horticultural requirements of the plants within. The building was a symbol of the courtly way of life, and the thought of producing a more appropriate environment for the growth of orange trees was secondary, if recognized at all.

Probably unbeknownst to the German architects of the Kassel orangery, the technology to create large expanses of window glazing had been developed several years previously. Although the Window Tax hampered the popularity of window glazing in England, glass manufacturing and use was faring better across the English Channel. A Frenchmen named Louis Lucas de Nedhou invented the process of pouring and rolling glass—what we know today as plate glass—in 1688, and with it the possibility to create truly flat, relatively clear sheets as large as 50in x 84 in (127.0 x 213.4 cm). The French recognized a good thing when they saw it and kept the process a secret, enabling them to monopolize the mirror-making industry in Europe for many years, and retarding the widespread development of plate glass use in European window manufacturing.

Fig. 1-6.
Unlike the Kassel orangery, although its chronological peer, the design of this pineapple house in Schwobber, Germany was better adapted for its horticultural use. (Courtesy of Rizzoli International Publications)

While orangeries were clearly an advance in the culture of exotic plants in western Europe, there were limits imposed on their practicality by the need for their adherence to prevailing architectural styles. A more direct precursor to the glasshouses of nineteenth century Europe was a pineapple house built in Schwobber, Germany, early in the eighteenth century (Fig. 1-6). Although permanent, it was a structure designed and built for horticultural purposes, and was not beholden to a style of architecture for its configuration.

Window Tax aside, the development of the glasshouse was spearheaded in Europe by the English, whose passion for gardening was complemented by their advances in technology made possible by the Industrial Revolution. Theirs was a modern industrial society while many other countries in northern and western Europe were still struggling to outgrow feudalism. Stone and brick were replaced by wood as a prime building material, but advances in the manufacture of iron soon pushed it to the forefront of construction technology, enabling great spans to be built without intermediate support. Cast iron was extremely brittle but readily forged; while wrought iron could tolerate stress well. The two were used in combination to maximize each others' attributes.

Heating Systems

Heating systems were vastly improved during the first part of the nineteenth century as well. Where previous structures would have a north wall made of stone to insulate and to reflect heat, the advent of steam and hot water heating in pipes beneath the floors allowed for the elimination of the stone wall, and glazing could completely encircle a structure.

The last major technological breakthrough of nineteenth century Europe relevant to our discussion was the introduction of prefabricated building parts and modular construction. Development of these processes greatly reduced construction cost and time and simplified construction techniques.

Yet another factor in the rise of glasshouses in nineteenth century England was the vastness of the British Empire's reach and the ability of its intrepid explorers to pique the interest of its citizenry by returning home with exotic plants. Oranges and other rare fruit trees once enjoyed the favor of the wealthy, but now tropical plants, particularly palms, were becoming sought after, and the desire to cultivate them on English soil increased. In 1774, the Royal Botanic Gardens at Kew began listing exotic plants growing in their gardens, and by 1789 they had catalogued 5,500 specimens.

The Glasshouse Phenomenon

Most people with a passing knowledge of nineteenth century glasshouse history believe that Joseph Paxton was the great innovator behind the nineteenth century English glasshouse, but it was another Englishman, John Claudius Loudon (1783–1843), who bore an indelible imprint on the use of iron and glass for architectural construction, the two materials on which the glasshouse phenomenon would depend. Many of the details and techniques which were to make the great glasshouses and wintergardens of Europe feasible during the middle of the nineteenth century were conceived by Loudon several decades earlier, when the use of iron and glass was still in an experimental stage.

Fig. 1-7.
The Syon House Conservatory, outside London (mid-1820s). This early glasshouse opened the roof to light with glass, but kept the stone facades of earlier structures. (Courtesy of Rizzoli International Publications)

The first glasshouses built in England early in the nineteenth century were constructed expressly for the growth and propagation of decorative or useful plants. The Syon House conservatory outside London (Fig. 1-7), designed by Charles Fowler and built between 1820 and 1827, is typical of the earliest glasshouses which were actually transitional in style between the Baroque orangeries and the all-glass structures to follow. Fowler increased the light penetration into the building by providing a glass roof, but kept the traditional stone facade on the central structure. Paxton's early work at Chatsworth, begun in 1836, shows structures built of glass from the ground up.

Fig. 1-8.
After the mid-nineteenth century, glasshouses were used as additions to buildings of various types, such as in this resort in southern England. (Courtesy of Rizzoli International Publications)

As the use of glass with iron became more prevalent and the ability to substantially increase the size of all iron and glass structures grew, the purpose of the structures gradually evolved from strictly functional to aesthetic. The first glasshouses were built strictly for the culture of exotic plants and were to be found only in conservatories, botanical gardens and other milieux dedicated to a horticultural intent. Their popularity began to expand after 1840, and the combination of iron and glass transcended the limitations of horticulture to be used in private homes, hotels, and spas, typical of the building types which took advantage of the new technologies to add a plant-filled, daylighted space to the more traditional ones. Iron and glass additions to multipurpose structures were built not only in large cities like London, Berlin, and Paris, but in English seaside resorts as well (Fig. 1-8).

Fig. 1-9.
The Crystal Palace was a landmark building in size, the use of materials, and use of prefabrication as a construction technique. (Courtesy of Rizzoli International Publications)

The Crystal Palace

It could be said that what Loudon started in the 1820s, Paxton finished, for the refinement of glasshouse design reached its zenith under his aegis. Paxton's pièce de résistance, the Crystal Palace (Fig. 1-9), was a gargantuan structure even by today's standards, and it is truly lamentable that it did not survive to the present day. It was 1,851 ft long, 456 ft (139.0 m) wide, 66 ft (28.1 m) high, and covered more than 800,000 SF (74,322 SM) in area. Built for the Great Exhibition of 1851 in London, the Crystal Palace took advantage of all the available advances of nineteenth century engineering technology, and represents the pinnacle of glasshouse architectural design. Typical of the later glasshouses of the era, the Crystal Palace was a multi-use facility in which plants were a prime, but not the only, attraction.

The Crystal Palace is generally considered to be the first major building in the world to be completely constructed of prefabricated parts. Paxton could never have built it otherwise, for he was given the commission in July 1850, a scant 9 months prior to the opening of the exhibition. It was so totally prefabricated and modularized, in fact, that it was dismantled, improved, enlarged and relocated to Sydenham, England, in 1854, where it survived until being destroyed by fire in 1936.

The success of the glasshouse in growing plants indoors is all the more remarkable when placed in its historical context. It must remembered that the electric light, mechanical ventilation, and air-conditioning, which play an undeniably important role in the use of indoor plants today, were still several decades from invention and more than half a century from common usage.

It was advances in technology that had allowed for the creation of the glasshouse and the ability of plants to survive and even thrive indoors. The continued evolution of the discipline of interior landscape design into the twentieth century would depend on widening the popularity of plants and the public's awareness of them; increasing the number of plant species which will tolerate the peculiarities of the indoor environment; further refining systems of glazing, heating, and ventilation; inventing (and refining) systems of lighting and air-conditioning; and improving the culture and shipment of plants from the places of growth to the end user.

As noted earlier, the popularity of plants increased dramatically during the seventeenth and 18th centuries when many European explorers sailed to the western hemisphere and south of the equator and brought back, among other things, exotic tropical and subtropical plants never before seen in western Europe. We earlier identified oranges, other fruit trees, and palms as being highly prized by the aristocracy, but more mundane species found their way back to the continent as well. Captain William Bligh (yes, *the* William Bligh) brought the first Heart-Leaved Philodendron (*Philodendron scandens*) back to England from the West Indies in 1793, along with several hundred other species (including 37 species of ferns) which made their way into the exotic species list of the Royal Botanic Gardens at Kew (Fig. 1-10).

Fig. 1-10.
Glasshouses at Kew Gardens: (top) the Palm House (Courtesy of Peter Cummin) and (above) the Temperate House (Courtesy of John Haederle).

THE VICTORIAN INFLUENCE

Fern cultivation reached a mania of sorts in England in the 1830s and 1840s, spurred by Nathaniel B. Ward, a surgeon who enjoyed many avocations, including entomology and botany. In 1830, Dr. Ward placed a moth pupa inside a large glass bottle, and when he inspected the bottle several months later to see if the pupa had undergone its anticipated metamorphosis, he discovered to his amazement that a tiny clod of moist soil also in the jar had sprouted a sprig of grass and a tiny fern. The grass and fern had apparently thrived for many months with no human help. Prior to this discovery, Ward had tried repeatedly to grow ferns in the foul London air, without success. Within the confines of a glass case, however, he found that ferns could prosper in their own unique environment, away from the London soot. Experimenting with many other types of ferns, he ultimately published a paper on his findings in 1841, entitled "Growth of Plants in Closely Glazed Cases." In deference to its creator, they became known as Wardian Cases (Fig. 1-11).

Fig. 1-11.
A Wardian Case

By 1860 over 800 species of ferns were in cultivation in Europe. One grower in mid-nineteenth century England offered more than 50 varieties of the Hart's-Tongue Fern alone, at costs in 1990 terms of as much as $50.

In the later stages of the nineteenth century, the glasshouse phenomenon, which heretofore had focused on public or municipal buildings such as the Crystal Palace or in botanical gardens throughout Europe, gradually became a featured addition to many Victorian homes. Even houses which had no glass conservatories began displaying plants in parlors whose ambient light availability may have been only slightly higher than the relatively dimly lighted rooms elsewhere. Palms remained a popular

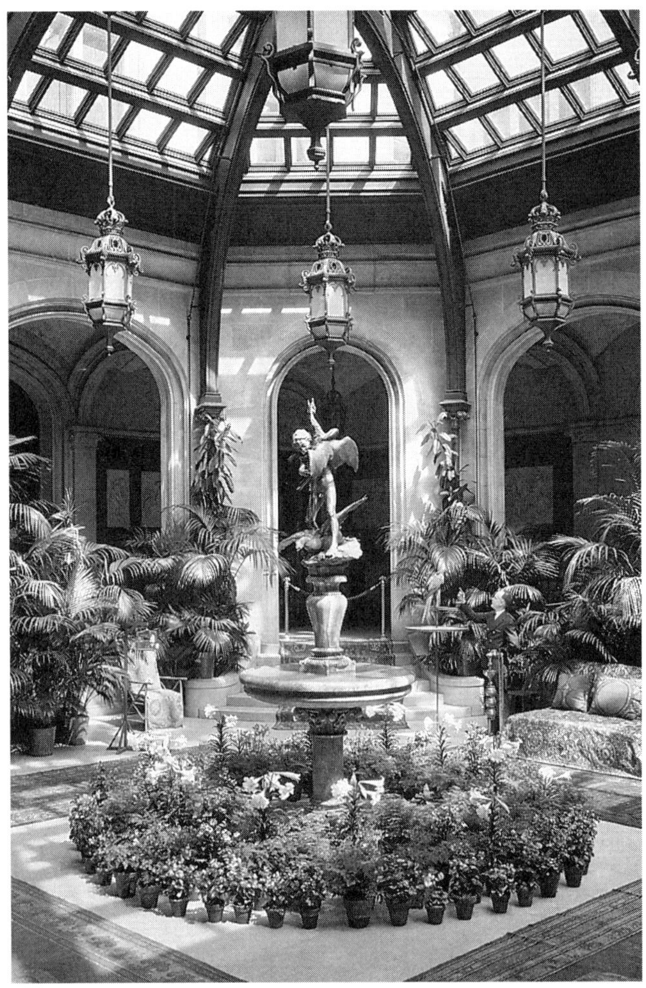

Fig. 1-12.
The Palm Court at the Biltmore Estate is a classic example of Victorian conservatory in the United States. (Courtesy of The Biltmore Estate, Asheville, North Carolina)

horticultural element of these parlor plantings, and the Kentia (*Howea forsterana*) was a palm of choice, as was the aptly named Parlor Palm (*Chamaedorea elegans*).

Typical of a more opulent parlor planting is the Palm Court at the Biltmore Estate in Asheville, North Carolina, designed for George Washington Vanderbilt by Richard Morris Hunt (Fig. 1-12). Generally considered to be the largest private home in the United States (although it is now a museum open to the public), it was begun in 1891 and completed in 1895, at the height of the American Victorian period. Note the use of species typical of the parlor plantings in Victorian England.

Other genera likely to be found in Victorian conservatories and parlors were *Agave, Aglaonema, Aspidistra, Aucuba, Begonia, Cissus, Dieffenbachia, Dracaena, Philodendron, and Pittosporum*. Despite the lack of light, flowering genera such as *Azalea, Fuchsia, Lantana, and Verbena* were also popular.

Even with the ample amount of light provided by the glass roofs and walls of the Victorian conservatories, it must be remembered that air circulation was extremely poor (i.e., when the windows were open and there was a breeze, there was air circulation; when the windows were closed, there was no air circulation) and was often exacerbated by the noxious fumes of gas lighting. In addition, air temperatures could not be as easily controlled prior to the advent of air-conditioning, and the air itself was quite dirty. No wonder that many of the plants known to have survived the indoors of the Victorian age are listed among the hardiest of the current interior landscape plants available.

The success of nineteenth century glasshouses in promoting the popularity of plants indoors is attributable in part to the type of glazing used. Only clear glass was available as a glazing component, a situation that most architects today would consider unacceptable because of its poor insulating qualities and aesthetic plainness. But prior to the advent of tinted or reflective glass, nineteenth century architects had only clear glass at their disposal, and their limitations were plant materials' gain. Light availability was extremely high in daylighted spaces, while the temperature of the glass-enclosed spaces fluctuated widely. The poor insulating qualities of single-pane, clear glass made heat retention in the winter difficult, while the heat gain in warm weather made these spaces uncomfortably warm. Heating systems of the time were able to provide for tolerable temperatures during cold spells, but the only method available of lowering sultry summer temperatures was to open windows to improve air circulation.

Two of the twentieth century's most important contributions to the technological capability of placing plants indoors—electric lighting and mechanical ventilation—were first developed in the nineteenth century. Edison's invention of a practical incandescent lamp on October 21, 1879 was the first of many developments in the field of electric lighting which would ultimately expand the possibility of plant use indoors. It didn't take long for the wonder of electric lighting to be applied to plant growth; evidence exists of electric lighting being used to supplement daylighting in greenhouses and cold frames in Belmont, Massachusetts, as early as 1888!

ELECTRIC LIGHTING

The incandescent lamp was the first electric light to achieve popular usage, but it has never received widespread acceptance as a light source for plant growth. With too much of its output generated as heat rather than light, and too much of its light energy concentrated in the red portion of the spectrum (and thereby causing poor growth characteristics), incandescent lamps even today are not appropriate light sources for plant growth. Other, more recently developed electric lamp types have filled that role: The introduction of fluorescent, mercury vapor, metal halide, and high pressure sodium lamps have enabled indoor plants to subsist entirely on light output from electric lamps. The combination of high efficiency, long lamp life, and horticulturally appropriate spectral energy distribution makes these four light sources superior to incandescent in their ability to assist in plant growth.

Mercury vapor lamps were first commercially manufactured in 1902 by the Cooper-Hewitt Electric Company. When first introduced, these lamps put out an eerie green blue light, but they had an efficiency of 12.5 lumens per watt (lm/W), quite a feat that early in the century. In 1934, high intensity mercury vapor lamps were first used, although they still had an unattractive greenish blue hue. Despite their higher efficiency and longer lamp life, their use remained limited until a means was developed to allow them to be used in a horizontal position and thus acceptable for street lighting in the 1950s. The color problem was improved with the introduction of red phosphors in the Deluxe White mercury vapor lamp, created in 1966 for use with color television broadcasting. Mercury vapor as a light source had by then reached social acceptability, and its use in interior environments increased dramatically. Mercury Vapor lamps remain today a popular light source for applications where the bluish cast they produce creates an appealing color rendition, such as the highlighting of jewelry in a department store.

The fluorescent lamp was introduced by General Electric on April 21, 1938 and made commercially available shortly thereafter by General Electric and Sylvania Electric Products, Inc. The various improvements to fluorescent since their introduction include an availability of many different colors, elimination of the need for separate ballasts, instant starting capability, higher output, and increased efficiency. These qualities make fluorescent lighting the most commonly used indoor electric light source in the world today.

Dr. Gilbert H. Reiling improved the mercury vapor even more by adding metallic vapors, creating the metal halide lamp in 1962. Made commercially available by General Electric as the "Multi-Vapor", it was a big hit at the 1964–65 New York World's Fair.

The newest of the high pressure, gaseous discharge light sources to be developed is the high-pressure sodium lamp, introduced in 1961 by William C. Louden and Dr. Kurt Schmidt of the General Electric laboratories at Nela Park, Ohio. It is the most efficient general lighting source used today. (Low-pressure sodium lamps are even more efficient, but their monochromatic yellow light renders them useful only in limited situations).

The nature of the three high-intensity discharge, (HID), lamps (mercury vapor, metal halide, and high pressure sodium) gives them an advantage over fluorescent lighting in their ability to sustain plant growth. While many of the fluorescent colors on the market provide acceptable plant growth lighting spectral energy, the innate design of the lamps and their fixtures prevent them from putting out enough light to be of use if they are located more than about 8 to 10 ft (2.4 to 3.0 m) from their target. Fluorescents' lack of directionality limits their acceptability as sources of plant growth lighting to ceilings of one story or less. HID lamps and fixtures can have their light output focused from a wide to narrow beam spread, and have the flexibility of higher wattages as well. As a result, they can be located, if necessary, several stories above plants and still provide sufficient output for plant growth.

Chapter Five will compare all the various electric lamp and natural light sources and their use in plant growth lighting.

AIR-CONDITIONING

The buildings being created in the last quarter of the twentieth century which support the growth of plants bear little resemblance to their predecessors of a century ago. The glasshouses of the 1860s used clear glass to let in light, used windows or ventilation openings to allow for the flow of whatever fresh air was available, and used prodigious amounts of energy to heat small portions of them due to the inefficiency of the heating systems and the low cost of fuel. The modern office building is designed for maximum human comfort in all its spaces and relies completely on mechanical means to heat, cool, and ventilate it. The lack of optional fresh air capability through operable windows forces inhabitants to rely solely on a building's mechanical systems for heat, ventilation, and air-conditioning. With no windows to open, plants located near them must have the benefit of cool air to keep them from excessively high temperatures.

The drive to control the interior environment has been led by Americans since the early nineteenth century, when New England ice merchants plied their trade internationally. Dr. John Gorrie of Florida patented the first ice-making machine in 1851, and a Texan transplanted from Scotland named David Boyle invented the first ammonia compressor in 1872, used to make ice. By the 1880s, mechanical refrigeration units were in use in breweries, restaurants, and meat-packing houses throughout the country. None of these uses, however, were designed for human comfort, which is not to say that Promethean efforts were not attempted in that area.

After President James Garfield was shot on July 2, 1881, he lay incapacitated in a White House bedroom with a bullet lodged in his back. The President's physicians attempted to keep him as comfortable as possible in the heat of the Washington summer. Less than a week after the shooting, naval engineers who were directed to cool the President's bedroom had worked around the clock and succeeded in building a device that cooled the room by 20 degrees and lowered the humidity in it as well.

The device was a coffin-sized, cast-iron box filled with dozens of terry-cloth cotton screens. Atop the box was a tank containing more than a half ton of ice, salt, and water. As the ice melted, it seeped down through the cotton screens. A fan at one end of the box pulled outside air through the box, which cooled the air as it passed through the screens, and was then pumped into the President's bedroom. Although the device did lower the temperature and humidity, it consumed over half a million pounds of ice during the 53 days of its operation! Recognizing its impracticality, President Garfield's doctors ultimately moved him to a seaside cottage on the Jersey shore to escape the Washington heat, and he died there on September 19, 1881.

Efforts to aid a mortally wounded President notwithstanding, most attempts to cool interior temperatures and lower humidity were expended not for human comfort but to help increase industrial productivity. In 1902, a practical method of lowering temperature and humidity in interior spaces was invented by Willis Haviland Carrier, who was asked by a publishing company to help solve a printing problem for a magazine: Colors printed on humid days during the summer did not line up with colors laid down on drier days. Combining the two emerging technologies

Fig. 1-13.
An air-conditioning unit at Allegheny Hospital, 1914. (Courtesy of the Carrier Corporation)

of electricity and refrigeration, he successfully produced a device which kept humidity down to 55 percent and had 10 times the cooling efficiency of the apparatus created by naval engineers for a dying President.

Carrier followed the success of his initial installation with solutions to other industrial problems throughout the country during the early years of the century. Meanwhile, efforts continued to develop air-conditioning systems for people. The New York Stock Exchange was first cooled in 1902 by an engineer named Alfred Wolff, and part of a commercial office building in lower Manhattan was fitted for air-conditioning equipment in 1906. It remained, however, a frightfully expensive proposition. Carrier continued to introduce many new improvements and refinements; he lowered the infant mortality rate at a Pittsburgh hospital maternity ward with an installation in 1914 (Fig. 1-13), and also installed the first home unit that same year in a mansion in Minneapolis.

Fig. 1-14.
Installation of air-conditioning in theaters like this (The Rivoli on Broadway, New York, 1925) did much to popularize its use. (Courtesy of the Carrier Corporation)

Carrier's cooling of theaters, starting in 1919, gave air-conditioning for human comfort the biggest boost yet, and the spread of this phenomenon increased dramatically throughout the 1920s (Fig. 1-14). The first multistory office building to be fully air conditioned was an 8-story structure in Fresno, California, in 1926, and a much larger, 21-story tower was air conditioned 2 years later in San Antonio, Texas.

Another Carrier introduction—the Conduit Weather-master System (1937)—allowed for the air-conditioning of skyscrapers by distributing conditioned air through narrow ducts at high velocity. Individually controlled units at the point of delivery then further cooled or heated it. This invention, with the help of the introduction of the fluorescent light, allowed architects more design flexibility by enabling them to heat, cool and light windowless rooms. It also allowed windows to be sealed, the impact of which will be discussed in the Epilogue. The United Nations Building in New York (1951) was typical of the new direction architecture could take as a result of Carrier's changes to the interior environment.

Employees were relatively slow to demand the introduction of air-conditioning into their work spaces. The Textile Workers Union of America finally made air-conditioning a bargaining issue in 1948, when temperatures in a North Carolina mill hit 95°F. Between the increased demand for cooled office spaces and the burgeoning of the residential market in the early 1950s, the popularity of air-conditioning in all interior spaces continued to climb. Today, cities like Houston, Texas, can claim to have air-conditioning in 95 percent of their office and residential spaces.

The mechanical control of the modern interior environment is now efficient and flexible enough to allow plant materials to thrive in virtually any part of a building a designer is so inclined specify. But the popularity of interior plants in the today's buildings is not just a result of technology's ability to allow plants to live indoors.

THE SOCIOLOGICAL PHENOMENON OF PLANTS

Although engineering technology has been responsible for the advances in lighting and ventilation, breakthroughs in other areas since the turn of the century were founded on more mundane methodologies. The appeal of plants continued to increase once their unique attributes were made known to the general population as a result of the success of the glasshouse. The popularity of plants during the Victorian Era reached a pinnacle during the latter part of the nineteenth century. After the turbulent world events of the first half of the twentieth century, plants have again, since the late 1960s, become an indoor "craze" as durable species were mass-marketed, making plants available to virtually everyone.

The Heart-Leaved Philodendron has a secure place in the history of interior landscaping, for it became the most popular of all house plants during the Great Depression when nurseryman John Masek of Orlando, Florida, "rediscovered" it in 1936 and began mass marketing it through five-and ten-cent stores. As late as 1972, one in five house plants shipped from Florida was the Heart-Leaved Philodendron. (Fig. 1-15)

Fig. 1-15.
The Heart-Leaved Philodendron (Philodendron scandens)*: Common house plant with a storied past.*

NEW INTRODUCTIONS

The Victorian Conservatory was able to keep plants healthy by utilizing a select number of species which were both available and tolerant of the indoor conditions of the time. The success and popularity of indoor plants today is due in large part to the variety of plant species tolerant of the typical indoor environment which have been introduced by the foliage nurseries in recent years. Using both traditional and modern propagation techniques like seeds, stem sections, cuttings, air layering, and tissue culture (Figs. 1-16), growers have responded to the demands of the marketplace by introducing new varieties that are more low-light tolerant, low-humidity tolerant, more

Fig. 1-16.
Three traditional propagation techniques: (top) air layering a Rubber tree, (center) a Coconut Palm grown from seed, and (bottom) a Dumb Cane grown from a stem section.

colorful, more insect- and disease-resistant, and better flowering than ever before. In addition to the work of botanists and plant physiologists, purchasing agents from major nurseries in Florida, California, Hawaii, and Europe continue, as did the eighteenth century English explorers before them, to comb the tropics looking for new varieties of plants which might have those same elusive qualities that will make it the next sales phenomenon.

ACCLIMATIZATION

It was only a short time ago, perhaps the mid-1970s, that most foliage nurseries in Florida grew almost all their nursery stock under full sunlight, the theory being that the faster the plants grew, the faster the growers could turn them over. But the contractors buying the stock found that sun-grown material either fared poorly on the job-site under considerably less light, or had to be kept in expensive holding areas on their property where plants could be "acclimatized" to lower light levels. The nurseries gradually responded by either acclimatizing plant material under shade houses for several months prior to shipment, or by growing containerized plants under shade from inception (Fig. 1-17). The result was higher survival rates, less turnover, and more satisfied customers. Acres of shade houses, some as high as 35 ft or 40 ft (10.7 or 12.2 m), are visible today in foliage nurseries in central and south Florida (Fig. 1-18).

ADVANCES IN TRANSPORTING PLANTS

The means of shipping plants from the nursery to the end user has been refined considerably even in the last 10 years. Nurseries have found that simply placing plants on trucks is no longer enough. Many of the growers now have prep rooms where plants are taken prior to shipment. Foliage is given a final application of insecticide and then subjected to high speed fans to dry incidental moisture from the foliage (Fig. 1-19). This helps avoid the formation of mold or mildew during shipping, even though they may have just been watered to prevent their drying out. Plants are then carefully sleeved in kraft paper or boxed to protect them from damage. Finally, the boxed or sleeved plants will be double- or triple-stacked in the cargo hold of truck trailers to maximize capacity and keep shipping costs down (Fig. 1-20).

Trucks and ships used to transport plants are climate controlled to optimize temperature and humidity while in transit. Transporting plants from Florida to Canada by truck or to Europe by ship has been found to cause virtually no permanent damage even when subjecting plants to complete darkness for weeks at a time. Hawaii has become a cost-effective source of foliage material now that plants can be shipped rather than air-freighted to California.

Fig. 1-17.
Shade structures and greenhouses are used by many foliage nurseries for growing plants directly from cuttings to a saleable size.

Fig. 1-18.
Originally used for acclimatizing plants once they had reached saleable size, shade houses like this (at National Nurseries) have been used increasingly as growth environments for many plants.

Fig. 1-19.
Overhead fans (at Michael's Nursery) are used to dry off foliage prior to shipment. This helps prevent spotting of foliage and formation of mold and mildew during shipment.

Fig. 1-20.
The efficient packing of tractor trailers increases shipping cost-effectiveness and decreases plant loss from breakage by keeping plants upright.

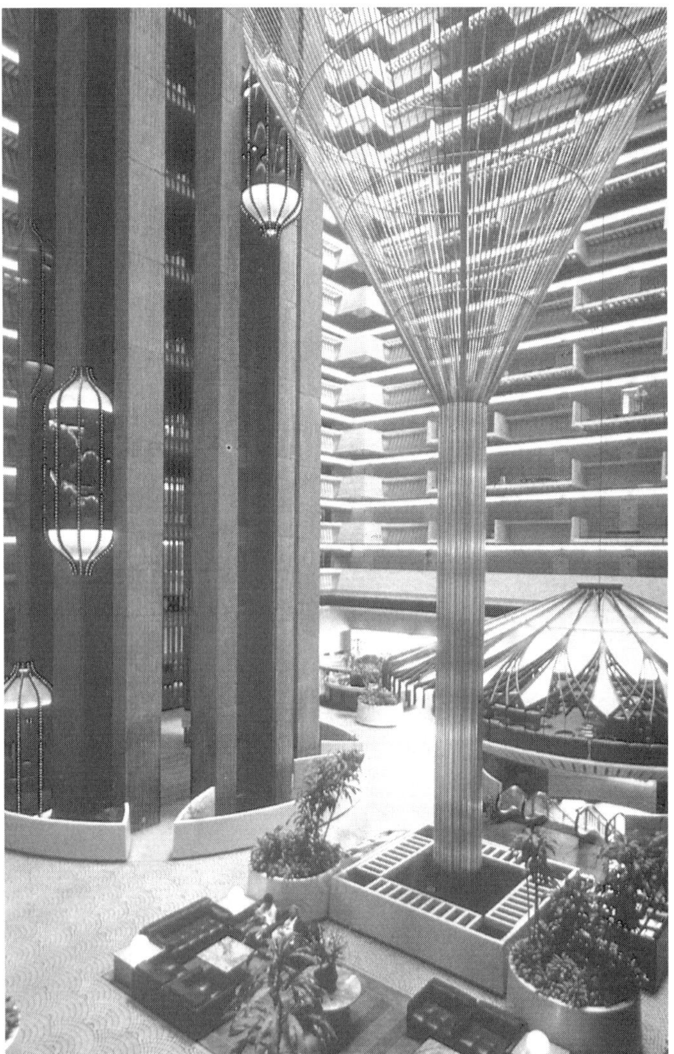

Fig. 1-21.
The Hyatt Regency Lobby, Atlanta, Georgia (1967): a landmark building in American architecture and in the history of interior landscape design. (Courtesy of John Portman & Associates, Inc.)

ARCHITECTURAL ADVANCES

We have seen that changes in architectural construction materials and techniques in the nineteenth century created the horticultural possibility of interior landscaping. The latter part of the twentieth century has seen changes in architectural style which further promote the use of plants by creating the need for landscaping as an integral part of the building's interior design.

The Atrium- Again

The Roman atrium of 2,000 years ago was a major advancement in the history of interior landscaping, for it marked the first use of plants within an architecturally surrounded environment. The re-introduction of the atrium in hotel design in the 1960s was just as significant an advancement, for it established the use of large scale interior plants as a planned component of a building's public spaces.

John Portman reinvented the concept of the grand public space with his design for the Hyatt Regency in Atlanta, an 800-room hotel with a 22-story atrium which opened in 1967 (Fig. 1-21). An instant critical and popular success, it was followed by other Portman hotels equally inspiring in scope and in style: the Hyatt Regency O'Hare in Chicago in 1971 (with a 10-story atrium, and the Hyatt Regency Embarcadero in San Francisco in 1973 (with a 17-story atrium). These landmark projects broke new ground in terms of their use of space, their solutions to structural, fire code, building code, and other life safety issues, and most importantly (for our discussion) in their re-establishment of the atrium as an architectural focal point of contemporary architecture.

The presence of large and dynamic indoor public spaces in these and other major buildings practically demanded the introduction of landscaping as basic elements within the context of the volume. The sheer grandiosity of some of the new atrium spaces was at once thrilling and intimidating. Plant material, especially large-scale trees and palms, serves to mitigate the textural starkness of the architectural environment, and at the same time provide a human scale to vast interior spaces, much as street trees serve a similar purpose along an avenue of skyscrapers.

PLANTS AS COMPONENTS OF "THE BOTTOM LINE"

The use of plants in interior spaces is now seen as a viable contributor to the financial success of malls, hotels, and other buildings dependent on high-volume pedestrian traffic.

Plant material is often displayed prominently in print advertisements and in television commercials as a means of establishing the proper ambience and inviting the shopper or overnight guest (Fig. 1-22). The cost of purchasing, installing, and maintaining extensive interior landscaping in these buildings is now recognized as a necessary component of the total design package.

"The Los Angeles Bonaventure has become the centerpiece of the new downtown."

"Crown Center brought a waterfall and tropical gardens to downtown Kansas City."

Fig. 1-22.
Ads like these testify to the importance placed on the use of indoor plants by commercial developers. (Courtesy of Westin Hotels & Resorts)

PLANTS AS INDOOR AIR CLEANERS

The NASA study of 1989 (see Epilogue) proved that plants can absorb harmful substances present in indoor air (the study focused on three common pollutants: formaldehyde, trichloroethylene, and benzene), and metabolize them into plant food without danger to humans. The implications of this study are vast, for the heightened awareness of indoor air pollution has made the public much more concerned about the omnipresence of trace substances like the ones on which NASA focused in their study. With plants available as a low-tech and low-cost option to purify indoor air, a substantial burgeoning of the interior plant business to take advantage of this benefit seems a reasonable progression.

As we near the end of the twentieth century, interior plants have reached a popularity unsurpassed in history. We continue to spur advances in their propagation, growth, shipment, and maintenance. Changes in contemporary architecture throughout the world have enabled plants to be considered as integral components of the interior commercial environment. And now, perhaps most important of all, plants are seen as a realistic contributor to the improvement of indoor air quality. All these factors will play a part in creating a future in which we can all enjoy the pleasures of an indoor environment filled with living plants.

CHAPTER TWO

DESIGN THEORY

The principles of design—form, symmetry, balance, rhythm, unity, and contrast are universal in their ability to address and resolve design issues. The various design disciplines utilize these principles similarly, but differ in the materials they employ to solve design problems. Plants, planters, and related accessories are the "paints" which landscape architects use to create their landscape art. It would appear logical that the interior landscape designer's identical requirement of plants, planters, and related accessories as the media needed to solve their design problems would make the landscape architect the ideal professional to address interior landscape design issues.

But just as the training needed to mold the talents of an architect, interior designer, or landscape architect establishes a uniqueness to each disciplinarian's skills, there are substantial differences between interior and exterior landscaping which make interior landscaping as singular a discipline as the others. The ability of the landscape architect to properly address them by virtue of personal academic or professional training in exterior landscape design becomes problematic.

The previous chapter, presented not as a history of our subject but as a series of milestones in technology which helped create the possibility of our subject, begins to identify why interior and exterior landscape design differ. Exterior landscaping is a blending of horticultural skills with the knowledge of design. The interior landscape designer begins with the blend of horticulture and design, but must also be much more attuned to the influence of human technology on the horticultural environment. To better understand how design theory specifically relates to interior landscaping, it is necessary to be aware of how comprehensively the environment of interior plants is controlled by people and not by Mother Nature.

Moreover, the success which some contractors have had in creating interior landscape designs bears testimony to their knowledge of these environmental requirements. Conversely, the inability of contractors to properly address design issues is generally because they lack training in the principles of design.

When teaching a class on design theory, the first slides I show (before the class falls asleep) are of contractors maintaining plants; then slides of artificial lighting systems; of skylights; and of watering systems (Fig. 2-1). The point made is that the plants of an

Fig. 2-1.
These four photos illustrate that a good-looking interior landscape must be a healthy one, requiring (clockwise from upper left) natural lighting, artificial lighting, regular maintenance and irrigation.

interior landscape must be healthy for any design to be successful, and healthy plants are dependent on a compatible environment. In painting, the artist must have a thorough familiarity with canvas, paint, and brushes before paint can be applied to a canvas with the flair needed to create great works of art. Similarly, the interior landscape designer must be familiar with the media of their art: plants, planters, accessories, and the environments into which they will be placed.

Fig. 2-2.
Contrast, balance, repetition, rhythm, and unity are universal design principles that apply to interior landscapes. (Courtesy of the Associated Landscape Architects of America)

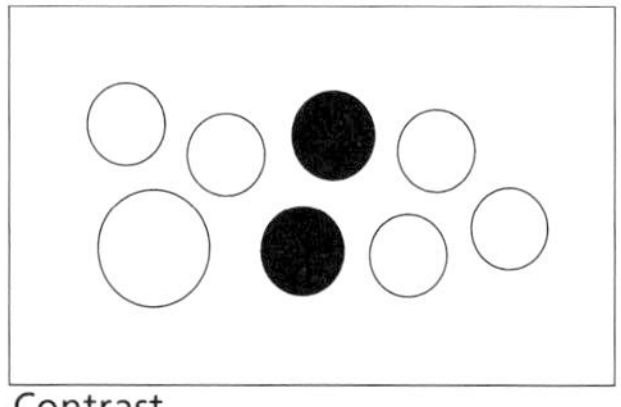
Contrast

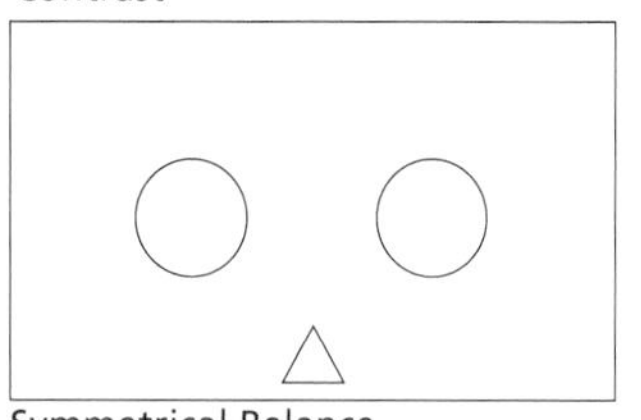
Symmetrical Balance

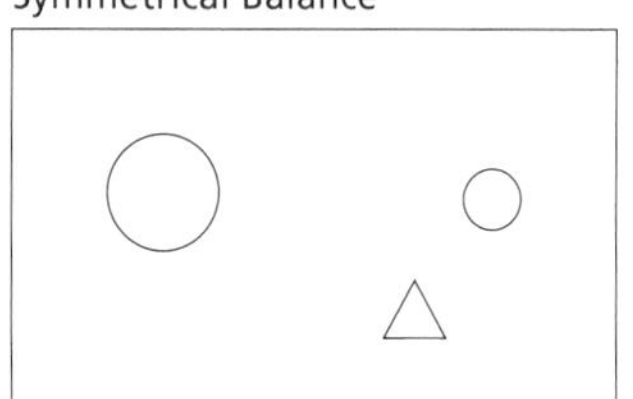
Asymmetrical Balance

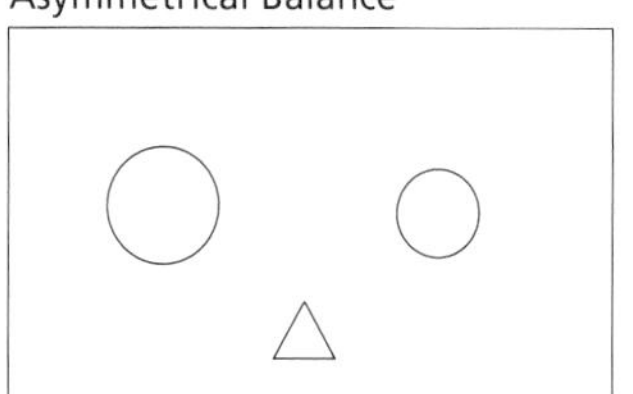
Visual Balance

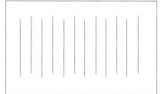

Repetition

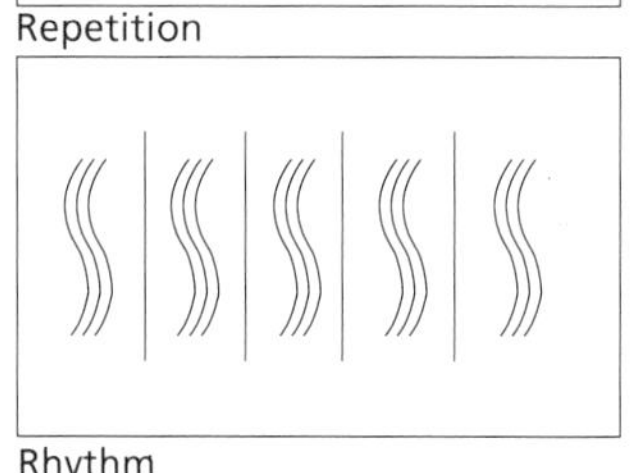
Rhythm

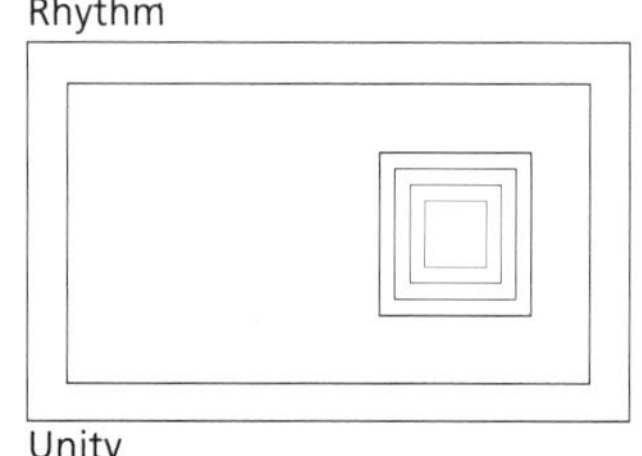
Unity

VISUAL CONFINEMENT OF THE INDOOR SPACE

That environment is a room; and this fact alone establishes a marked difference between interior and exterior landscape design. The milieu of the exterior plant can extend horizontally to the horizon, vertically to the clouds. The interior milieu stops with walls and ceiling. Even a multistory atrium will have a skylighted ceiling that is often visible without tilting the head back; so limited is the vertical cone of view indoors.

These, then, are the two major differences between interior and exterior landscape design: the dependence of plants on an artificially created environment which is necessary for their sustenance, and the visual limitations of that environment. Working within these differences, one can successfully apply the time-tested theories of design to the interior landscape.

The subjectivity of design tells us that what appeals to some may be abhorrent to others. Despite this contradiction, several rules of design are universally accepted as contributors to an appealing result: Unity is the characteristic occurring when all the elements within a design combine to promote an undivided total effect. Several methods can be used to create unity. If I were to describe my own perception of unity as a principle of design in a word or two, it would be clarity or order, the quality of having a visual hierarchy that subconsciously leads the viewer's eye from element to element within a design. This concept is fostered by rhythm (Fig. 2-2) and movement (Fig. 2-3), the means by which the eye is led, by focal points, the goals of the eye movement. The location, number, and hierarchy of focal points of an interior landscape will be key factors in the design's success, for they will determine where and how long the viewer's attention will be focused perhaps subconsciously. The antithesis of clarity and order—visual confusion or disorder—is characterized by a variety of undefined images that tend to isolate the viewer rather than draw them into a design (Fig. 2-4a,b).

These concepts are manifested in the interior landscape using plant materials as the medium. The subconscious movement of the eye within the space is initiated by the use of focal points; traffic signals directing the viewer through the interior space. Plants are a medium well adapted to serve as focal points, for they possess many qualities suitable for the purpose: height, color, texture, and habit of growth.

Fig. 2-3.
Movement from one focal point to another keeps the viewer's eye absorbed with a design. (Courtesy of Plantscape, Inc. and the Associated Landscape Contractors of America)

Fig. 2-4a.
Massing of similar species reinforces the creation of focal points, helps the eye move from place to place, and gets the viewer involved in the design.

Fig. 2-4b.
With no order in the hierarchy of images, a design can appear confusing, thus isolating the viewer.

Fig. 2-5.
These Ponytail Palms are only 12 in (30 cm) above grade, they have become focal points because they are taller than the surrounding ground cover.

Fig. 2-6.
These Ficus trees, approximately 25 ft (7.6 m) high, help scale down the massiveness of the atrium space.

Fig. 2-7.
Palms add a distinct ambiance to an interior space. (Courtesy of M. Paul Friedberg & Partners)

HEIGHT

Placing a taller specimen among shorter ones is the most common way to create a focal point. The key is relative size, not actual size. A low shrub, perhaps only 18 in (45.7 cm) tall, will become a focal point within a ground cover bed that is only 4 or 5 in (10.2 or 12.7 cm) above grade (Fig. 2-5). An equally important use of height, however, is the establishment of the interior tree not only as a focal point of the interior space but as a means of providing scale to those multistory atria that may dwarf the inhabitants, much as the row of shade trees on an urban street helps bring the scale of the skyscraper down to human tolerance (Fig. 2-6). A major difference is that the 90 ft (27.4 m) tall street tree may seem insignificant next to an urban skyline, while a 25 ft (7.6 m) tall interior tree will dominate even large atrium spaces (Fig. 2-7).

LIMITED CHOICES

Another difference is that the 90 ft street tree may be one of 50 or more different species available to the landscape architect in virtually any climate in the United States. The interior landscape designer will not be so fortunate. The tropical foliage nurseries providing plants to the interior landscape industry will generally stock only one genus of tree in the 25 ft range—*Ficus*—that will live in "typical" lighting found in most interior environments. Other trees which can be found at that height, such as Black Olive, will not tolerate lower light levels as well as *Ficus*. Many palms which can tolerate similar light levels, and are available in the 25 ft range, are simply not trees, and will be ruled out by clients (or designers) who want the look of branches and leaves, and not fronds (Fig. 2-8).

COLOR

There are two typical ways in which the attribute of color can capture the viewer's attention in the interior landscape: first, by using placements of flowering plants whose color is temporary (Color Section C2-1 to C2-8); and second, by using permanent or semi-permanent placements of non-green or variegated plants as counterpoints to the green plants around them (Color Section C2-9 to C2-14).

The first option is potentially more spectacular, but it is also more expensive. Because of this, cost may limit some clients to a flowering plant option only during certain times of the year, such as Pointsettias (*Euphorbia pulcherrima*) at Christmas. Overuse of flowering plants can also be visually confusing in addition to being very costly (Color Section C2-15). A year-round flowering plant program generally rotates plants every 2 to 3 weeks (depending on the species; some can be as often as weekly, some can be as rarely as monthly). A 2 to 3 week schedule translates into 18 to 26 rotations per year. At a cost of $8 to $15 (again, depending on species, and at 1991 prices), a client can end up spending $144 to $390 per plant per year for a specimen like *Chrysanthemum* which rarely exceeds 2 ft in height. Needless to say, the designer must use rotational flowering plants with discretion unless a client is willing to invest substantially in the rotation program. The impact of flowering plants can be considerable enough, though, that even small quantities can produce outstanding visual effects (Color Section C9-8). One reason for this is that the vibrant colors of flowering plants can be much more intense than the color provided by non-green or variegated permanent plants.

Fig. 2-8.
Trees can recreate the feeling of an outdoor space in a northern temperate climate.

Fig. 2-9.
Subirrigation can prolong the blooming cycle, or reduce the watering interval, of flowering plants, which generally require additional water when in bloom.

FLOWERING PLANT CONSTRAINTS

In spite of the temporary nature of the flower rotation, environmental constraints will still exert their influence on their care. Flowering plants will generally require more frequent watering than permanent plants, for specimens in flower are in the peak of health and are expending a great deal of energy. This facet of flowering plants can pose maintenance concerns to accounts locked into a 7 day or greater watering cycle. The problem is often mitigated by the use of subirrigation, planters with built-in reservoirs of water, which can increase watering cycles dramatically and keep the plants healthier in the process (Fig. 2-9).

Another problem associated with flowering plants is insects. Permanent foliage plants normally take several months to become salable, during which time they are invariably treated several times with insecticides. Flowering plants will in many instances take only several weeks to become salable, and often are not subject to the use of pesticides. The result is that flowering plants can often cause the introduction of pests into an interior landscape that had painstakingly been kept insect-free.

The last innate constraint of flowering plants is that even though these specimens are temporary, the length of their rotation is ideally kept as lengthy as possible to ensure maximum cost effectiveness, and this rotation length is solely dependent on the physical appearance of the blooms. Under most conditions, rotation length will be idealized only under very bright light, the kind of conditions which are normally required to grow flowering plants in the first place. Under "typical" indoor conditions, light availability will be so low it will force flowering plants through their blooming cycle much faster than under brighter conditions.

Fig. 2-10.
This Bird-of-Paradise (Strelitzia nicolai) *has leaves approximately 7 ft (2.1 m) long. A plant this coarse will stand out wherever it is specified.*

Fig. 2-11.
Part of the charm of palm trees is the enormity of their fronds.

VARIEGATED AND NON-GREEN PERMANENT PLANTS

The drawbacks of blooming rotational plants—cost most prominent among them—make owners and designers look to other methods of creating interest through the use of color in the interior landscape, and the foliage growers have responded with an extremely diverse assortment of variegated or non-green cultivars available, many of which are low-light tolerant as well. These plants allow designers to make subtle or abrupt changes in the tonal quality of a planting without altering other characteristics. Examples of dramatically variegated, yet low-light tolerant genera are Chinese Evergreen (*Algaonema 'Maria'*, A. 'Silver Queen', and many others), Dumb Cane (*Dieffenbachia* 'Camille', *D.* 'Picta', *D.* 'Tropic Snow', etc.), and Pothos (*Epipremnum aureum* and E. 'Marble Queen'). The amount of variegation in a Chinese Evergreen can vary from virtually all green (A. 'Queen Juliana') to predominantly white (*A. 'Pseudobracteatum'*), and makes this genus a very popular one as a result. Typical of variegated or non-green specimens which require higher light levels are Croton (*Codieaum* 'Karen' and C. 'Norma'), Treebine (*Cissus discolor*), and Wandering Jew (*Tradescantia fluminensis* and *Zebrina pendula*). Many genera of green plants have been cultivated by the nurseries to produce variegated varieties of what are usually all green plants. *Ficus* and *Schefflera* are two "green" genera for which variegated cultivars have been successfully introduced.

Under ideal indoor lighting conditions, a designer may be fortunate enough to specify a flowering plant which actually can subsist as a permanent plant in the interior landscape. Though few plants flower profusely in deep shade outdoors, a few, such as *Impatiens*, *Hibiscus*, *Schlumbergera*, and *Begonia*, can survive indoors under bright light.

Fig. 2-12. (top)
At the other end of the textural scale, Tree Ferns like this one at the Isabella Stewart Gardner Museum in Boston, MA. have extremely lacy foliage.

Fig. 2-13. (above)
The startling changes in texture in this detail of the Conservatory at the Opryland Hotel in Nashville, TN, make it a feast for the visual palette.

TEXTURE

The term "exotic" is often used to describe interior plants, and the characteristic most responsible for that description is texture. Northern and southern temperate plants rarely have the enormous disparity in leaf size and structure which can be found on plants of the tropics and subtropics, where many species lay claim to leaves of several feet in length (Banana, Bird-of-Paradise, etc.; see Fig. 2-10), or palm fronds many times larger than that (Fig. 2-11). The exotic textural nature of these plants is an attribute of plants that is not considered as a design tool as often as height or color. This is regrettable, for the textural qualities of many tropical and subtropical plants are prime contributors to the atmosphere created by "exotic" interior plants. From the airy lacyness of Tree Ferns (Fig. 2-12) to the coarseness of the aforementioned Bird-of-Paradise, the differing textures of tropical plants can psychologically transport the casual observer in a New York shopping mall to the Caribbean or South Pacific in a matter of moments. When juxtaposed to one another, textural changes can be dramatic (Fig. 2-13).

Fig. 2-14.
The Southern Yew (Podocarpus macrophyllus 'Maki') *is often sold as a stiffly columnar specimen. Its foliage is similar to the Yews commonly specified outdoors.*

Fig. 2-15.
Norfolk Island Pine (Araucaria heterophylla) *displays the pyramidal shape typical of many exterior coniferous evergreen trees.*

Fig. 2-16.
Screw Pine (Pandanus utilis) *has a unique habit consisting of a hemispherical series of sharp spikes.*

Fig. 2-17.
The thick mass of aerial roots on some Weeping Java Fig Trees (Ficus benjamina) *makes them distinguished specimens.*

HABIT OF GROWTH

The exterior landscape boasts many different habits of growth: Weeping Willows, Birches, and Beeches; picturesque, contorted Japanese Black or Bristlecone Pines; columnar plants like Lombardy Poplar or Cypress; pyramidal evergreens like Fir and Spruce; and wide spreading trees like the Royal Poinciana. Similar examples exist within the interior landscape: Weeping Podocarpus (*Podocarpus gracilior*) carries on the tradition of the willow, while its generic sister, the Southern Yew (*Podocarpus macrophyllus,* Fig. 2-14), is columnar. Many interior landscape specimens exhibit contorted trunks or limbs, such as the Madagascar Dragon Tree (*Dracaena marginata,* when specified as "with character") or Ming Aralia (*Polyscias fruticosa*). Norfolk Island Pine (*Araucaria heterophylla,* Fig. 2-15) displays the sharply pyramidal shape of many exterior evergreen trees. Then there are some interior plants exhibiting habits of growth one would rarely encounter out of doors north of Florida or southern California, such as the stiffly symmetrical, hemispherical daggers of a Screw Pine (*Pandanus utilis,* Fig. 2-16) and the intricate aerial root maze of the Weeping Java Fig Tree (*Ficus benjamina,* Fig. 2-17).

The use of plant height, color, texture, habit of growth—and more often, combinations of some or all of these traits—give the designer many options to create focal points, the number and importance of which will be determined by the size, complexity, and budget of an interior landscape.

The creation of visual movement throughout an interior landscape using focal points can be reinforced when the landscape elements between focal points (let's call this the "field") are down-played as much as possible, using a kind of reverse methodology. To clear the visual palette, the plant field wants to eliminate the textural, size, color, or shape qualities that make the neighboring focal specimen so dominant. This is achieved by massing plants of similar species together, creating an extended area of monochromatic and monotextural foliage. The finer the texture and the lower the foliage, the more the field becomes the background for the focal planting.

IMPORTANCE OF GROUND COVERS

You've probably noted by now that fields of plants between focal specimens will often be ground covers, since they exhibit many of the qualities required of plants to serve as "background" elements. Ground cover plants can be extremely effective tools for enhancing visual movement through a space, so much so that I call ground covers the "glue" that can hold an interior landscape design together (Color Section C2-16).

Fig. 2-18. Baby's Tears (Soleirolia Soleirolii) *at left, below, provides as close a textural feel to lawn as you will find in an interior ground cover.*

It would follow that an ideal ground cover for serving as the background would be lawn, whose texture is so fine that individual plants disappear entirely, and its height is so low—presuming it is kept mown—that all other plants will be taller. In the exterior landscape, lawn serves this function quite admirably because of its aesthetic qualities and low cost per square foot. It may average as little as one-tenth the cost of planting ground covers in its place. Alas, lawn has met with only limited success indoors, and only when light availability is extremely generous.

There is no shortage, however, of ground cover plants available for interior use. Next to lawn, the ground cover most useful as "design glue" might be Baby's Tears (*Soleirolia Soleirolii*), whose color and fineness of texture rivals those of any lawn (Fig. 2-18). Unfortunately, it, too, suffers from substantial horticultural limitations which must eliminate it from consideration in many interior landscapes: it requires reasonably high light (although not as much as lawn), and high humidity. So let's start at the other end of the horticultural spectrum and discuss some interior ground covers which have virtually no horticultural limitations.

Fig. 2-19.
Devil's Ivy or Pothos (Epipremnum aureum *and its cultivars) is an excellent low-light tolerant ground cover or hanging plant.*

Fig. 2-20.
English Ivy (Hedera Helix *and its cultivars) makes a neat, low, thick, spreading ground cover or climbing vine.*

TRAILING OR SPREADING GROUND COVERS

Since a ground cover, by definition, "covers the ground", the best type of plant to specify for this use is a trailing or spreading plant, one whose runners "cover the ground" as they grow. The most commonly and successfully grown plant for interior use is such a plant: Pothos, or Devil's Ivy (*Epipremnum aureum* and its cultivars) (Fig. 2-19), whose widespread acceptance is much more the result of its ability to tolerate low light, low humidity, uneven irrigation, pests and diseases than its usefulness as a design tool. It has two marks against it as such: (1) its leaf size identifies it as a relatively coarse-textured plant, and (2) its foliage color—light green or light green with variegations—make it stand out from many other plants. But in spite of my objections to it from an aesthetic standpoint, I have probably specified it more than any other ground cover (perhaps even more than any other plant; and to pay it the highest compliment of all, I have more specimens of Pothos in my home than any other plant as well!), because as stated at the outset of this chapter, an attractive planting must be a healthy one, and nowhere is this fact more true when it comes to ground covers, where uniformity of growth is both a key to visual appeal and an indication of its health. Pothos will grow vigorously and fill in to a dense, green mat within a matter of weeks when properly specified, and will create the healthy background which a focal point ideally plays against.

Many other spreading plants are available for indoor use. One such grouping is English Ivy (*Hedera* spp., Fig. 2-20), which contains a myriad of species adaptable for the interior. Like Pothos, which sends out aerial roots from trailers that grow down into the soil as the runners spread out, *Hedera* species will spread out from trailers, rooting as they go, but they can also be climbers, since their aerial roots have a facility for adhering to vertical surfaces as well. *Hedera* species are not particularly low-light tolerant, but will do well with perhaps 100 footcandles (fc) if they can be kept free from mite infestations, to which they are quite susceptible.

Philodendron is another genus which contains many species adaptable to interior use (Fig. 2-21). Although the most common species is Heart-Leaved Philodendron (*P. scandens*), it and many others are readily available and most are tolerant of reasonably low light levels. Like Pothos, it is relatively free of insect problems.

Fig. 2-21. Heart-Leaved Philodendron (Philodendron oxycardium) *is a low-light tolerant, disease-free ground cover.*

Grape Ivy (*Cissus* spp.) consists of two very popular species (*C. rhombifolia* or Grape Ivy, and *C.* 'Ellen Danica' or Ellen Danica Ivy) (Fig. 2-22a,b) and several that are less well known. The dark, glossy green foliage associated with *Cissus* species makes an extremely attractive ground cover which will grow quite dense under medium light. It is relatively free of insect problems, but is prone to powdery mildew. As a result, soil moisture should be carefully monitored when it is used.

Fig. 2-22a. One of the prime attributes of Grape Ivy (Cissus rhombifolia) *is the glossiness of its foliage.*

Another spreading ground cover which can offer excellent results indoors is *Ficus pumila* (also known as *F. repens*), the Creeping Fig (Fig. 2-23). Its many qualities include fine-textured, dark, glossy green leaves about one inch across and an ability to grow as a dense mat both horizontally and vertically when attached to virtually any type of surface. Although pest- and disease-resistant, it does best in relatively good light, perhaps 100-150 Fc or more.

SMALL SHRUB GROUND COVERS

Ground cover plants are not limited to those whose habit of growth enable them to spread over the ground and root as they go. Any plant that grows very low to the soil level can be considered a ground cover, and that encompasses many plants known as small shrubs.

One genus of small shrubs that has become very popular recently because of the introduction of many different species which are low light tolerant, vary widely in size, and flower persistently under low light is *Spathiphyllum*. While many species are sold in containers of up to 14 in (36 cm) and will grow 4 or 5 ft (1.2 to 1.5 m) in height (such as *S.* 'Sensation'), at least two of its species,

Fig. 2-22b. (above)
Not as glossy as Grape Ivy, Ellen Danica or Oak Leaf Ivy (Cissus *'Ellen Danica') has a more interesting leaf shape.*

Fig. 2-23. (left)
Creeping Fig (Ficus pumila) *requires more light than the previously mentioned species, but when provided with good light it grows very densely and climbs as well as any indoor vine.*

Fig. 2-24.
Maria or Emerald Beauty Chinese Evergreen (Aglaonema *'Maria' or* A. *'Emerald Beauty') is a low-light tolerant, compact-growing small shrub usable as a taller ground cover.*

Fig. 2-25a.
Boston Fern (Nephrolepis exaltata 'Bostoniensis') *is one of many species of fern that can be used as an indoor ground cover to simulate a forest floor.*

Fig. 2-25b.
The circular foliage of Button Fern (Pellaea rotundifolia) *make it quite distinctive.*

S. wallisii and *S.* 'Starlite', stay small enough to be considered excellent ground covers. Besides their flowers, all *Spathiphyllum* species feature highly glossy, dark green foliage that can stand on their own without flowers to justify their worth. The foliage of both Wallisii and 'Starlite' are long and narrow, perhaps 1.5 to 2 in (3.8 to 5.1 cm) in diameter, substantially less than many of larger species available.

Aglaonema is a second genus of low-light tolerant small shrub, some of whose species are appropriate for use as ground covers. Like *Spathiphyllum*, some *Aglaonema* species can be found in pots up to 14 in (35.6 cm) diameter, though they tend to grow lower than Spathiphyllum. *A.* 'Maria' is a particularly attractive, compact shrub appropriate as a ground cover (Fig. 2-24). It will generally mature at a height of about 6 to 12 in (15.2 to 30.5 cm) above the soil line, well within reasonable limits for a ground cover plant. Although *Aglaonema* as a genus is famous for the variegation of its foliage in its many cultivars, *A.* 'Maria' is one of the less variegated, being virtually all green, and hence appropriate for its use as a "design glue".

These are two exceptional genera of plants for use as ground covers. They are both low-light tolerant, relatively disease- and insect-tolerant, and generally easy to care for. But they are by no means the only options when considering small shrubs for ground-cover use. Ferns, most of which are identified botanically with the family *Polypodiaceae*, are one of the largest families in the plant kingdom and one already shown to have played a pivotal role in the history of interior landscaping. They contain a large number of genera and species adaptable for use both indoors and as ground covers. Moreover, since hardy ferns are a common sight as the natural ground cover in northern temperate forests, the use of ferns as an understory planting indoors makes them especially desirable when an interior landscape is proposed to emulate the outdoor landscape. Boston Fern (*Nephrolepis exaltata 'Bostoniensis'*), Holly Fern (*Cyrtomium falcatum*), Table Fern (*Pteris* spp.), Button Fern (*Pellaea rotundifolia*), and Squirrel's Foot Fern (*Davallia* spp.) are only five of a number of fern genera and species that can successfully be specified indoors with proper lighting and humidity considerations (Fig. 2-25a,b).

DECREASED LIGHT AVAILABILITY

It should be noted that light availability for ground cover plants can sometimes be misleading. Many ground cover plants are placed in locations under taller plants which will block out much of the light available to the space beneath them. Calculations of footcandle levels are a necessary tool in the proper design of the interior landscape. These calculations will address lamp wattage, lamp type, height above the floor, beam spread, percentage of transmission for skylights, and solar orientation, but they cannot accurately take into account the decrease in light caused by upper-story plants well above the ground plane. It is helpful in such situations to consider low-light tolerant ground covers, for actual footcandle levels will be difficult to predict in advance, even with a computerized lighting study.

IMPORTANCE OF PROPER SPACING

The spacing of ground cover plants can be critical to the success of an interior landscape. When planted outdoors, ground cover plants rarely can be spaced to appear from the outset as a massed planting; if they were, they would be prohibitively expensive to install and would become much too crowded within a few growing seasons if they grew properly. For these reasons, a spreading or trailing outdoor plant like English Ivy, many species of which are hardy as far north as New England, must be planted with room to grow. Rooted cuttings with perhaps four or five leaves on it could be spaced at 9 to 12 in (22.9 to 30.5 cm) on center and look completely filled in after three or four seasons with good care. Larger plants like spreading Juniper can be planted with an initial spread of 15 to 18 in (38.1 to 47.2 cm) per plant, spaced 2 1/2 to 3 ft (0.76 to 0.91 m) on center, and be expected to fill in in a few seasons (The old gardener's tale regarding the growth of ground covers is "The first year they sleep. The second year they creep. The third year they leap.")

By contrast, a 6 in (15.2 cm) potted interior English Ivy or Pothos with five or six runners from 8 to 10 in (20.3 to 25.4 cm) in length will usually have to be planted 12 to 15 in (30.5 to 38.1 cm) on center indoors, unless light availability is quite generous. If plants that size were to be planted outdoors, the spacing could probably be increased to from 24 to 30 in (61.0 to 76.2 cm).

Interior ground covers must be addressed in a different manner. It is rare that interior landscapes, especially at the ground plane, where low plantings may be situated beneath taller ones, have the luxury of many hours of direct sunlight per day to promote rapid growth. As a result, the spacing of ground covers indoors must take into account the visual appeal desired versus the environmental conditions versus available budget. It almost always seems that there is a need to space ground covers to make them appear filled in, or virtually filled in, at the time of planting.

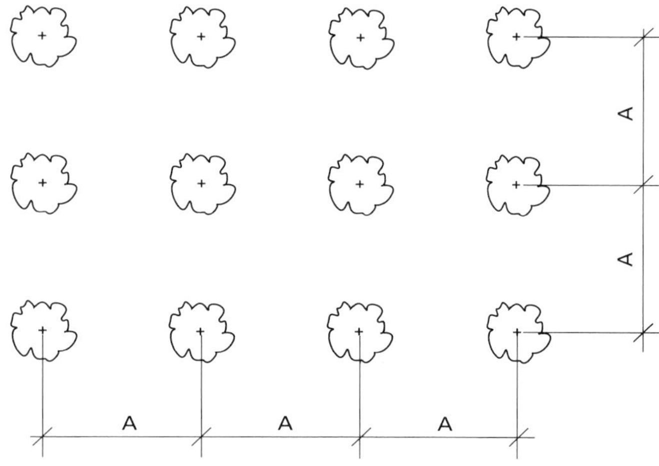

Fig. 2-26.
A rectangular grid pattern provides "even" spacing, but the spaces between rows can be too visible until the plants fill in.

The spacing of small shrubs (*Aglaonema, Spathiphyllum*, etc.) to be used as ground covers makes the potential growth issue academic. Because they are shrubs and not trailing plants, they won't fill in with time under bright light or dim light. They must be spaced closely together regardless of lighting conditions; for they will grow outward only a slight amount and will not reproduce across the ground as the trailing ground covers will. These small shrubs must be spaced at 12 to 18 in (30.5 to 45.7 cm) on center for most six in (15 cm) potted specimens, and 15 to 24 in (38.1 to 61.0 cm) for most eight in (20.3 cm) specimens, depending not on light availability, but on the fullness of the specimens themselves.

The distance between plants is only one factor in the spacing of ground cover plants. Equally important is the configuration of the spacing. Ground cover plantings could be placed in a grid of rows and columns whose dimensions are equal in both directions (Fig. 2-26). Doing so, however, will cause the individual plants to look like soldiers lined up for inspection, with noticeable gaps between plants, until they have had the opportunity to fill in. To avoid that pitfall, staggering the spacing according to the table in Fig. 2-27 will allow the plants to appear filled in faster and look less military. This table will also provide the means to determine the required number of plants per square foot or per square meter for a given area. Taking into account the cost per plant, one can also calculate the cost per unit area.

While on the subject of the expense of ground covers, it may come as a surprise that ground covers can be an extremely cost effective method of covering large areas of interior space, if the alternative is presumed to be planting beds of larger plants without any ground covers. Covering the ground with mulch or gravel is less expensive, to be sure (to install *and* to maintain!), but the appearance of mulch as a ground cover element can quickly lose its appeal when overused. And, of course, it will not serve as a "design glue" as successfully as will ground-cover plants.

One complaint leveled against ground-cover plants is that they are visible only when viewed from above or from very close to the plants; that their visual impact is diminished when pedestrians are farther away from planting. This can be true if the landscape is flat. But if the topography of the plant bed is sloped, or angled, the foliage immediately becomes more visible (Fig. 2-28). Incorporating topography into the plant bed creates other benefits as well. A "rolling" bed of plants is a more natural way to display plants and makes the planting appear more integrated to the interior design of

Plant Spacing Chart

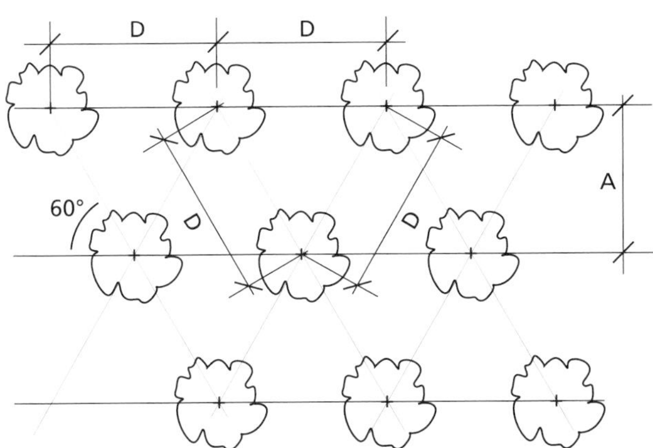

Fig. 2-27.
Ground cover spacing chart (English and metric) The use of staggered spacing creates a more even visual appearance, even when the plants have not had an opportunity to actually grow together.

ENGLISH

Spacing D on center	Row A	No. of Plants	per Area Unit
4 in	3.46 in	10.40	
6 in	5.20 in	4.62	
8 in	6.93 in	2.60	/ 1 SF
9 in	7.79 in	2.05	
10 in	8.66 in	1.66	
12 in	10.39 in	1.15	
15 in	12.99 in	8.66	
18 in	15.59 in	5.13	/ 10 SF
24 in	28.78 in	2.08	
30 in	25.98 in	1.85	
36 in	31.18 in	1.28	
4 ft	3.46 ft	7.23	
5 ft	4.33 ft	4.62	/ 100 SF
6 ft	5.20 ft	3.21	
8 ft	6.93 ft	1.80	
10 ft	8.66 ft	1.15	
12 ft	10.39 ft	8.02	
15 ft	12.99 ft	5.13	/ 1,000 SF
20 ft	17.32 ft	2.89	
25 ft	21.65 ft	1.85	
30 ft	25.98 ft	1.28	
40 ft	34.64 ft	7.22	/ 10,000 SF

METRIC

Spacing D on center	Row A	No. of Plants	per Area Unit
10 cm	8.66 cm	115.47	
15 cm	12.99 cm	51.32	
20 cm	17.32 cm	28.87	/ 1 SM
25 cm	21.65 cm	18.48	
30 cm	25.98 cm	12.83	
40 cm	34.64 cm	7.22	
45 cm	38.97 cm	5.70	
60 cm	51.96 cm	3.21	/ 1 SM
75 cm	64.95 cm	2.05	
90 cm	77.94 cm	1.43	
1.0 m	.86 m	11.63	
1.5 m	1.30 m	5.13	
2.0 m	1.73 m	2.89	/ 10 SM
2.5 m	2.17 m	1.84	
3.0 m	2.60 m	1.28	
4.0 m	3.46 m	7.22	
5.0 m	4.33 m	4.62	
6.0 m	5.20 m	3.21	/ 100 SM
7.0 m	6.06 m	2.36	
8.0 m	6.93 m	1.80	
9.0 m	7.79 m	14.26	/ 1,000 SM
10.0 m	8.66 m	11.55	

Note:

To find the number of plants per unit area for any given spacing, use the formula $\frac{1}{D \times A} = N$, where the dimensions D and A are as shown above, and N is the number of plants. For example, when D equals four feet and A equals 3.46 ft, the number of plants per square foot at 4-ft spacing is $\frac{1}{4 \times 3.46}$ or 0.0723 plants per square foot.

To find the number of plants per square foot for any given spacing when the spacing is in inches, use the formula $\frac{12}{D} \times \frac{12}{A} = N$

For example, when D equals 4 in and A equals 3.46 in, the number of plants per square foot is $\frac{12}{4} \times \frac{12}{3.46} = 10.40$ plants per square foot.

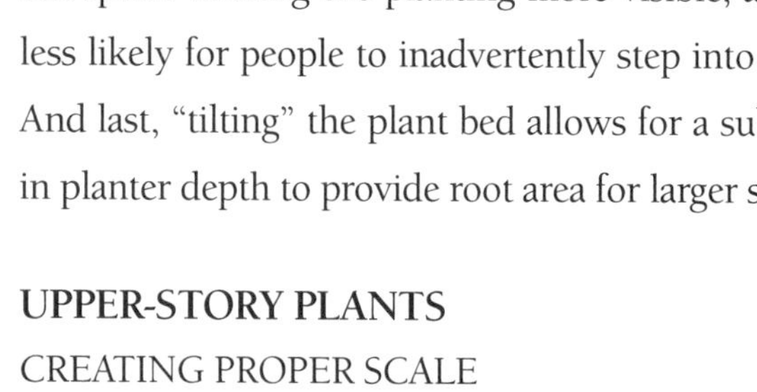

the space. Making the planting more visible, also makes it less likely for people to inadvertently step into a plant bed. And last, "tilting" the plant bed allows for a subtle increase in planter depth to provide root area for larger specimens.

Fig. 2-28.
Angling the plant bed makes ground covers and low shrubs more visible at a pedestrian's eye level.

UPPER-STORY PLANTS

CREATING PROPER SCALE

At the opposite end of the height spectrum from ground covers, upper-story plants serve different but equally important functions in the interior landscape. As stated in the beginning of this chapter, large trees and palms can provide scale to an otherwise intimidating interior architectural space. Just as the wide open prairies or the skyscrapers of our cities create environments that are out of human scale, the multi-story atrium space can sometimes cause its occupants to feel dwarfed by the monumentality of the space around and above them. The interior landscape can be used to help mitigate that feeling by establishing a perceived limit to the height and breadth of the space within its actual architectural limits.

Fig. 2-29.
The Weeping Java Fig Tree on the right was installed at a height touching the ceiling. Besides looking out of place, it can be noted that the foliage on the right side of the plant is dying off because it is too far from the fluorescent fixture.

For example, a person who looks up at an overhead mass of foliage will tend to ignore the existence of the built ceiling above it; the foliage becomes the perceived, or psychological, ceiling of the space. Similarly, a mass of foliage in front of someone effectively bisects a space vertically.

THE "TWO-THIRDS" RULE

In specifying materials designed to create a sense of height in spaces with low [under 10 ft (3.0 m)] ceiling heights, there is a general rule of thumb that should be followed in determining the maximum heights of the plants: The tallest plant material in the space should not exceed two-thirds the height of the space. Therefore, a room with a 9 ft (2.7 m) ceiling height should have no plants more than 6 ft (1.8 m) tall in them; in an 18 ft (5.5 m) high room, there should be no plants more than 12 ft (3.6 m) tall; and so on.

There are three reasons for this rationale, two practical and one aesthetic. First, specifying plants with heights exceeding these limits gives the plants little room to increase in size as part of the normal growth process (This issue can be mitigated by specifying prunable plants such as *Ficus*. Non-prunable plants such as palms should not be considered where reasonable growth will cause plants to outgrow their spaces.) Second, the closer the foliage is to the top of the space, the more difficult it is to provide even lighting to the entire crown of the plant, unless it is skylighted from above. And third, plants whose heights exceed two-thirds of the available space tend to look too confined, even if they do fit within the space's physical dimensions (Fig. 2-29).

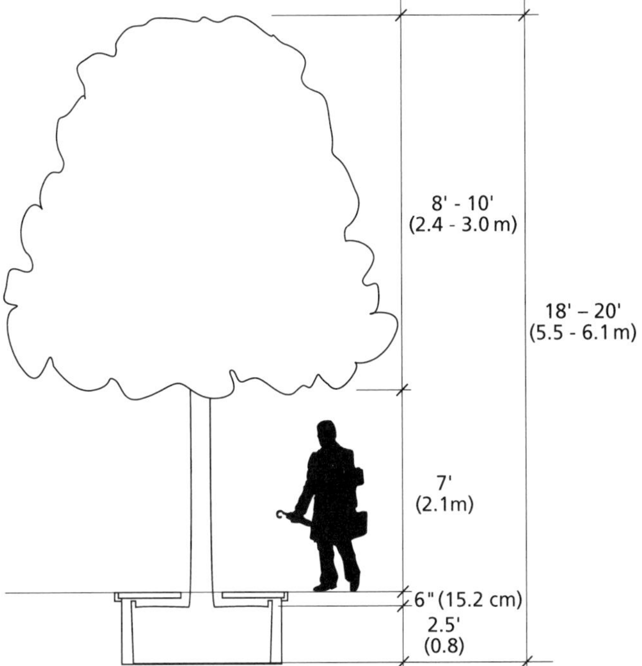

Fig. 2-30.
Using tree grates can produce excellent results, but it requires the use of fairly large specimens.

This rule of thumb applies principally to lower ceiling heights. It also does not mean that the tallest plants in a space *must* be two-thirds its height (A 180 ft [54.9 m] atrium does not require a 120 ft [36.5 m] tree!). When greater than normal ceiling heights are present, another rule of thumb has a bearing on plant specifications: Once a focal tree or palm reaches 12 to 15 ft (3.7 to 4.6 m) in height (and particularly if it has considerable crown spread), it will effectively create a perceived enclosure for a space, becoming a psychological "ceiling". One excellent way of using large trees and palms to establish scale indoors and concurrently replicate the outdoor environment is to place large plants in a row or grid and space them closely enough together for the crowns to touch (creating an actual ceiling instead of a perceived one).

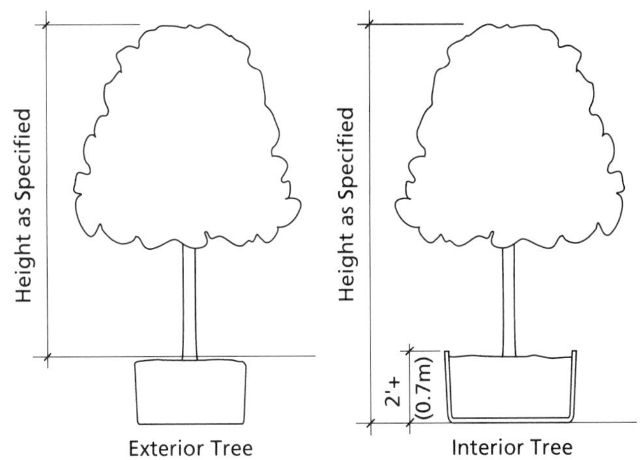

Fig. 2-31.
The difference between height specifications for exterior and interior plants can have substantial impact if the designer is not familiar with the idiosyncrasies of each.

TREE GRATES

Trees in these types of plantings may also be installed in tree grates so that pedestrians can walk beneath their canopies. For this type of planting to be effective, the trees must be in the vicinity of 18 to 20 ft (5.5 to 6.1 m) in height (about 2 1/2 ft [0.18 m] for the root ball; six in [15 cm] of space between the top of the root ball and the top of the tree grate, or finish grade; 7 ft [2.1 m] from the tree grate to the first branch, or bottom of the crown; and 8 to 10 ft [2.4 to 3.0 m] of crown proper) (Fig. 2-30). It is important to point out that unlike exterior plant material, whose height is measured from the top of the root ball to the top of the plant, an interior plant is measured from the bottom of the root ball to the top of the plant (Fig. 2-31). Skimping on the 7 ft dimension from the tree grate to the first branch can cause impediments to pedestrian circulation; skimping on the crown height can yield trees that look comically inadequate.

The use of tree grates indoors can do wonders for large atrium spaces, but they also present certain challenges to an interior landscape designer, especially when they are used over occupied space. These challenges are:

PLANTER DEPTH: Plant materials large enough for use in tree grates require plant pits with several feet of space available beneath finish grade. Besides the space requirements already mentioned, additional space is needed for drainage beneath the root ball. The bottom of the planter must be dropped at least 3 ½ ft (1.1 m) below finish grade. If planters are specified in locations over occupied space (as in first floor atria located over underground parking, or atria located above the first floor), additional depth must be provided to accommodate the structure of the floor slab itself, which must be determined by a structural engineer. When planted on grade, each plant pit should be encased with a concrete bottom and equipped with a drain tied to the building's plumbing system. The detailing for planting in tree grates is shown in Chapter Three: "Design Documentation."

"Bottomless" planters (i.e., those built on existing subgrade) should be avoided for two reasons. First, certain soil gases or liquids in the subgrade may filter up into the planting medium and harm the plant (They might even filter into the interior space itself). Second, overwatering a tree in a bottomless planter may undermine the subgrade of the floor slab and lead to slab failure. Both are relatively far fetched possibilities, but it is better to be safe by not considering this option. If it is to be considered, a sub-surface soil investigation to determine the presence of potentially harmful gases or liquids should be commissioned to supplement a geotechnical report. In these days of environmental awareness, it is a very likely possibility that such an investigation will have been performed to uncover potential hazardous waste materials when the property is transferred.

PLANT WEIGHT: Trees more than 15 ft (4.6 m) tall can have densities (weight per unit area) exceeding the minimum standard loading requirements of more floors (usually 100 to 200 pounds per square foot [1012 Kilograms per square centimeter]; check your local building codes). Should that be the case, the structural engineer must supply a more substantial structural design for the flooring when large trees are planted over occupied space. This can have significant cost and scheduling implications.

DRAINAGE: Drains placed in the bottoms of tree pits 3 ft below the finish grade of the first floor of a building will probably have lower rim elevations than any other interior drains in the building (unless there is a basement drainage system as well). It is therefore necessary for the mechanical engineers to be aware of these constraints early enough in the design process to incorporate modifications to their designs. It costs virtually nothing to lower the piping a few feet early in the design process, but it could be prohibitively expensive during construction, or afterward.

The alternative to the internal drain is the observation tube (Fig. 2-32), a pipe extending the depth of the planter through which the presence of water can be monitored and, if necessary, siphoned out. This is particularly effective in retrofit situations where a planter is placed over an existing structural slab. Observation tubing is not recommended as a substitute for a planter drain in new construction.

Fig. 2-32.
The observation tube (here wrapped in filter fabric to keep out fines) allows maintenance staff to check water levels at the bottom of planters, and if necessary, siphon excess water. 4 inch (10 cm) diameter is wide enough to enable one to look in without the need for a dipstick.)

LIGHTING: Providing plant growth lighting for large trees and palms is not as straightforward as it may seem. The basic solution, locating light directly above the trees, will cause the plants to grow straight up, which is fine. But if the light comes from a "point source" (such as a single electric light), that source will create an "umbrella effect". When this happens, the outer shell of leaves remains viable but the inner foliage drops or dramatically thins because of lack of light.

The best source of light for large trees is abundant daylight, preferably with some direct sunlight. It not only provides the proper spectral energy, but it is normally a more diffused light source, staving off the development of the umbrella effect. Barring that, a combination of daylight and electric light will often work satisfactorily. Using only electric lighting can also be successful if more than one illumination source is allocated for each specimen. As stated in the discussion of ground covers, the use of large plants will often block much of the light from reaching the understory plants below. This can be resolved by

1. Specifying upper-story plants with foliage crowns thin enough for light to penetrate (palms would perform this function better than trees; fine-textured trees would perform this function better than coarse-textured trees).
2. Specifying understory plantings which can tolerate very low light levels.
3. Selectively pruning the upper-story plantings to allow light to pass through to the ground plane.
4. Specifying supplemental lighting angled to illuminate the understory plantings. (Angled plant growth lighting can, however, cause glare, and must be used with discretion.)
5. Using a combination of these measures.

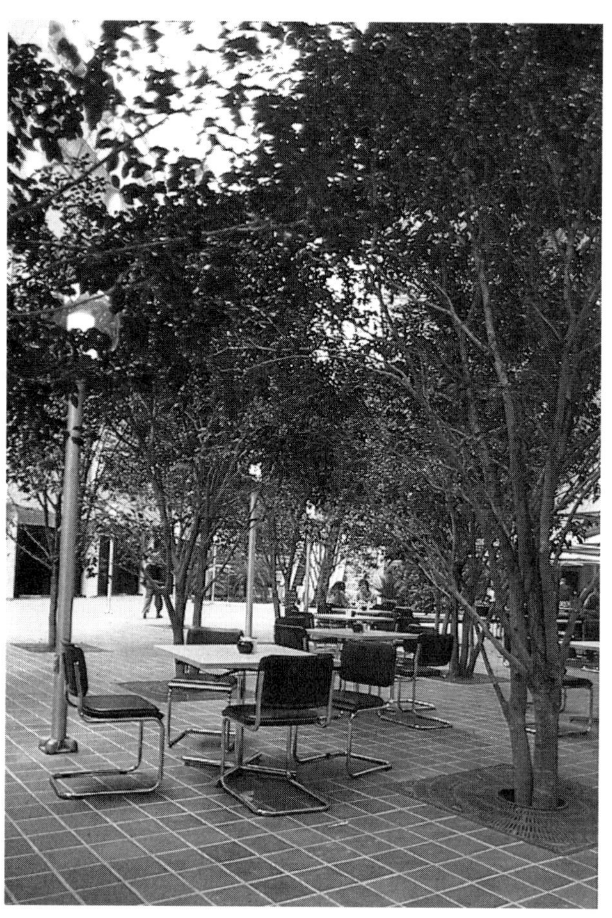

Fig. 2-33.
The Weeping Java Fig Tree (Ficus benjamina)*: ubiquitous, attractive, and versatile.*

This problem cannot be successfully resolved simply by directing higher intensity light at the tree from above. Other lighting issues are addressed in Chapter Five.

UPPER-STORY CHOICES

The use of upper-story plants in the exterior environment is bolstered by the availability of a diverse variety of species, a diversity needed to offset the various climates throughout the world. Many species are hardy enough to be adaptable in several different places, and the result is that a relatively large number of different upper-story species will be at the landscape architect's disposal in most locations. The interior environment must rely solely on upper-story plants grown in the tropics or subtropics which also have been acclimatized to grow indoors. And because upper-story plants are by their definition the tallest plants in a given area, they are accustomed to receiving full sunlight. These three factors conspire to severely limit the number of upper-story species at the interior landscape designer's disposal.

Trees

FICUS: *Ficus* species are by far the most commonly used interior tree, for several reasons. First, they will survive indoors with minimal care if given moderate light, about 250 fc at the mid-crown height of the plant (see Chapter Five; "Plant Growth Lighting"). Second, they are grown in large sizes (in excess of 12 to 15 ft (3.7 to 4.6 m) in many nurseries throughout the world. Third, they are available in a variety of shapes and sizes not only within the genus, but within individual species as well. Fourth, unlike palms, they closely resemble the types of trees found outdoors in northern temperate climates (or, in the southern hemisphere, in southern temperate climates). And last, they can be extremely attractive specimens (Fig. 2-33).

Ficus benjamina and, to a lesser extent, *F. retusa* (Weeping Java Fig Tree and Indian Laurel Fig Tree, respectively) are species with so many styles of tree within them that they could easily be presumed to be a genera of their own. Normally readily available in sizes up of to 25 to 30 ft (7.6 to 9.1 m) depending on market conditions and weather in the growing areas, they can be provided in even taller sizes with proper lead times. *F. benjamina* and *F. retusa* can be purchased in bush form—foliated to the ground—in smaller sizes (below 6 ft [1.8m]), and in larger sizes as a single- or multiple-stem tree (Fig. 2-34). The multiple stem can consist of several major branches coming from one

Fig. 2-34.
Three of the many habits of growth available from Ficus species: (top) single stem; (left) true multi-stem; and (right) multiple stems in one grow pot.

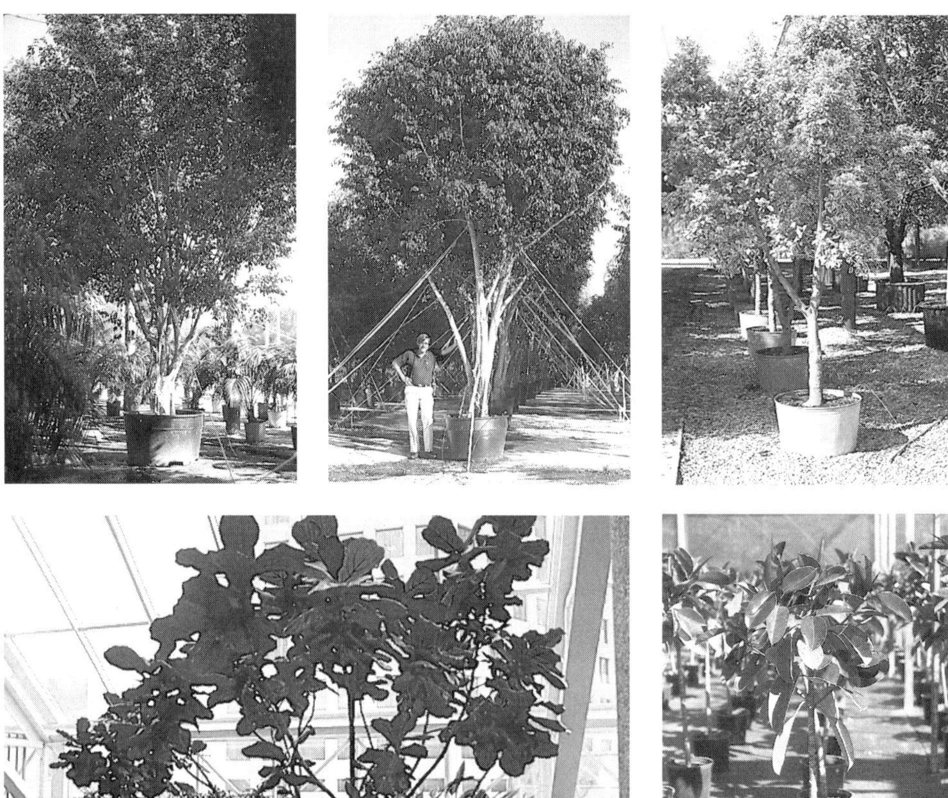

(Clockwise, from top left)

Fig. 2-35a,b.
Differences in crown width can make a big difference in appearance.

Fig. 2-36.
One of several cultivars of variegated Ficus.

Fig. 2-37.
A cultivar of the India Rubber Tree (Ficus elastica *'Burgundy'*).

Fig. 2-38.
Fiddle-leaf Fig (Ficus lyrata)

trunk, or several trunks which have been planted in the same container. They can both also be purchased with wide spreading crowns or relatively narrow crowns (Fig. 2-35a,b), and with a variety of bottom-of-crown heights. They can be purchased with natural, sculptured, or braided trunk forms. Both species can be purchased with either clear trunks or trunks with many aerial roots. And lastly, there are cultivars of both *F. benjamina* and *F. retusa* available with variegated foliage (Fig. 2-36).

Other *Ficus* species are commonly available as well. The coarse-textured India Rubber Tree and its cultivars (*F. elastica* 'Decora', Fig. 2-37) is very popular as a house plant and is normally readily available in sizes below 10 ft (3.0 m). Larger sizes are more difficult to find under cultivation for interior use, although it does grow much taller in the wild. Several noteworthy cultivars have been developed with variegated or offgreen foliage.

The Fiddleleaf Fig (*F. lyrata*, Fig. 2-38) has the largest leaves of any *Ficus* cultivated for interior use, making it the most coarse-textured choice. Its deep, glossy green foliage makes it both unusual to see and difficult to ship, for it is prone to breakage, as is the India Rubber Tree.

Fig. 2-39.
Lesser known Ficus species available in Florida nurseries (Clockwise from upper left): F. 'Alii', *which is becoming more popular; the Zulu Fig Tree,* F. 'Nekbudu'; F. 'Nuda'; *and Rusty Fig Tree,* F. rubiginosa.

Other *Ficus* tree species have been used, but not with the regularity of the previously mentioned. Some of the lesser used *Ficus* trees are the F. 'Alii', Zulu Fig Tree (*F. 'Nekbudu'*), F. 'Nuda', Rusty Fig (*F. rubiginosa*), Mistletoe Fig (*F. deltoides*), and Moreton Bay Fig (*F. macrophylla*) (Fig. 2-39).

Fig. 2-40.
Black Olive (Bucida buceras) *cultivars are supplied in several different habits of growth: (above) with a distinctive, flat-topped crown; and (below) as a standard shade tree.*

Next to the many species and cultivars of *Ficus*, all other interior-cultivated upper-story trees pale into insignificance in terms of quantities shipped, but can be excellent choices, and are worthy of mention.

BUCIDA: The Black Olive (*B. buceras*), which has become much more popular within the last 10 years, can deliver excellent results in reasonably bright light, perhaps 500 fc. The Black Olive can be purchased with two different leaf sizes, one of which is extremely small and thus differentiated from all *Ficus* trees. Black Olive can also be purchased with either a distinctively flat-topped, asymmetrical crown or a more standard, oval shape. They are normally available up to about 20 ft (6.1 m) (Fig. 2-40).

ARAUCARIA: For the design which desires to emulate the northern temperate exterior, a Norfolk Island Pine (*A. heterophylla*, Fig. 2-41) provides a good imitation of a typical coniferous evergreen tree, replete with needles and a sharply pyramidal habit of growth. They are seldom stocked in excess of 15 ft (4.5 m) in height, but field grown specimens can be acclimatized. Specimens as tall as 45 ft (13.7 m) have been installed indoors. It needs about 300 fc to do well.

PODOCARPUS: Another interior plant which successfully imitates the prevalent coniferous evergreen species of the northern temperate climate is the Southern Yew (*P. macrophyllus* 'Maki'), grown as a columnar specimen (see Fig. 2-14, earlier) or well-branched tree (Fig. 2-42). Like the Norfolk Island Pine, it requires about 300 fc to sustain healthy growth. *Podocarpus* can be found in sizes up of to 20 ft (6.1 m) in nurseries, and larger than that in the field.

One excellent advantage of Southern Yew is that its slightly increased hardiness enables it to tolerate lower temperatures better than many other interior plants. For this reason, it is an excellent specimen to locate near windows and doors where drafts may be a problem for other, more delicate plants. As a case in point, three large Southern Yews were planted as part of the original design of the entrance lobby of a Boston hotel in 1983. In January 1984, a fire in the hotel caused the heat in the lobby to be shut off for 3 days. Temperatures in the lobby dropped to the high thirties, yet the three Southern Yews were the only original plants to survive, and they remain perfectly healthy as of this writing (1991).

Weeping Podocarpus (*Podocarpus* 'Gracilior') is a relatively new plant, becoming popularized in the last 10 years. While it has cultural characteristics similar to those of the Southern Yew, it has a completely

Fig. 2-41. (far left)
Norfolk Island Pine
(Araucaria heterophylla)

Fig. 2-42. (left)
The well-branched version of Southern Yew (Podocarpus macrophyllus 'Maki')

Fig. 2-43. (below left)
An excellent specimen of African Fern Pine or Weeping Podocarpus (P. gracilior) *about 15 ft (4.6 m) tall.*

Fig. 2-44. (below)
The Umbrella Tree or Schefflera (Brassaia actinophylla) *used as an upper story specimen in the atrium of the Household Finance Company Headquarters.*

different habit of growth, with graceful, arching branches giving it a weeping effect. It is available as a shrub or small tree up to perhaps 10 to 12 ft (3.0 to 3.7 m) in height (Fig. 2-43).

BRASSAIA: The Umbrella Tree or Schefflera (*B. actinophylla*, Fig. 2-44) is a popular interior shrub sometimes grown as an upper-story plant. As such, it should receive more light, about 400 to 500 fc, than it normally gets as a shrub. It is very common in sizes of up to 10 ft (3.0 m), but can be found up to 30 ft (9.1 m) or more. With foliage consisting of many large palmately configured leaflets, the Umbrella Tree gives a unique appearance as an upper-story plant.

Palms

Hortus Third, one of the industry's standard reference books, states that the palm family (Palmae) consists of "about 210 genera and 2,780 species of evergreen, shrub-like or tree-like plants or vines." The foliage nurseries in the southern and western United States have thus far been able to grow and distribute plants from approximately 15 to 20 of those 210 genera, many of which can be successfully used as upper-story plants.

Palms fall into two basic groups: the cluster types and the solitary types. These growth habits often determine how individual species are used in the interior landscape. The cluster types produce secondary shoots by suckering at the base, creating dense growths at the ground plane that make these plants suitable for use as shrubs when young. The solitary palms do not sucker; instead, they produce single or multiple trunks that are unfettered by secondary shoots.

I have distinguished between trees and palms in the discussion of upper-story specimens because their growth habits, and to a great extent their use characteristics, are completely different from the aforementioned tree genera. Palms offer several design advantages that are unique to their plant family: First, no other group of plants can create the ambiance of a "tropical" environment as readily as palms. Second, the distinctive vertical character of solitary-trunked palms makes these plants ideal for use in tall, narrow spaces that would be too confining for trees of similar height. Third, and converse to the second point, the natural growth habit of many palms are out of plumb (i.e., tilted) or curved, making for trunks with rakish angles or graceful bends. Such characteristics can add much interest to an interior landscape. Fourth, the fibrous root systems of palms enable them to tolerate transplanting into containers that, on average, are smaller than those needed by trees of similar height. This advantage becomes particularly useful when it is difficult to get containers of other large plants onto a job site. And fifth, many of the palms that can be used indoors can tolerate reasonably low light levels, a worthwhile and somewhat unusual trait for plants in the 15 to 40 ft (4.6 to 12.2 m) height range.

One serious drawback of palms, however, is that they cannot be pruned to keep their height constant, as can be done with *Ficus* and many other tall trees. In skylight-equipped atria, where daylight will provide optimal growing conditions, many palms can outgrow their spaces within months, thereby necessitating replacements.

As might be expected, none of the palms tolerant of low light levels (less than 100 fc+/-) fall into the upper-story plant category, for these palms are typical of species found in the wild under the canopies of larger plants above them. There are, however, several excellent palms able to tolerate moderate light (100 to 300 fc) which are available as upper-story plants.

Fig. 2-45.
A row of Queen Palm (Arecastrum Romanzoffianum), *about 18 ft (5.5 m) in height.*

Fig. 2-46.
Kentia Palm (Howea forsterana) *(Courtesy of Architectural Supplements, Inc.)*

ARECASTRUM: Queen Palm (*A. Romanzoffianum* Fig. 2-45) is probably the most commonly available palm in Florida nurseries over 15 ft (4.6 m) in height. They are grown as straight, narrow, solitary plants in heights from 6 to 35 ft (1.8 to 10.7 m). Its medium green pinnae arch downward in ribbons from heavy midribs in a manner that is quite distinctive to the species. Also known in the trade as *Cocus plumosa*, it is an excellent choice for tall, narrow spaces.

HOWEA: Kentia Palm (*H. forsterana*, Fig. 2-46). This species has been used indoors for more than a century, as a favorite of the Victorian parlor planting. With its classic arching shape; dark green fronds; disease, pest, and low-light tolerances; and slow-growing nature, Kentia Palm has achieved a well-earned place as one of the most popular interior plants on the market. And it has achieved this status despite its high cost compared to other similar species such as Areca Palm. Kentia is most commonly available in heights of 3 to 12 ft (0.9 to 3.7 m), with three to five or more plants per pot (ppp). It can be very difficult to find in larger sizes. The arching habit of Kentia Palm is relatively pronounced, and the spread often equals the height, fairly uncommon for many palm species. Kentias can tolerate as little as 50 fc and maintain a healthy appearance.

Fig. 2-47.
Very popular in smaller sizes, the Areca Palm (Chrysalidocarpus lutescens) *makes a spectacular large specimen cluster palm, like this 18 footer (5.5 m).*

Fig. 2-48.
Pygmy Date Palm (Phoenix roebelenii).

CHRYSALIDOCARPUS: Similar in initial appearance to Kentia, the Areca Palm (*C. lutescens*, Fig. 2-47) has lighter green foliage with yellow-green frond stems. It grows very quickly, and so is both relatively inexpensive and popular, but has several drawbacks with regard to its cultivation and use. While it appears to tolerate relatively low light (perhaps as low as 100 fc), it does much better in bright, indirect light of 200 fc or more. Direct sunlight can burn the foliage. It suffers from water stress (too much or too little) under low light, and from mite damage as well. Unlike Kentia, it suckers with age, and becomes a dense, striking specimen as it gets older.

PHOENIX: The genus *Phoenix* contains the Date Palm (*P. dactylifera*) a species known to have been cultivated for thousands of years. Although the Date Palm is used only rarely indoors because of its need for great quantities of light, the genus *Phoenix* does contain several species adaptable for interior use, the most common of which is the Pygmy Date Palm (*P. roebelenii*). This palm has very delicate, medium green, 2 to 5 ft-long fronds that droop down. Both the fronds and trunk are rough and stiff, making the plant difficult to handle. The Pygmy Date Palm, available in heights to 18 ft (5.5 m), is attractive enough to use as a single-trunked specimen, but it is also offered in double- and triple-trunked forms and in clumps. Unlike the Date Palm, the Pygmy Date Palm can tolerant moderate light levels of perhaps 250 fc (Fig. 2-48).

Two other *Phoenix* species are adaptable to a higher light intensity indoors: the Senegal Date Palm (*P. reclinata*), and the Canary Island Date Palm (*P. canariensis*). The Senegal Date Palm is usually offered as a multi-stemmed clump with crooked trunks. The dark-green fronds are up to 6 ft long, with 80 or more pinnae on each side of the midrib. Very sharp thorns, up to 6 in long on the lower parts of the midribs, make this species distinctive to look at and difficult to handle. It is available in heights up to 25 ft (7.6 m) (Fig. 2-49). The Canary Island Date Palm is similar to the Senegal Date Palm, but has a much stouter trunk (Fig. 2-50).

CHAMAEROPS: The European Fan Palm (*C. humilis*), like all fan palms, has a markedly different texture from palms whose fronds have pinnae. The small, silvery-green, thin-bladed, fan-shaped fronds are 2 to 3 ft (0.6 to 0.9 m) wide, and they hold very erect on the trunk, which is covered with burlap leaf sheaths. It is available in heights to 18 ft (5.5 m) (Fig. 2-51).

Fig. 2-49.
Senegal Date Palm (P. reclinata).

Fig. 2-50.
Canary Island Date Palm (P. canariensis).

Fig. 2-51.
European Fan Palm (Chamaerops humilis).

Fig. 2-52.
Chinese Fan Palm (Livistona chinensis).

Fig. 2-53.
MacArthur Palm
(Ptychosperma Macarthuri).

Fig. 2-54.
Manila Palm
(Veitchia merrillii).

Fig. 2-55.
Triangle Palm
(Neodypsis decaryi).

LIVISTONA: The Chinese Fan Palm (*L. chinensis*) differs from the European Fan Palm in that it has larger, coarser, light green fronds, (Fig. 2-52) the tips of which droop as they mature. It is generally grown as a solitary palm with a clear trunk, but it is also available as a shrub-type specimen with little or no trunk. It is usually offered with the frond stems removed, giving a smooth appearance to the trunk. It is available in heights to 30 ft (9.1 m).

PTYCHOSPERMA: The genus *Ptychosperma* offers two attractive specimens: The Alexander or Solitaire Palm (*P. elegans*), and the MacArthur Palm (*P. Macarthurii*). The Alexander Palm, the more popular of the two, is available up to 30 ft (9.1 m). This solitary-type palm is commonly grown in a 2- or 3-ppp multi-stemmed form. It has a cement gray trunk with frond scars (bands) that are about 5 to 6 in (12.7 to 15.2 cm) apart and a large green growing tip. The medium green fronds are about 6 to 8 ft (1.8 to 2.4 m) in length. The MacArthur Palm, much rarer, has foliage similar to that of the Alexander Palm, but it grows in clumps. It also has a smaller-caliper trunk and is less tolerant of low light than the Alexander Palm, preferring medium to high light (Fig. 2-53).

VEITCHIA: The Manila Palm (*V. merrillii*) is similar to the Alexander Palm, with a straight, solitary, cement gray trunk. Its fronds are also medium green, but shorter (5 to 6 ft [1.5 to 1.8 m]) and more erect. The growing tip is shorter, and the bands between frond scars are about 2 to 3 in (5.1 to 7.6 cm) apart. It is available to 30 ft (9.1 m) in height (Fig. 2-54).

NEODYPSIS: The Triangle Palm (*N. decaryi*) is named for the triangular pattern in which its silvery-gray fronds form around the trunk. It is available in heights to 20 ft (6.1 m). This species is unique in ability to survive drought, requiring water no more than once every 6 to 8 weeks (Fig. 2-55).

DECORATIVE CONTAINERS

The material presented so far has dealt with the atrium landscape, the use of plants designed to be "built in" to an interior environment. This is the most challenging, complex, and costly type of interior landscape, but by no means the most common. The "bread and butter" accounts of all interior landscape contractors throughout the world are the ones in which plants are placed in decorative containers as individual specimens or small groupings in commercial office spaces. Much of the design work—i.e., the selection of plants and planters—associated with these accounts is performed by the contractors themselves without the benefit of a design professional's assistance, for clients will often contact a contractor to request that they "put some plants in our office". Unfortunately, that is precisely what many contractors do: *put* plants in offices, rather than *designing* with plants and planters.

Unlike the atrium landscape, which is an integral part of the interior design of the space and one for which a relatively high cost per unit area will be planned by architect and client, the planting of a commercial office space is often the last element to be considered after all the other factors in a tenant fit-up: partition locations, wall and floor coverings, furnishings, window treatments, lighting, etc. Even artwork is often thought of prior to plantings; in fact, plantings are sometimes provided as part of an art budget. With plantings that low on the priority scale, it is often difficult to do much with the remaining budget. Regardless, it is possible to *design* with plants in a commercial office space, which, for the purpose of our discussion in this book, we will call the "office landscape" (see Glossary, Appendix B).

Budget constraints are not the only restricting factor in an office landscape: Lighting—or lack of it—is another common hindrance, as is low ceiling height. Both will serve to limit the types and sizes of plants which can be used, and the ability to maintain plants in the office environment. The most critical constraint of all may be the schedule. Since plants may be an afterthought, their use is often not considered until after the space is built and fit up to the last piece of artwork on the walls. The next factor, delivery dates, becomes a problem: The selected plants and their decorative containers may not have to be the best ones for the space, they have to be the ones that can be delivered within 2 days!

All these constraints can be overcome, or at least dealt with, by the designer who is conversant with the idiosyncrasies of the office landscape. The cost issue is addressed by being familiar with low end plants and planters. Lighting concerns can be resolved by knowing the plants most tolerant of low light and by being familiar with methods of increasing light intensity. Scheduling concerns are mitigated by the designer who knows where in the project's market area plants and planters are kept in stock, or from where they can be quick-shipped.

Designing the office landscape involves three key relationships:

1. A decorative container to its surroundings
2. A plant to its decorative container
3. A "planting"—a plant in its container—to the function and ambiance of its surroundings

The container / interior space-relationship

Fig. 2-56.
Wicker planters are popular because of their low cost, but also add warmth to a design.

Fig. 2-57.
Trompe l'oeil in the interior landscape: inexpensive materials can be finished to look like expensive materials. (Courtesy of Topsiders)

The element that provides the unity between the decor of a commercial office space and its interior landscaping component is not so much the plant as its decorative container. The designer with a comprehensive knowledge of available container materials, styles, shapes, and colors will best be able to provide that unity. The interior environment will invariably feature combinations of textures and materials, and it becomes the container's role to match, blend with, or complement one or more of the materials of the space. Matching materials can be difficult, because interior finishes commonly consist of wallcoverings, carpeting, wood trim, plastic laminate, and painted surfaces, while planter finishes commonly consist of wicker, plastic, terra cotta, ceramic, fiberglass, and metal. Fiberglass and metal containers can be painted, and so can match other interior colors readily (although the gel coat required of a custom color fiberglass finish will invariably cost more and require more time to order than custom colors on metal planters. Containers can also be appliqued with wall or floor covering material to match. Wood planters, on the other hand, can be purchased from manufacturers as off-the-shelf items in a limited but attractive variety of wood types and shapes, or they can be custom-built (budget permitting) to match the grain of a wood used elsewhere in the interior.

The other decorative container materials can only blend with or complement their interior finishes. Normally, the introduction of other materials for plant containers in a space is not a problem, especially for the low-end project, since wicker and plastic plant containers are very popular because of their cost-effectiveness (Fig. 2-56). They are also among the easiest containers to find in stock, should scheduling be an issue. Several manufacturers of plastic and fiberglass containers offer within their product lines faux finishes approximating the color or texture of more expensive materials like marble, granite, or wood (Fig. 2-57).

The plant-container relationship

This is the most basic design relationship in our industry, yet few designers take sufficient time to properly address it. Its essence is one of proportions: A tall plant is generally (not always) inappropriate for a low container and vice versa; a narrow plant is inappropriate for a wide container (Fig. 2-58). There are both aesthetic and horticultural exceptions to this, but it is a reasonable rule of thumb. It is a common fallacy that one must use the smallest decorative container that can accommodate the grow pot. Unfortunately, a client may feel the smallest compatible planter is the most appropriate in terms of cost, a hurdle which may be difficult to overcome.

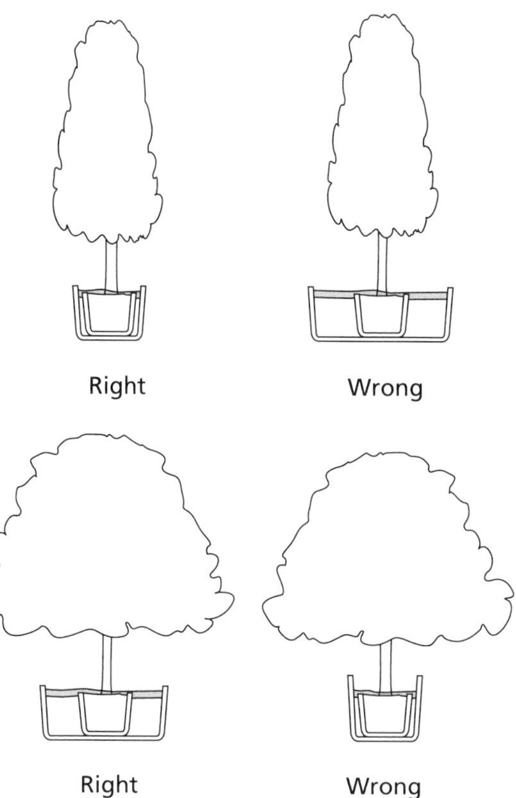

Fig. 2-58.
It is often helpful, though not essential, for the height-width proportion of a plant to blend with the height-width proportion of its planter.

Achieving the desired proportion between a plant and its decorative container can succeed only if the specifier is thoroughly familiar with both the shape of the plant and the specifications of the container. In many instances, design professionals with little hands-on experience in interior plants may not be aware of the height-width ratios of the plants they are specifying, the result of which might be a disproportionate relationship of plant and container. The specifier must be familiar with not only the height but the typical shape and habit of growth of the specified plants (Fig. 2-59).

Fig. 2-59.
The specification of a planter should not be made unless the designer is familiar with the height and width of the plant specified.

The planting-function relationship

The last key design concern of the office landscape is the relationship of the plant or plants in their container ("the planting") to the function and ambience of the space in which they will reside. Because plantings are almost always the last element to be addressed in an office landscape, it is reasonable to presume that little room will be left for them. Prudence must therefore be in specifying the locations of floor plants, because most of the floor space that has not already been used for site furnishings will be relegated to

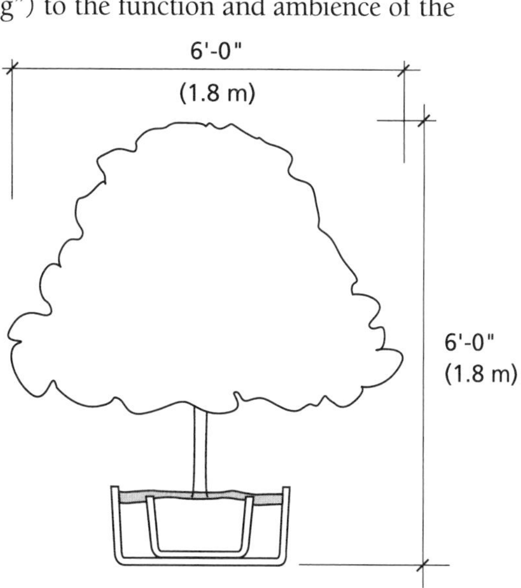

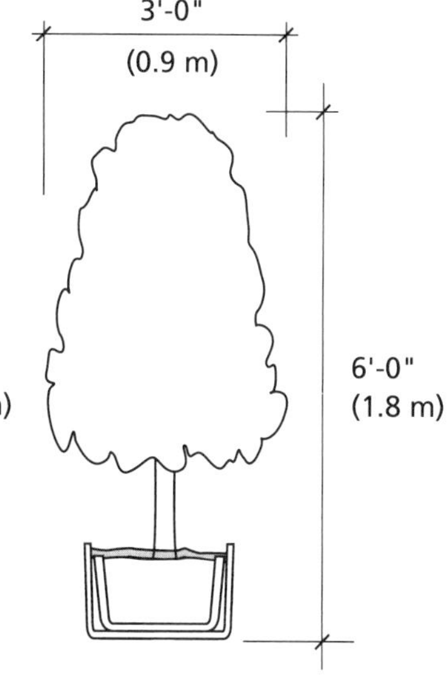

Fig. 2-60. Using planters whose colors are formulated to match partition or file manufacturers can help integrate plants more fully into the interior design of a space. (Courtesy of Topsiders)

Fig. 2-61. The repetition of a long row of files can be mitigated by plants. (Courtesy of Topsiders)

Fig. 2-62. Plants atop files serve both aesthetic and functional uses. (Courtesy of Topsiders)

pedestrian circulation, and plantings that infringe on traffic flow will become nuisances and maintenance problems.

Tall, narrow floor plantings should be considered for such spaces, because they maximize the visual impact of the foliage while using minimal floor space. Even better are hanging plants and those placed atop files, credenzas, tables, or partitions which can provide the color and textural interest of plants without usurping any floor space. This concept is being expounded by several companies that market container systems specifically designed to be placed atop partitions or files and will match the colors of major file and partition manufacturers (Fig. 2-60).

Not all plants must be placed in corners, out of harm's way. They can be used to provide direction to pedestrian circulation or create focal points at the ends of corridors. Plants are much more effective for intentionally changing the flow of traffic or for interrupting the dullness of a long corridor than are file cabinets or partitions (Fig. 2-61).

Plants placed atop file cabinets for aesthetic purposes provide textural relief at or above eye level. They also keep employees from using these spaces as repositories for miscellaneous junk. Here again, planter boxes can be purchased which precisely match the colors of major file manufacturers, allowing the introduction of planters that fit handily into the office landscape (Fig. 2-62).

Decorative mulch

A fairly large specimen, perhaps 10 ft (3.0 m) in height, may have a foliage crown beginning several feet above the top of the decorative container, leaving the top bare. Placing an ornamental mulch atop the grow pot ordinarily finishes off a "planting." Decorative mulches can vary in terms of appearance and cost almost as much as containers, and can help unite a planting with an interior decor almost as much, too. Because wood chips or bark nuggets are so widely used in the exterior landscape, landscape architects often specify bark nuggets even when other choices might be preferable. Some alternatives to bark nuggets are: gravels of many different colors and sizes, river cobbles, granite chips, marble chips, excelsior, and cork nuggets (both natural and colored) (Fig. 2-63). Besides color, size, and cost, availability may also vary widely as well. Check local fire codes to determine if organic nuggets (wood chips, bark, excelsior or cork) must be specified as fire retardant, or if they can be specified at all.

Fig. 2-63.
The selection of aggregate mulches available to the interior landscape designer is not limited to gray gravel. Choices vary in color from black to white, tan, brown, and rust, green and blue; sizes vary from sand or pea gravel to stones as large as 3 in (7.6 cm); textures range from sharply jagged to naturally smooth to polished river cobbles.

PRESERVED PLANTS

While walking through an interior landscape trade show several years ago, I slowly approached a *Ficus benjamina* tree about 8 ft (2.4 m) tall. The first thing I noticed, while I was still about 20 ft (6.1 m) away from it, was that its shape and fullness seemed almost perfect. It appeared to be a singularly outstanding specimen. And the beauty of this specimen didn't diminish as I got closer. It wasn't until I got to within about 5 ft (1.5 m) of it that I noticed it wasn't a *Ficus* at all. In fact, it wasn't a real tree; It was a dead trunk onto which were affixed hundreds of replicas of *F. benjamina* leaves fashioned from polyester fabric.

I had two equal and opposite reactions. The first was "Wow, they sure have made artificial plants realistic! This is great!" The second was "What is this world coming to, where people are spending their time manufacturing plants that look more like plants than the real plants do?" My initial exposure, many years previous, to the concept of artificial plants was vehemently negative: The first artificial plants were hopelessly unrealistic, and the use of artificial plants defeated the whole purpose of having plants indoors. As a landscape architect, I have undertaken a role to "preserve, protect, and defend" the environment. Does the destruction of trees, to be appliqued with plastic leaves and placed indoors serve that purpose? No. What benefit, therefore, can there be in using artificial or preserved plants?

Plants have become so ubiquitous in our indoor environment that there is scarcely a location where someone hasn't specified a plant: They are used as focal points, they help direct traffic, they fill voids, they add color, they add texture. Many of these applications in which plants are desired are not appropriate horticulturally, and for one reason or another, plants will not sustain themselves. The purist in me says that in such cases we either should not use plants at all or should alter the environment to make it horticulturally appropriate. The pragmatist in me says that as long as real plants can't live there, and a client wants the look of plants, and they are now as realistic as they are, why not?

I do *not* believe that artificial or preserved plants should be substituted en masse for live plants simply because a client or tenant thinks it will be easier to deal with a non-living plant. But I can justify the limited use of preserved plants in certain situations:

The Case for Preserved Plants

INSUFFICIENT LIGHT: We all know there are settings where live plants won't survive because there is not enough light. We also know there are clients who will want plants in such places, but who are not willing to pay for the constant replacement of plants which fail, or who do not wish, for whatever reason, to install appropriate supplemental lighting.

TOO MUCH LIGHT: In rarer cases, plants are placed in conditions where light is so intense that they either outgrow their space too quickly, or the combination of light and heat makes for intolerable conditions. Most designers wish for the luxury of copious amounts of light, but there can be an excessive light in certain instances.

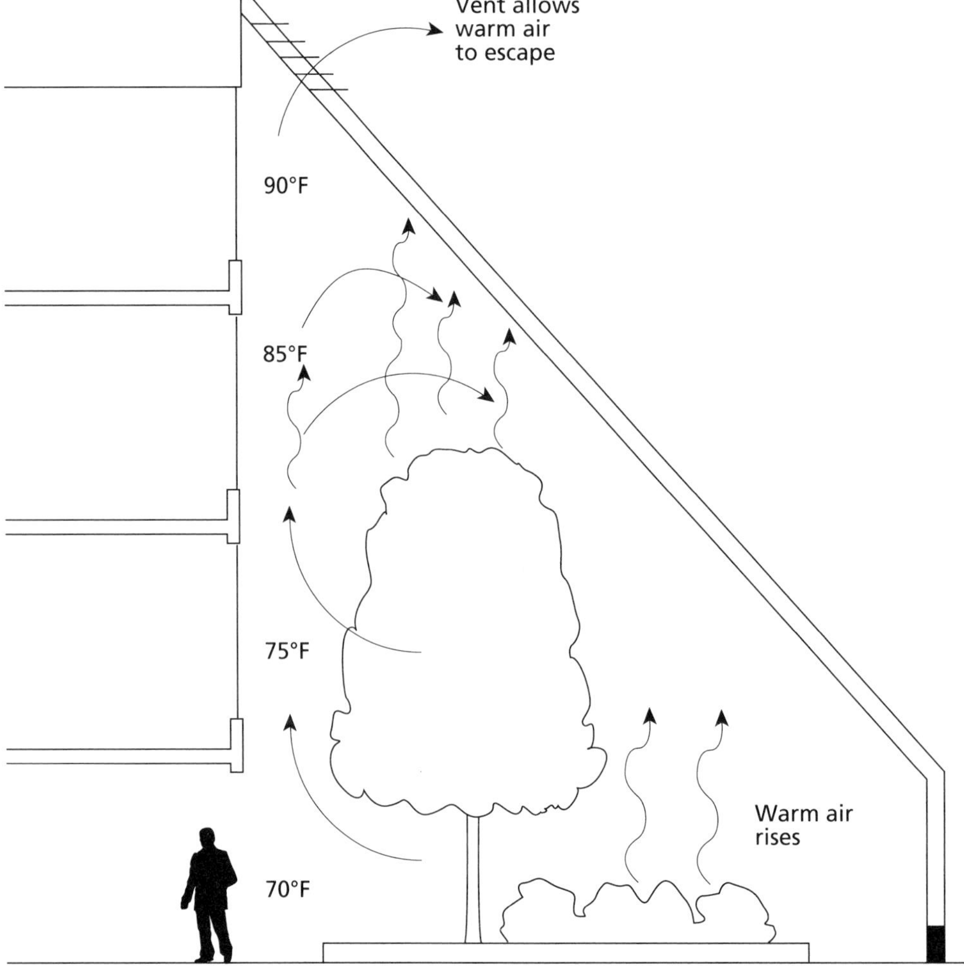

*Fig. 2-64.
The Greenhouse Effect: Warm air will be trapped at the top of multi-story spaces, unless it is expelled through roof vents or mechanically recirculated. During cold weather, air warmed by solar energy at the top of an atrium can be used to help heat a building by recirculating it through the building's HVAC system. Foliage within the upper portions of these spaces can be severely damaged.*

UNSUITABLE TEMPERATURES: Tropical plants do best in tropical temperatures, but providing such conditions everywhere in a building can sometimes be difficult. For example, plants placed near doors in northern temperate climate buildings can be subjected to blasts of freezing air for several seconds at a time, easily long enough to cause damage to tender foliage.

Heat build-up can also cause problems, as can happen to plants placed on south-facing window sills in buildings with marginal ventilation systems, or buildings whose ventilation systems are cut back on weekends. Similarly, the crowns of tall plants in skylight-equipped atria can suffer from the "greenhouse effect" as heat builds up in the upper portions of these multistory spaces. (Fig. 2-64)

Last, plants placed too near heating or air-conditioning outlets can be subjected to extremely hot or cold air being ejected from this outlets. Even air from a fresh air make-up vent that is room temperature can dry out a plant enough to cause damage.

INACCESSIBILITY: Many architects and clients create locations for plantings with degrees of inaccessibility that defy the ability—and courage—of even the most intrepid service technician. Knowing that service will be difficult, some architects intentionally design such spaces with artificial plants in mind. The archetypal example is the planting along a balcony that is separated from the pedestrian area with a glass handrail.

WEIGHT: The desire to use large specimens in an interior landscape must sometimes be tempered by the reality that the floor slab upon which the plants are to be placed cannot support the weight of the specified materials. Most building codes require load tolerances of 100 to 150 lb/ft^2 (1012 to 1519 Kilograms per square centimeter) for "typical" floor conditions. Some larger plant specimens—generally in excess of 15 to 20 ft (4.6 to 6.1 m)—may have densities greater than 100 lb/ft^2. In such cases, the use of live plants will be dependent on the ability of a structural engineer to design increased load tolerances. This requires close coordination and additional time and cost for both the design and construction of the structural slab.

ENVIRONMENTAL CONSIDERATIONS: Despite the results of the NASA study (see the Epilogue) on the air-cleaning capabilities of plants, there are still many people who believe that live plants are harmful to interior environments or their inhabitants. As an example, every so often one hears of hospital administrators who direct staff to remove live plants from hospital rooms, claiming the plants will cause allergic reactions or more serious problems for patients. Although I am aware of no data to support this claim, this belief, however founded, can be very difficult to overcome.

MAINTENANCE COST: The client who already deals with live plants knows that they must be watered, fertilized, trimmed, rotated, pruned, cleaned and sometimes replaced. The time and expense of providing this service is often thought to disappear when dealing with artificial or preserved plants. Maintenance costs will not disappear for non-living plants, but they are lessened.

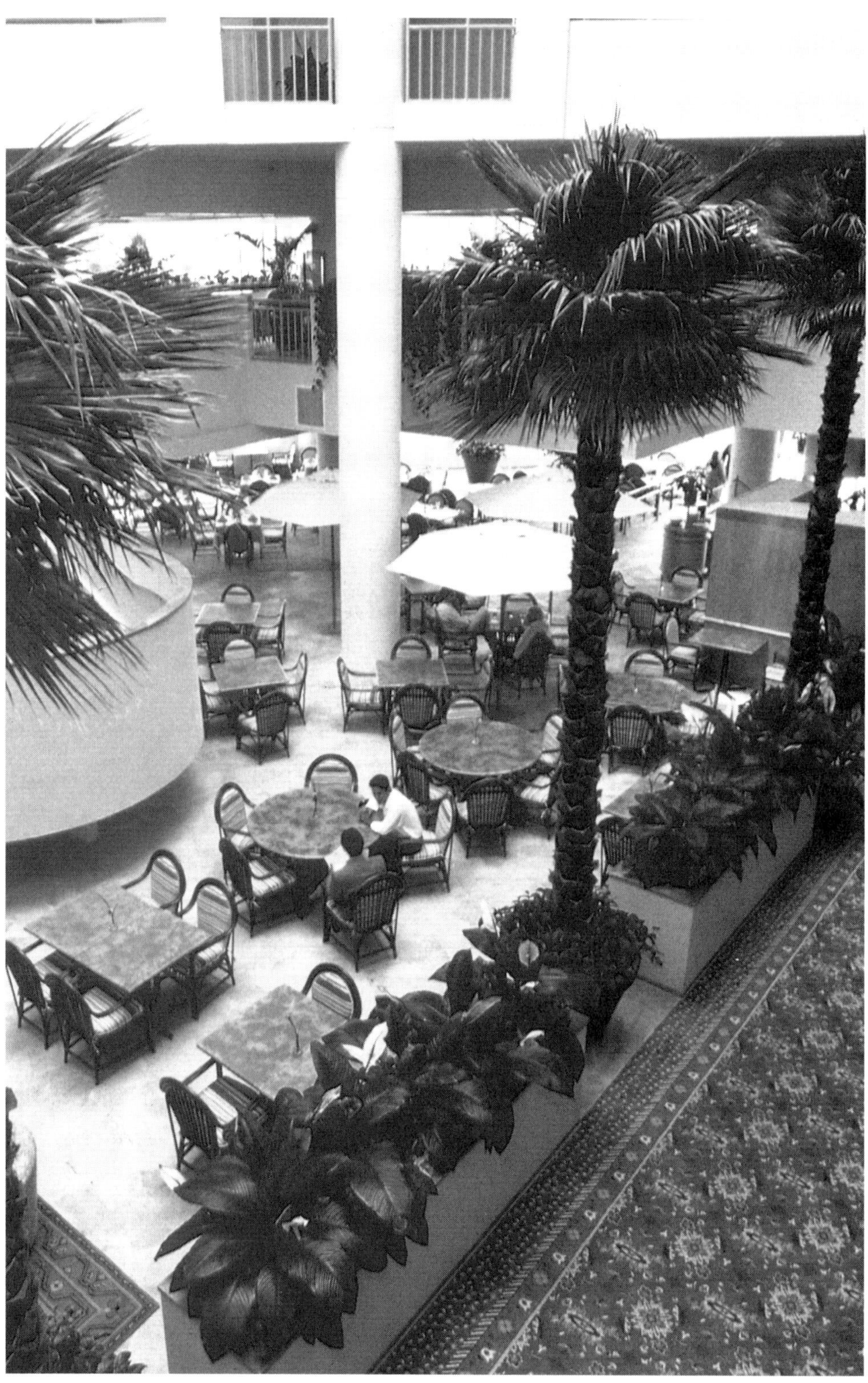

Fig. 2-65.
Combining preserved plants with live plants offers a convincing way to integrate both into an interior landscape. In this hotel lobby, the palms are preserved and the underplantings are live! (Courtesy of Associated Plantscapers, Inc.)

The Case for Live Plants

Although all these factors have merit, the use of artificial and preserved plants must be tempered by the very strong rationale for using live plants indoors:

Fig. 2-66.
Artificial flowers can be extremely realistic, and allow a client to create flowering plant programs more cost-effectively by rotating the same flowers continually.

HEALTH BENEFITS: The NASA study has proven beyond a reasonable doubt that plants do, in fact, absorb harmful chemicals from indoor air. One area that the NASA study did not explore is the prevalence of some of these and other chemicals. Further research should focus on the omnipresence of pollutant substances in "typical" indoor air, and how effective certain types of plants are in metabolizing these pollutants into harmless plant nutrients. Over and above their ability to mitigate levels of harmful chemicals, plants also remove carbon dioxide from air and replace it with oxygen and water vapor. This basic act of the process of photosynthesis helps mitigate excessive levels of carbon dioxide in indoor air, itself a contributor to "Sick Building Syndrome." As better monitoring equipment permits the accurate measure of pollutant presence, and the pervasiveness of indoor air quality concerns is better documented, the call for corrective actions will become more vocal. Plants can play a pivotal role in this process.

DIVERSITY: Live plants change. They grow up, they branch out, their leaves get larger, they flower, their leaves turn color. Even qualities perceived as detrimental—wilting when in need of water, dropping leaves, leaves turning yellow—offer evidence of the dynamism of living plants.

PSYCHOLOGICAL BENEFITS: Studies have proven that plant use indoors creates positive mental attitudes and increases worker productivity.

COSTS: The costs to purchase and install live plants are generally less than those for artificial and preserved plants, except where extremely large live specimens are used, and labor costs to install them can be considerable.

The listed factors justifying the use of non-living plants are reasonable, yet many design professionals– myself included—have philosophical objections to their specification. It would seem that the ideal use of non-living plants would be their integration within a context of living plants in an interior landscape (Fig. 2-65). Few people would advocate the creation of a design utilizing mostly or totally non-living plants. Even the manufacturers and distributors of these products recognize the limitations of widespread use. But the conditions warranting non-living plant use are often unavoidable.

The landscape architect's involvement in an interior landscape design will occur during the design of a building, before structural steel is fabricated or concrete is poured, and significantly, before the environmental systems of the building are irrevocably defined. Many interior landscape contractors who are given the responsibility to do design work do not have that luxury, and are forced to adapt a design to "given" conditions. It is this situation that makes the specification of non-living plants logical.

The incorporation of a flowering plant program in an interior landscape design can be an interesting application for artificials. Besides their realism, artificial flowers that are either rotated within a design or stored between uses can provide clients with substantial cost savings over natural flowers, with their high cost and short life span (Fig. 2-66).

The introduction several years ago of preserved plants has expanded possibilities in the non-living plant arena. Preserved plants consist of real leaves (or fronds, in the case of palms) which have been harvested as living specimens and chemically treated to maintain their appearance. They are then attached to a manufactured or natural trunk. While artificial plants—plastic or polyester—can often have a distinctly artificial appearance, most preserved plants appear to be real to the great majority of people who view them. The use of preserved plants, especially in conjunction with real plants, can often produce excellent aesthetic results.

One final note relative to non-living plants: Many people refer to them as "silk" plants. An interior landscape contractor who installed artificial plants which he called "silk" was threatened with a lawsuit when his client noted that they were not silk but polyester. In this litigious society, honesty is the best policy.

The use of plants—living, artificial, or preserved—adds grace, texture, color, and warmth to the interior environment. The selection of appropriate plants for a given interior space need not be a complicated process, nor is it magic. The application of the fundamentals of design, coupled with the knowledge of interior plants and the special requirements of their environmental well-being, will provide the designer with the means to create lasting beauty with plants.

CHAPTER THREE
DESIGN DOCUMENTATION

The classic cartoon shows a person lost in thought, trying to solve a problem. Suddenly an idea is born, signified by the light bulb which glows brightly above the now ecstatic person's head. The successful interior landscape design may possibly be born in a burst of creative energy—although it sure doesn't happen to *me*—but more often it is the result of a painstaking process of effort and refinement, repeated many times until the design intent is acceptable to client and designer, and the documentation is detailed enough to be built by a contractor.

The Design Process

While the solution to a problem may be agonizing to attain, the mechanism exists to achieve that solution, a process allowing the designer to identify the scope of the project and the elements within it; to establish the proper juxtaposition of the various elements with respect to each other; and to develop and refine the necessary detailing from bubble diagram to scaled, hard-lined plan.

An interior landscape can vary from a few plants in decorative containers occupying a small office, to the planting of many entire floors of a skyscraper, to the creation of a large indoor park which re-creates an entire exterior environment under glass. Its size, complexity, schedule, and budget will determine the amount of documentation needed to satisfy a client's level of interest and involvement in the design process, and the contractor's requirements during the construction period. It must be remembered that an overriding reason for establishing a process at all is to keep a client abreast of refinements as a design progresses, and to get the client to agree with the course the design is taking.

The most complex and large scale projects will require the most definitive possible documentation. Lesser projects will be able to avoid many of the various steps along the way.

Predesign

The first steps in the design process are technically not part of the design process at all, but steps considered part of "Predesign": Programming and site analysis. It is programming that permits the designer to delve into the client's wants, needs, and budget; in effect, to "scope out" the project. The success which the designer has in extracting information from the client during this phase will help shorten the remainder of the design process and should substantially reduce the number of revisions necessary because the designer was unaware of the client's wishes.

As programming permits the designer to learn about the clients' intended plans, the site analysis enables the designer to learn about the constraints and opportunities which the site offers for the proposed project.

PROGRAMMING

During programming, the designer should request the following information:

1. All potential locations to receive plants. A client (or architect) may hire a designer to provide an atrium planting, not realizing that many other areas within a building may benefit by having plants in them. The designer should take a pro-active role in helping the client to determine which areas within a building should have plants.

2. The interior landscape. Once the areas to receive plants have been identified, the nature of the interior landscape should be discussed. Will there be a modest use of plants, perhaps a few plants in decorative containers, or will there be a large interior garden in the space? If they are decorative containers, will they be wicker baskets, custom thrown pottery, or some other material and color? The answers will depend on the degree of interest the client has in having plants in the space (or the interest in plants the designer can *generate* in the client), the programmatic need for plants, and, of course, the budget. The designer should again play a pro-active role in assessing the implications of these issues.

3. The design process and outcome. Does the client have any preconceived notions of what is to be designed? Many clients know precisely what they want, and lack only the skill to present their ideas on paper. Other clients may not have a clue as to what they wish to see. The designer must ascertain this information, for the client may not even realize that they can provide a direction to the design work. The more interactive the client can be with the design process, the faster a mutually achievable goal will be reached. The exception to this is the client who places implicit faith in the designer to arrive at an acceptable solution, and allows the designer to proceed without power of review because the client is ultimately willing to accept whatever the designer presents.

4. Non-plant elements. Will the designer be responsible for elements other than plants: paving, planters, water features, seating, furnishings, etc.? The responsibility of adding non-plant elements into an interior landscape often "falls through the cracks" when a scope of work is being established. The interior landscape designer should determine what elements the client wishes to have in the space if it has not been determined by the client or architect. If the interior landscape designer is not capable of properly specifying these elements, the task must fall on someone else on the design team, or a new consultant must be retained. Because changing a scope of work carries with it the

burden of adding fee to a job, this determination should be completed as early in the design process as possible.

5. Schedule. When must the design work be completed, and when must the construction be completed? Have intermediate dates been set-up for design reviews, or for public presentations?

6. Budget. The $64,000 Question! What is the client prepared to pay for the installation of plants? Is the client aware of the anticipated cost of *maintenance* of plants? The mere mention of maintenance may cause a client to be taken aback, not realizing that an on-going cost will be required for any interior landscape. Is the client prepared to pay the installer to maintain the plantings after installation? Or will the client's own staff maintain plants after the installation?

Many clients have no idea what interior plants will cost to purchase, lease, *or* maintain. To help provide the client with this information, the designer must prepare a design of sufficient detail that the client can envision what plants will do for a space, and then accurately estimate the cost of the work prior to its construction. This topic will be addressed in detail in Chapter Seven: Conceptual Cost Estimation.

SITE ANALYSIS

The site analysis portion of the Predesign phase is devoted to collecting data about the location(s) to receive plants. For an interior landscape, the site will fit into one of several categories: It will be an existing building being retrofitted for plants, a new building (or addition) recently completed, a new building under construction, or a new building about to be built. To a great extent the category will determine how much information is available. Whatever the case, the designer must be responsible for *assessing*, if not actually establishing, all the environmental and aesthetic factors which will ultimately determine the ability of plants to thrive in that space. These factors are

1. **Size of space:** What are the dimensions of the space(s) to receive plants: length, width, height?

2. **Location of space or access:** Will the space(s) to receive plants be located on the ground floor? If not, how high up or down will they be? Will elevators be available to bring materials in? If so, how big are the elevators? If elevators will not be available, how will plants be brought into the space?

3. **Structural parameters:** What is the structural configuration of the floor slab, or more specifically, what is the loading capacity of the floor? Can large specimens be properly supported if necessary? Is there flexibility in depressing the slab if desired? Is there occupied space below, such as a garage? If so, is it heated?

4. **Lighting parameters:** What is the light availability going to be in the space? Will light come from natural or artificial means, or both? If the space is skylighted, is the glazing clear, tinted, or reflective glass? Is it a translucent material? If lighting is from sidewall (i.e., window) glazing, what are the sizes and heights of the windows? What type of window glazing will be used? What kind of window treatments are being used? Will the designer have any control of the use of window treatments? What is the percentage of light transmittance for the glazing? If the space is electrically lighted, what is the type of light source to be used? Are they on special timers? Are they properly aimed? What will the light intensity be? Has a lighting analysis of the space been done to determine light levels? If not, is it possible to do it later?

5. **Water supply:** Will a source of water be available near the plantings? Will it be softened? Will it be tempered? Is the client willing to consider either subirrigation or drip irrigation? If so, is the client aware of the up-front costs of sub- or drip irrigation?

6. **Temperature:** What temperature range are the mechanical engineers planning to use for general building comfort? Will thermostats be set to conserve energy? Will temperatures be automatically set back on weekends or evenings?

7. **Ventilation:** Where will sources of air supply and return be located, and will they conflict with potential plant locations? What will be the temperature and velocity of heated or air-conditioned air coming out of these vents?

8. **Interior finishes:** With what materials are the walls and floors covered? Will they be light colored or dark? Will they be shiny or flat? Can they be washed? Will their colors blend or conflict with any of the materials the interior landscape designer is using?

9. **Maintenance:** If the interior landscape is a substantial one, is there a maintenance facility (i.e., storage room with sink) near the potential plantings?

All these facts will have an impact of one kind or another on the success of the interior landscape design, or on its cost, or on its ability to keep plants horticulturally sound. Many of these facts will be undetermined at the time the designer is retained, to be set by the interior landscape designer. Many, regrettably, will be unknown and the designer will have no way of discerning them until late in the design process, or even after the plants are installed. The designer must make a concerted effort to understand all the environmental factors which will affect plant health.

The predesign phase of a small project may consist of the first 15 minutes of the first interview with a client, and may not need to identify answers to many of these questions. The more complex project, on the other hand, may generate many other questions in addition to the ones stated, and may take weeks to complete, since information may have to come from several different sources. A site visit to an out-of-town location may be required to inspect existing conditions.

Once the designer has reviewed the program sufficiently to become conversant with the client's desires, and has reviewed the site information available enough to be knowledgeable about it, the process of design can begin.

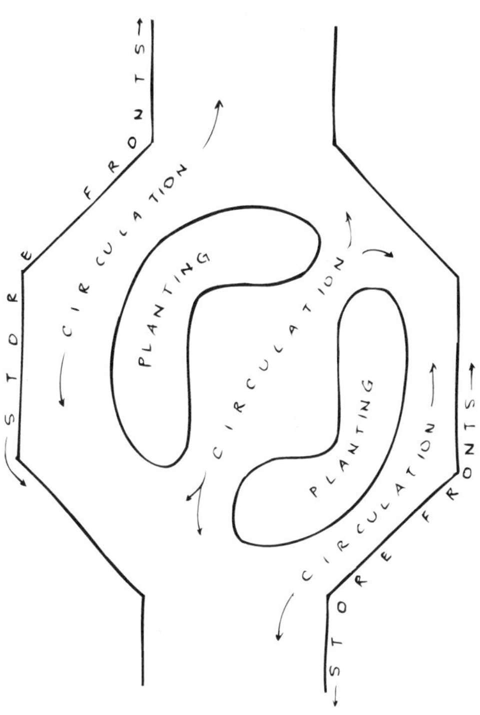

Fig. 3-1.
The "Bubble Diagram" is the first step in the graphic depiction of a design intent. It establishes the juxtaposition of the components within an interior landscape. This bubble diagram is for a hypothetical shopping mall atrium, whose purpose is to broadly define the "land use" of the atrium space, creating approximate area percentages of planting to circulation space and the approximate locations of plantings relative to circulation and the storefronts.

Schematic Design

The most basic phase of the design process is schematic, or conceptual, design, a phase in which elementary decisions are made that will form the basis for more refined and detailed decisions later in the design process. The most preliminary element of schematic design is the "bubble diagram", a means used to accomplish nothing more than deciding where key elements will exist in relation to each other. At this early stage, no scale is used, the specific idiosyncrasies of the site might be ignored, and attention to detail is not an issue. (Fig. 3-1)

SCALE

The most commonly used scale in the United States for drawing architectural plans is 1/8 in = 1 ft 0 in. For projects virtually anywhere else in the world, the metric system is used, and the nearest metric equivalent of the so-called "eighth" scale is 1:100 (the actual metric conversion of eighth scale is 1:96). Eighth scale is popular because it offers sufficient size to show a reasonable amount of detail, yet it is small enough that many entire buildings will be able to fit on a typical drawing sheet. Large buildings will often be drawn at the schematic design phase, or even the later design development phase, at 1/16 in = 1 ft 0 in (nearest metric equivalent, 1:200) or 1/32 in = 1 ft 0 in (1:400), simply because a building may be so large that it will not fit on a typical (i.e., 24 x 36 in (61.0 x 91.4 cm) or 30 x 42 in [76.2 x 106.7 cm]) drawing sheet, and it is imperative that an architect present buildings early in the design phase to a client that are inclusive on one sheet. Once the building is finalized, drawings suitable for construction will be drawn at a scale of 1/8 in = 1 ft 0 in regardless of the number of drawings needed to depict the extent of the building.

The so-called "eighth scale" is suitable for many interior landscape plans. An exception might be a very complex, garden-type installation where plants are densely spaced and detail requirements force the use of a larger scale, perhaps 1/4 in = 1 ft 0 in (1:50), or 3/8 in = 1 ft 0 in (1:30). Another exception might be the office landscape plan so packed with furnishings and other interior design elements that the identification of plants may be difficult.

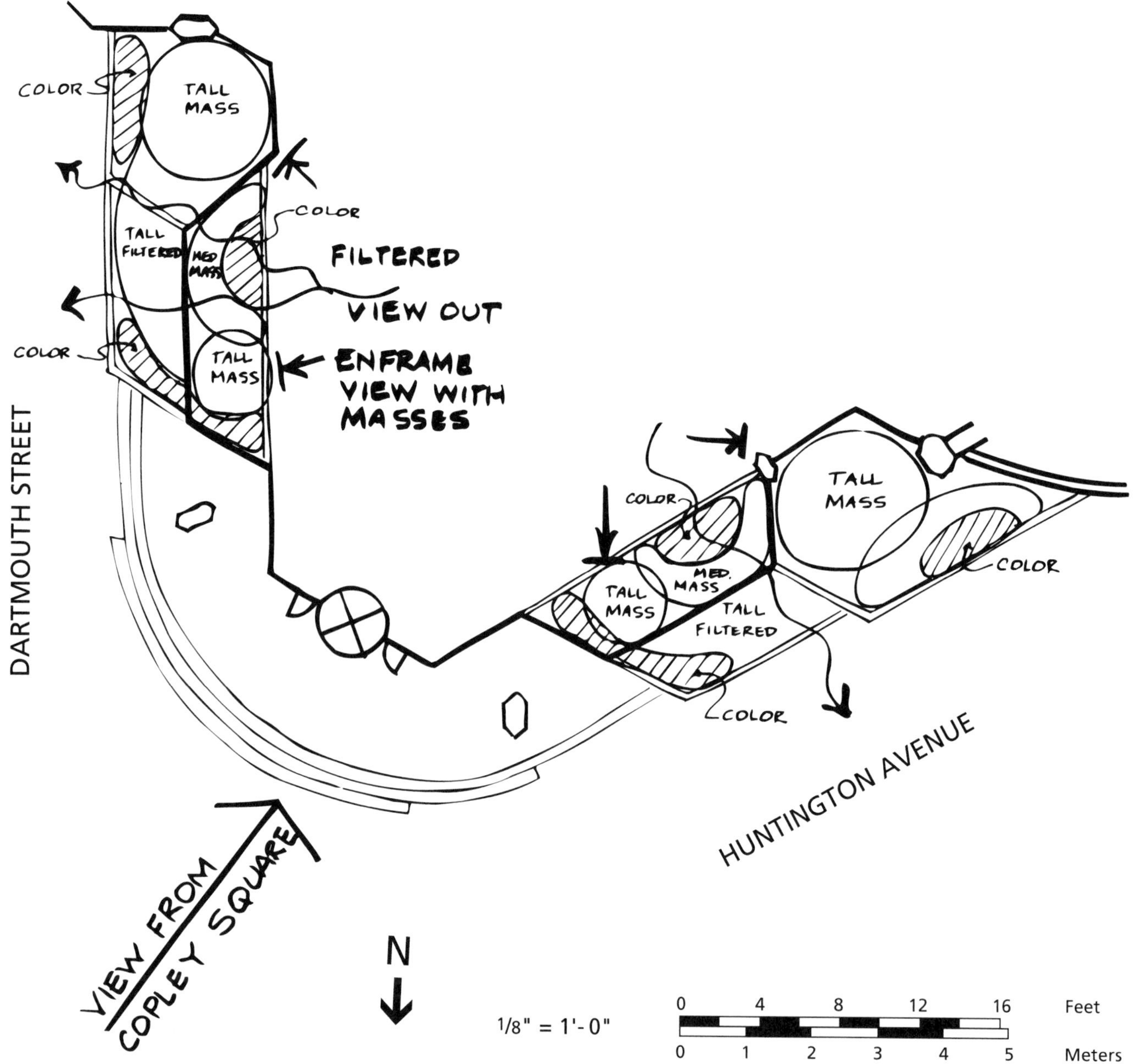

Fig. 3-2.
This conceptual plan is the first graphic representation prepared for the design of a built project, the entrance lobby planting of the Westin Hotel at Copley Place, Boston, MA. Its primary purpose was to create and define an interrelationship between the interior and exterior plantings on either side of the glazing of the lobby entrance, represented by the heavy black lines. The north arrow and street names have been added to the original sketch to help orient the viewer. (Courtesy of The Architects Collaborative, Inc.)

The completed bubble diagram will present the correct juxtaposition of interior landscape elements. The next refinement of the bubble diagram will incorporate this juxtaposition within the bounds of the scaled plan, a drawing we can call a "conceptual plan" (Fig. 3-2). Circles used to indicate the spread of particular plants will approximate their actual size. In order to get a feeling for the type of plants to be selected, they might be described in basic terms, such as "tall palm tree"; "fine-textured ground cover"; or "low, spreading shrub". Specific decisions with regard to plant species will occur in later phases, as will a plant list, essential to the proper specification of plants. The depiction of the schematic design on paper is first performed as a working tool to allow you, as the designer to express your thoughts to yourself. This "in-house" or "study" drawing is for the designer's eyes only, not for the client's consumption. Here, neatness doesn't count, ideas do (Fig. 3-3).

COORDINATION

One factor many designers wait too long to deal with, or even ignore entirely, is coordination with other disciplines. In any given interior space, plants will be dependent on the mechanical systems of the room in which they are located for their survival. Although the thorough designer will investigate the mechanical elements of the design as part of the site analysis, a continuing dialogue with the architect, interior designer, and the engineers—HVAC, plumbing, electrical and structural—during the entire design process will ensure that no surprises lurking within the horticultural environment greet the designer and contractor during construction. Unless directed otherwise, it is reasonable to presume that mechanical, plumbing and structural consultants will design their respective engineering systems for nothing more than the basic requirements of the people who will be using the space, and not for plants.

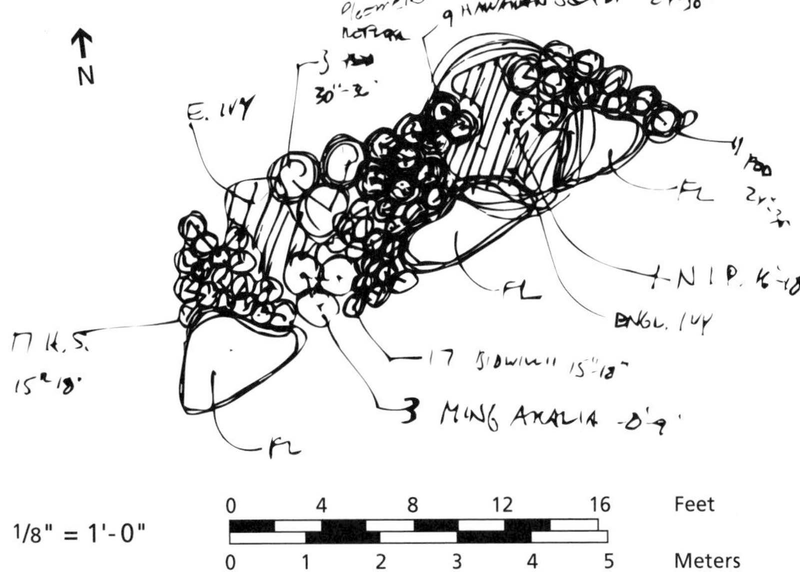

Fig. 3-3.
An in-house working sketch of the Huntington Avenue interior planter begins to identify specific plants by genus and species.

Abbreviations used in this sketch.

E. IVY – English Ivy
FL – Flowers
HS – Hawaiian Schefflera
N.I.P – Norfolk Island Pine
POD – Podocarpus macrophyllus

(Courtesy of The Architects Collaborative, Inc.)

It is also reasonable to presume that these consultants will have been brought into the design process long before the interior landscape designer is retained. It follows that the responsibility to alert the engineering consultants to any unique requirements of plants should rest with the interior landscape designer.

The last and perhaps most important element of the schematic design phase is the presentation to the client. In many cases, the schematic design presentation will be the first documentation the client will see from the designer, and could solidify the impression the client will forever have of the designer, regardless of how the designer may perform in later stages of the work ("You get only one chance to make a good first impression"). The schematic design presentation requirements can usually be satisfied with a rendered plan showing locations of plants, perhaps graphically depicted to be characteristic of the horticultural

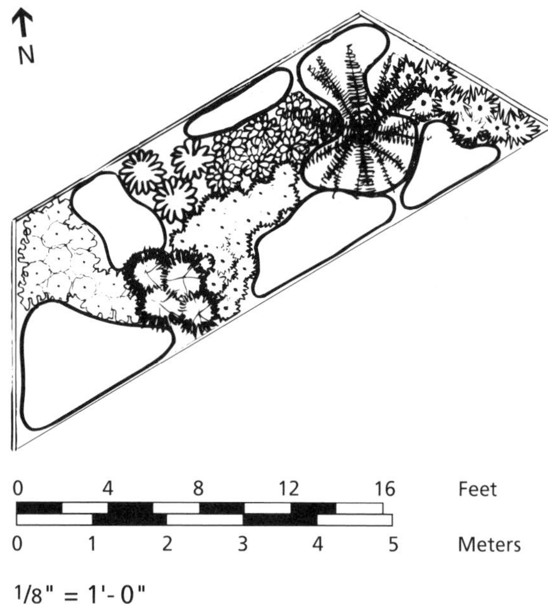

Fig. 3-4.
A schematic design presentation plan of the Huntington Avenue interior planter portrays the plants to the correct scaled size without identifying individual plant names. The graphic representation of the plants is done in a manner which helps the viewer interpret the texture of the proposed plants. Plant names have been kept off to allow the landscape architect to keep the oral presentation to the client as flexible as possible. (Courtesy of The Architects Collaborative, Inc.)

qualities of the plants (Fig. 3-4). Demanding clients or projects with considerable horticultural complexity may require elevation drawings, or one or more perspective sketches. The size of the project, and hence its design fee, might determine your need or ability to retain the services of an illustrator to assist with the preparation of sketches if you or your firm lack the in-house expertise to prepare appropriate graphic presentation materials.

Some clients may wish to become better acquainted with specific plant types at this stage.

As the designer, you have three options:

(1) Show the client photos of selected specimens from either your own collection or those which have been previously published (Figs. 3-5 to 3-7);

(2) show the client drawings of plants from published sources, drawings you have had commissioned for you, or, if you are artistically inclined, sketches you have prepared (Fig. 3-8); or

(3) accompany your client on a tour of a local greenhouse (perhaps your own facility, if you are a contractor) to show the client first hand what plants they might consider in certain instances (Fig. 3-9).

Plant lists—in which the plants are identified by botanical and common name, size, quantity, and any special characteristics—are not appropriate at this time. If planters are to be included in the design, the schematic phase might indicate their material, without yet calling out a size and shape.

Schematic design is the first point at which an estimate of the construction cost might occur, especially if the client is cost-conscious to the point where future direction of the design will be dictated largely by budget factors. One of the sources of data a contractor will use to determine costs is the specifications, which provides detailed descriptive data on the materials and methods of construction for the work involved. Although the schematic design phase is premature for a complete specifications package, an "outline" specification might sometimes be included within a presentation at this time. The outline specification will simply list, without descriptions, the materials to be employed.

Fig. 3-5.
My own photo of a Maria Chinese Evergreen, taken at a Trade Show of the Interior Plantscape Division of the Associated Landscape Contractors of America's Annual Meeting. A camera is a must for landscape architects fortunate enough to attend such meetings. The primary use of my slide collection is for my own personal reference, but I will often present slides like this to clients to familiarize them with plant species proposed for a design.

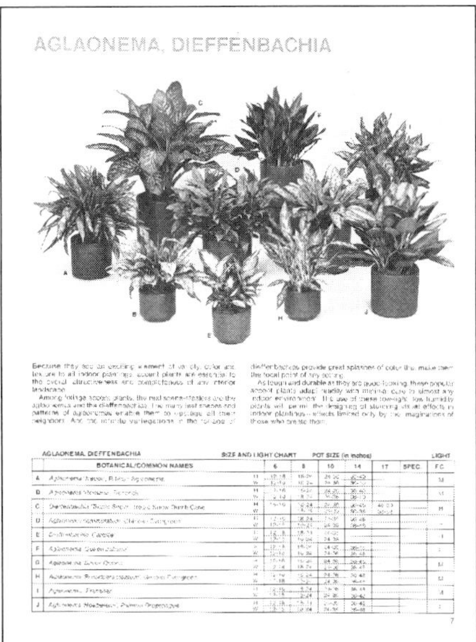

Fig. 3-6.
"Plants for Interior Landscapes", published by the Interior Plantscape Division of the Associated Landscape Contractors of America (ALCA) is a full color brochure featuring many popular plants which can be purchased from ALCA for use as a sales tool, or for informational purposes. (Courtesy of the Associated Landscape Contractors of America)

Fig. 3-7.
Many interior landscape contractors provide plant selector guides like this to potential clients. (Courtesy of Rentokil Tropical Plants, Inc.)

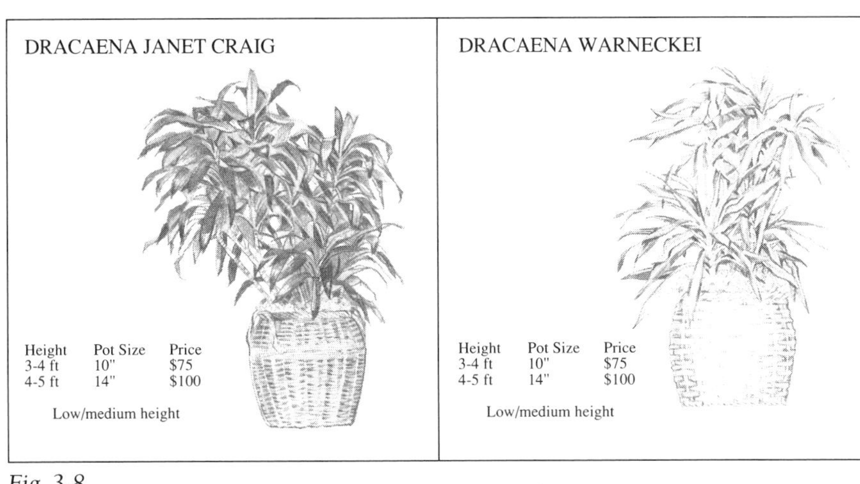

Fig. 3-8.
Sketches of plants, even if they are prepared by someone other than yourself, convey a sense of artistry to a potential client. These were prepared by professional illustrator Bill Owen for Tata White of mr. greenjeans, inc., and are used as a marketing tool. (Courtesy of mr. greenjeans, Inc.)

Fig. 3-9.
A plant holding area in an interior landscape contractor's headquarters prepped to receive a group of potential clients. (Courtesy of Southern Tropic of Plants, Ltd.)

Design Development

Once the client has seen and approved the initial concept, a second stage of design is begun in which the results of the schematic stage are taken to a higher level of detail, but short of the detail necessary to actually give the documents to a contractor for construction. This allows the client to follow the progress of the design without the designer expending a great deal of time and fee going in a direction divergent from the client's wishes. Measurements become an important consideration at this time. The precision of determining exactly where program elements will be located within the space is now as important as the overall design concept.

The elements of a design development submission might be:

1. An **illustrative plan**, drawn to scale (probably 1/8 in = 1 ft 0 in ; 1:100), showing locations for all plants, preferably in juxtaposition with other elements in the space, such as pavement, curbing, water features, and seating. This plan will show plants as circles or perhaps more horticulturally accurate graphically, and will identify plants by specific names (Fig. 3-10).

2. If the design is to be a garden-type, **a preliminary grading plan** might be necessary, to indicate any changes in the finish grade of the planting.

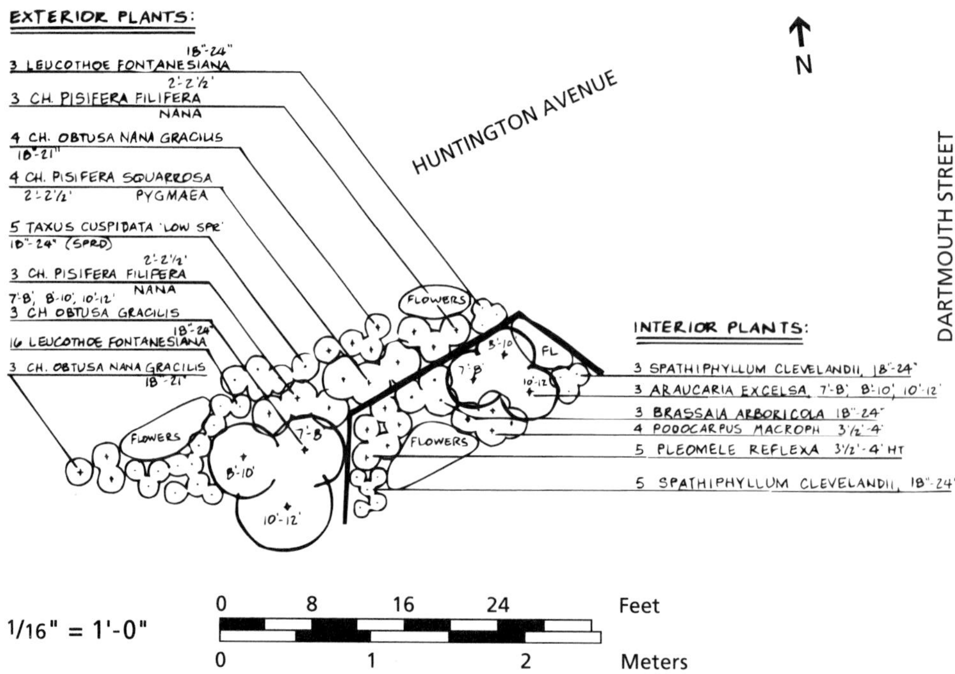

Fig. 3-10.
The in-house design development plan prepared for the Huntington Avenue planter of the Westin Hotel at Copley Place. Although in sketch form, it contains almost as much information as the final planting plan.
(Courtesy of The Architects Collaborative, Inc.)

3. A **plant list** should be provided, indicating quantities, plant names, and sizes. The plant list may actually be as detailed as the final plant list for the construction document phase (Fig. 3-11).

4. **Sketch details** which indicate how plants are planted in section might be helpful at this time to give the client an idea of what the composition of the plant bed or decorative container might be (Fig. 3-12).

Quantity	Name	Size
Permanent Plants		
7	Bunya-Bunya Pine	30" ht
1	Norfolk Island Pine	8' ht
1	Norfolk Island Pine	10' ht
1	Norfolk Island Pine	12' ht
11	Hawaiian Schefflera	5' ht
5	Pleomele Reflexa	4' ht
220	English Ivy	6" pot
4	Southern Yew	4' ht
4	Southern Yew	5' ht
4	Southern Yew	6' ht
4	Southern Yew	8' ht
20	Peace Lily	24" ht
Seasonal Plants		
110	Accent Plants (Various species)	8" pot

Fig. 3-11.
The design development plant list (this one for the Westin Hotel at Copley Place) is primarily a tool for cost estimation. It will identify the types, sizes, and quantities of plants, yet need not be specific enough for construction. (Courtesy of The Architects Collaborative, Inc.)

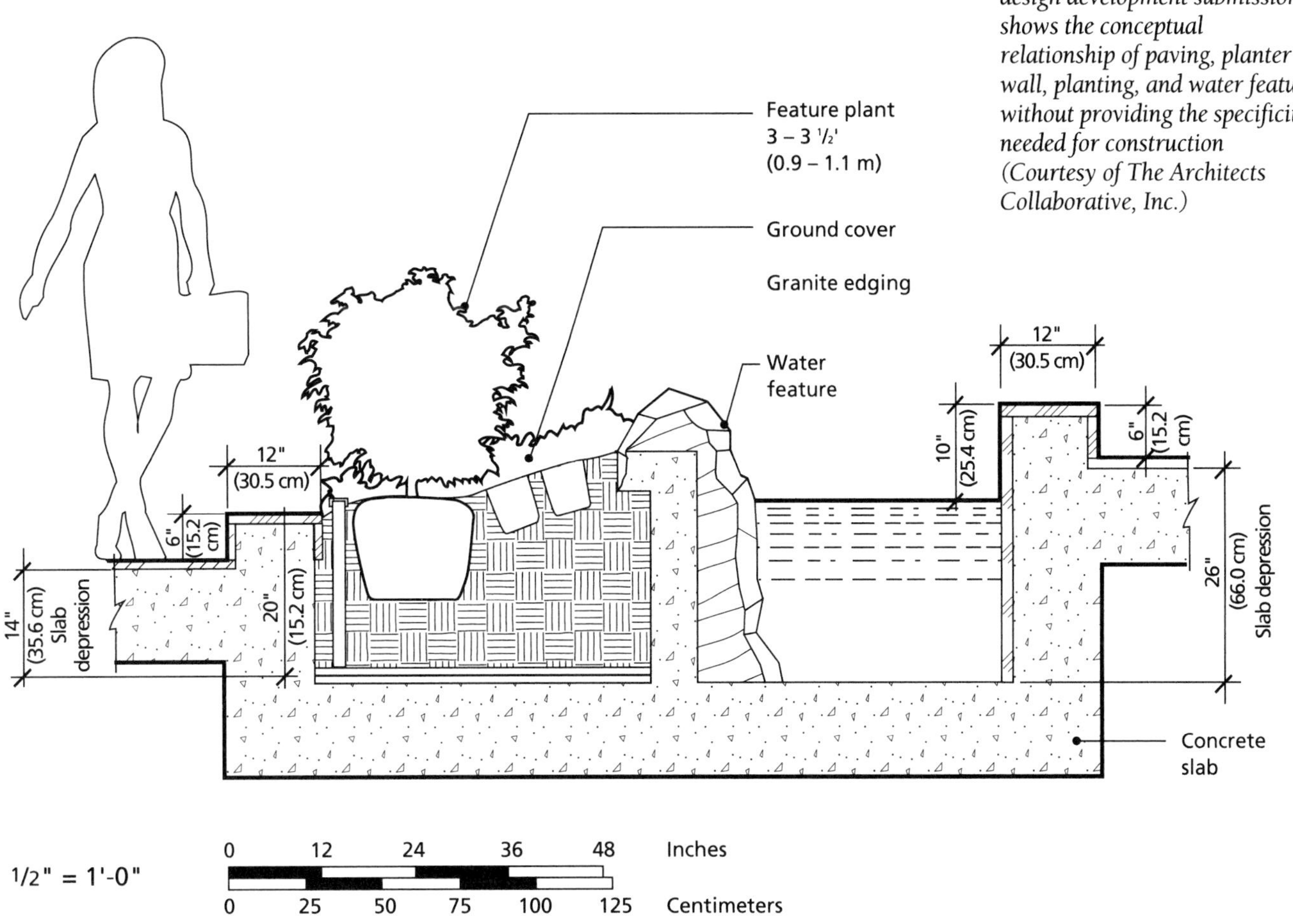

Fig. 3-12.
This detail, included in a design development submission, shows the conceptual relationship of paving, planter wall, planting, and water feature without providing the specificity needed for construction (Courtesy of The Architects Collaborative, Inc.)

5. As an adjunct to sketch details, one or more **perspective drawings** might be necessary to convey the design concept to the client. Many lay people can not fully comprehend the information shown on plan drawings. The preparation of perspectives is an excellent method of providing a three-dimensional visualization of a proposed design, especially if a) the designer is adept at such skills, or b) the design budget can afford retaining a professional renderer to prepare them (Fig. 3-13).

6. **Models** are often used in architectural presentations to convey the intent of a three-dimensional design. As with professionally prepared illustrations, professionally built models can be surprisingly life-like (Fig. 3-14). Realistic models can, however, be quite time-consuming and expensive to build. In addition, the realism which can be achieved in replicating architectural elements at reduced scale is difficult to match when attempting to replicate horticultural elements.

Fig. 3-13.
Urban Investment and Development Company, Inc., the developers of the Copley Place mixed-use project in Boston, needed a means to convey the project's design intent to potential investors and tenants prior to the realization of the actual building's completion. The architects for the complex, The Architects Collaborative, Inc., commissioned a series of professional renderings early in the design process to accomplish this critical marketing strategy. This rendering (at left) focuses on the Shopping Galleries' Central Atrium and its interior landscape. The differences between the rendering and the actual atrium (at far right, facing page) are due more to design changes subsequent to the rendering's execution than from inaccuracies in the rendering itself. (Courtesy of The Architects Collaborative, Inc.)

7. **Outline specifications**, an option in the schematic phase, should be provided in the design development phase. Unlike the specifications portion of contract documents, which are intended to provide detailed information about the materials and procedures to be employed in the construction phase, outline specifications are meant to allow client and consultants to better determine the scope of work at the pre-construction phase, and are intended to provide useful information for cost estimation. A typical outline specification will consist of a listing of materials to be supplied and installed by the interior landscape contractor:

Section 12800 Interior Landscaping

1. Plant Materials—Contractor shall supply and install all trees, shrubs, ground covers and vines as shown on the drawings.
2. Planting Medium—Shall be proprietary soilless planting medium sold in bags and formulated for use with interior plants.
3. Filter Fabric—Shall be a non-woven polyester fabric installed above drainage fill and beneath the planting medium.

Fig. 3-14.
Models have their place in the presentation medium repertoire, being able to three-dimensionalize an idea far better than drawings. This professionally commissioned 1/4" = 1'-0" (1:48) scale model of the Copley Place Shopping Galleries' Central Atrium (above left), compares with an opposite side view of the constructed atrium (above). Models built to this level of detail will be time-consuming and expensive, and while the architectural elements can be reproduced with startling accuracy, scaled representations of plant material rarely attain a similar quality.

4. Drainage Fill—Shall be styrofoam pellets.
5. Observation Tubing—Shall be perforated polyethyene tubing, 4 in (10.2 cm) in diameter; one per planter.
6. Planters– Shall be circular aluminum, no lip, with brass finish. (Note: Planters are often included in the interior finishings specification. If an extensive quantity or range of materials of planters is called for, a separate specifications section—both outline and final—may be warranted.)

8. If the project is to be irrigated by some automated or semi-automated means, the system should be identified at this stage and indicated in some preliminary fashion in the plans. (See Chapter Six, "Irrigation")
9. A cost estimate will, as accurately as possible, indicate the cost of the plants and related accessories of the project. (See Chapter Seven, "Cost Estimation")

When a client accepts a final design development submittal, he or she should be sufficiently familiar with, and approve of, the design and its detailing that the documents necessary to construct it can now be executed.

Contract Documents

The intent of contract documents is much different from the drawings created in earlier phases. Schematic design and design development are prepared to allow designers to graphically depict, to themselves and their clients, *what* a design is. They allow the client to take part in the design process and approve intermediate iterations of the design work. Contract documentation is simply a vehicle for illustrating to the contractor *how* to build the design. Where style and substance characterize the schematic and design development drawings, clarity, legibility, detail, and thoroughness are the hallmarks of high quality contract documents.

Contract documents consist of two complementary packages: specifications and working drawings. Using an analogy of my youth—when I was a Revell Master Modeler's Club member—the instructions for building model planes and ships consisted of illustrations and written directions. The same principle applies with our "full scale" models: The written directions are the specifications, and the illustrations are the working drawings. As stated earlier, the smaller, simpler projects may require as little as a single drawing and no specifications to satisfactorily convey design intent to the contractor, while the larger, more complex projects may require a set of 20 or more drawings and a specifications book an inch thick. The key is to provide the clearest, most thoroughly prepared expression of the design possible to the contractor. Potential elements of a set of working drawings for a relatively complex interior landscape might be as follows:

LAYOUT PLAN

This plan, drawn at a scale of 1/8 in = 1 ft 0 in (1:96), 1/4 in = 1 ft 0 in (1:48), or perhaps 3/8 in = 1 ft 0 in (1:32), will provide dimensions for all proposed non-planting elements within the design; it will show references to details which might be provided on separate drawings; and it will identify the materials of non-planting elements within the interior landscape. Particularly complex projects may require a separate materials plan from the layout plan. The non-plant elements identified in the layout plan will be those for which the interior landscape designer will be responsible, and might include– but not be limited to– walkway pavements, handrails, lights (up-lights, wall lights, light standards, or other lights not ceiling-mounted), planter walls or curbs, seating walls, free-standing seating, and water features, whose detailing can be extremely intricate, involving the delineation of free-form curbing of cast-in-place or fiberglass reinforced concrete (Fig. 3-15).

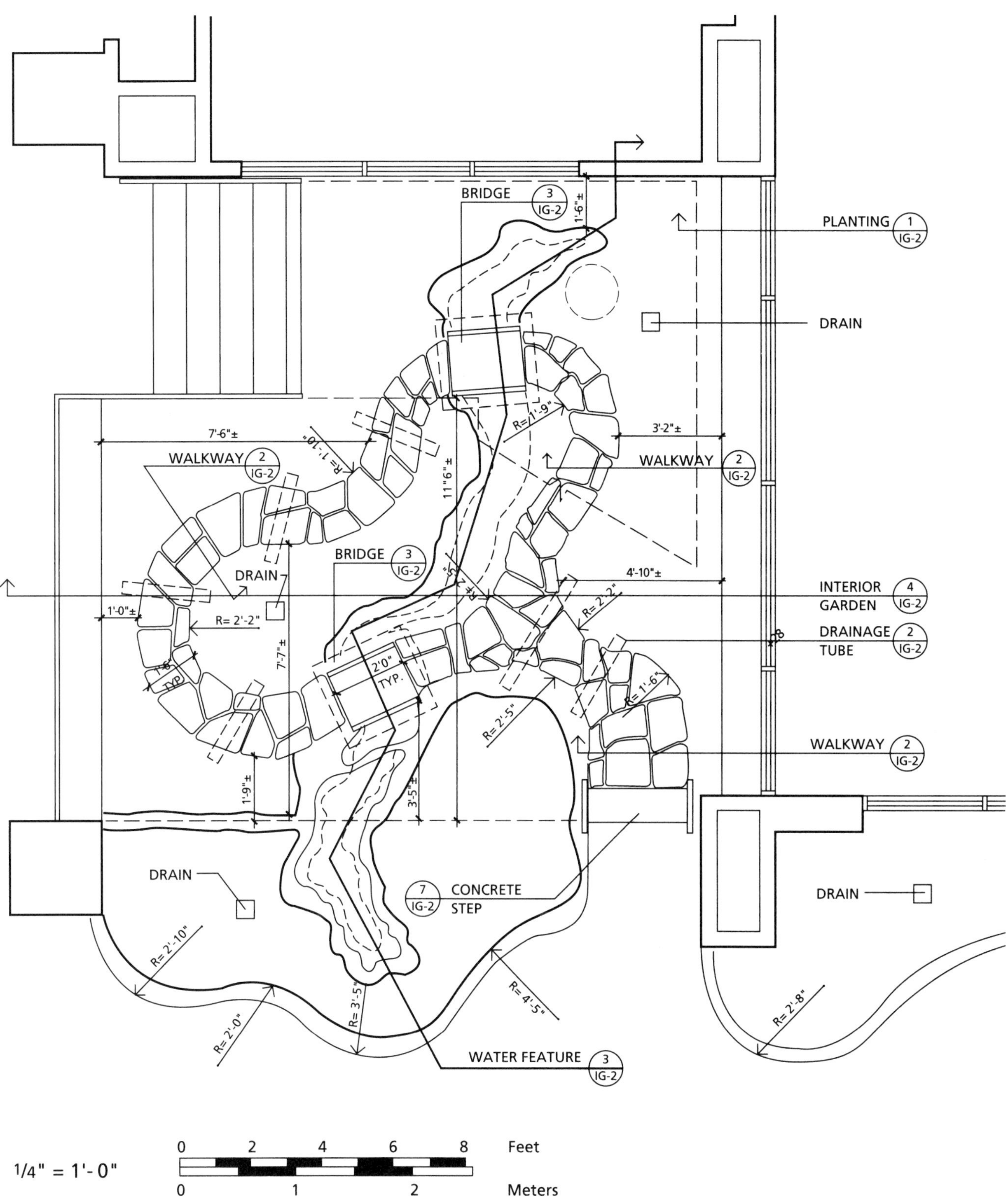

Fig. 3-15.
The Layout Plan of an interior (or exterior) landscape serves three functions: To provide dimensions of proposed site improvements, to identify materials to be used, and to provide references to any details needed to further describe the procedures of construction. The circles indicate the detail number (top) and drawing number (bottom) where the detail can be found (Courtesy of Earl R. Flansburgh + Associates, Inc.)

GRADING PLAN

Showing grades will be necessary when an interior landscape is placed within a planting bed whose upper surface is not flat. To document the shape of the surface, **contour lines** (lines of equal elevation) and spot elevations will be provided. Exterior landscape grading plans typically employ spot elevations for identifying the grades of relatively flat areas or specific locations, such as the top of a curb at an intersection point. Contour lines are generally used to provide topographic data for the contractor. In the exterior landscape, existing topography is typically indicated with dashed contour lines, while proposed grading intent is shown with solid lines. Indoors, existing topography is not relevant, and contour lines can be shown either way.

The **contour interval** (the vertical distance between contour lines) of exterior grading plans is almost always 1 or 2 ft (0.3 or 0.6 m). Indoors, the smaller size and more precise requirements of the surface of the planting bed may generate the need to make the contour interval smaller, perhaps 6, 4, or even 3 in (15.2, 10.2, or 7.6 cm).

The grading plan of an exterior landscape project is an integral component of the storm water management of the site. It indicates how surface runoff is handled, and is used in conjunction with the drainage plan (sometimes shown on the same drawing—a **grading and drainage plan**), which describes the subsurface drainage design. The grading plan of an interior landscape need not deal with runoff—the purpose of topography in the interior landscape is aesthetic—but it can be part of the water management of the interior. Since excess irrigation water will filter through the planting medium and flow to a drain, the grading plan can be a useful drawing to document the drain location and size, although a drain connected to a building's plumbing system must also appear on the project's plumbing drawings as well (Fig. 3-16).

PLANTING PLAN

This plan is the essence of the interior landscape design, and will show locations, types, numbers, and possibly sizes of plants. For garden-type installations, it will show the juxtaposition of plants to each other; for office landscape installations, it might be incorporated as a reproducible copy of a furnishings plan, enabling the designer to portray the location of plants in relation to other fixed objects in the space.

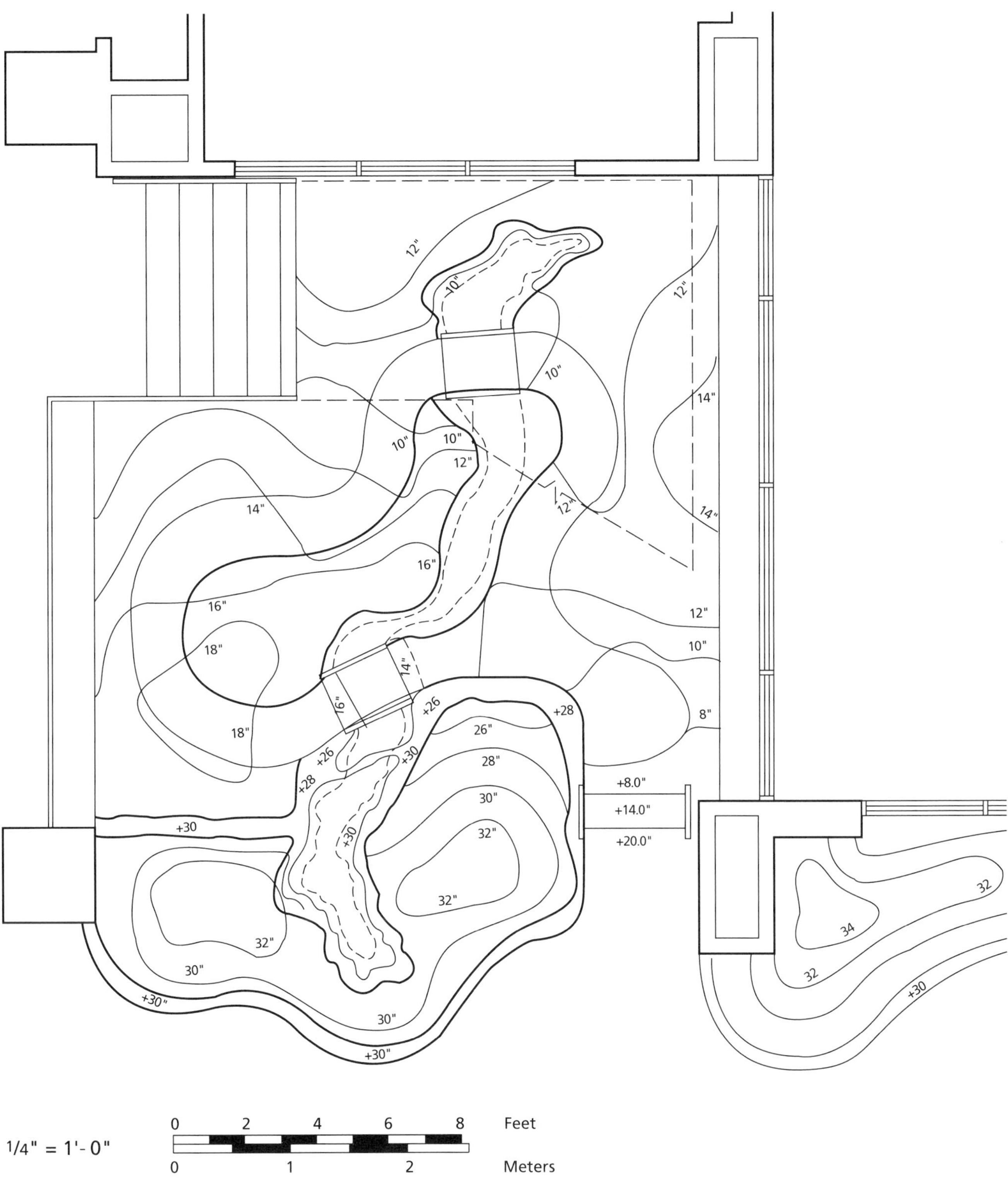

Fig. 3-16.
A Grading Plan will be necessary only for garden-style installations, and then only when the finish grade is meant to vary within the landscape. The intricacy of this grading plan suggested the use of a 2 in contour interval. (Courtesy of Earl R. Flansburgh + Associates, Inc.)

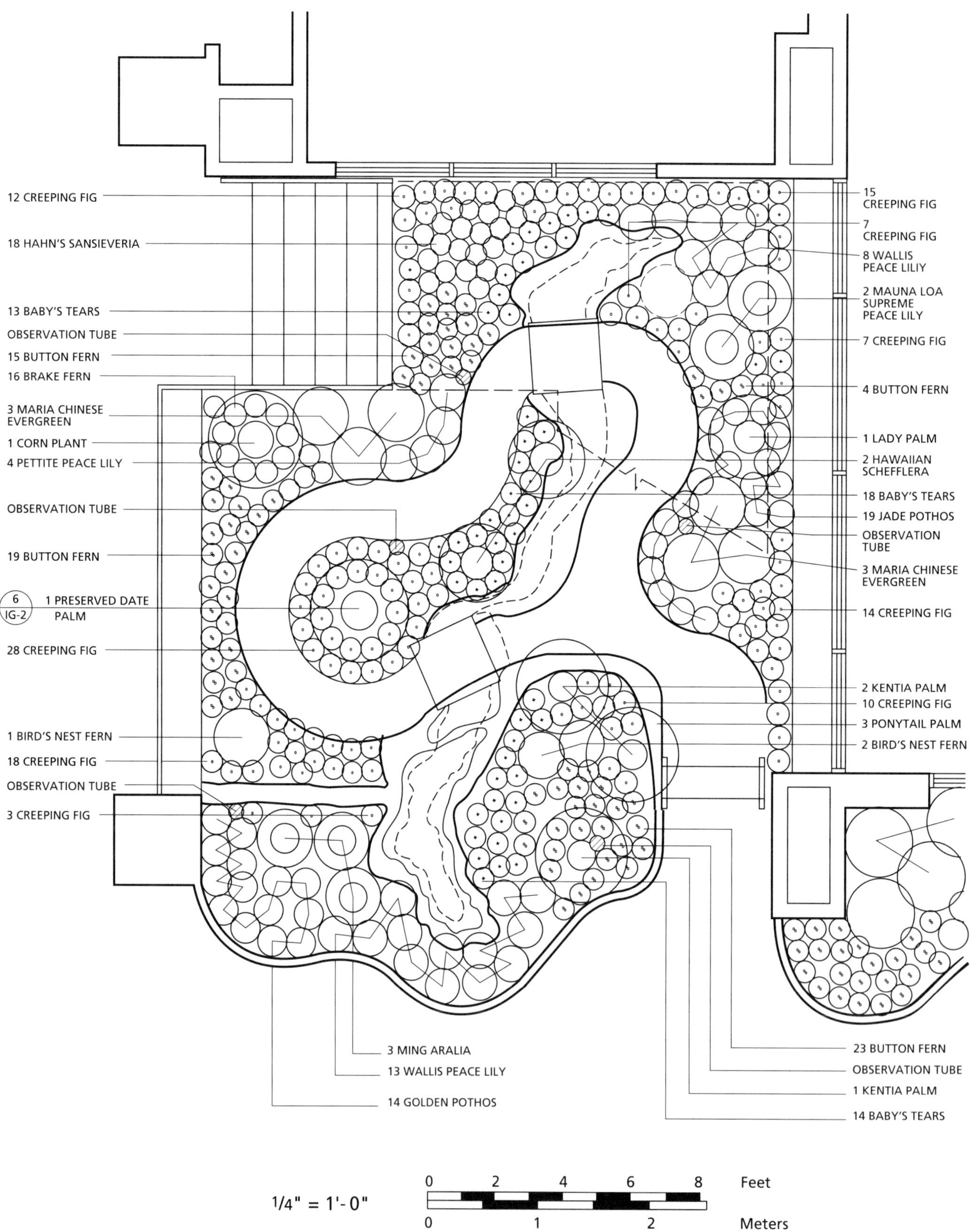

Fig. 3-17.
The Planting Plan is the core of the interior landscape documentation. This scheme is drawn at a scale large enough to show even the ground covers individually without making it too busy to read. (Courtesy of Earl R. Flansburgh + Associates, Inc.)

The planting plan is very often the only document given to the contractor for construction. Small scale gardens or office landscape plans can sometimes be represented on one plan, perhaps without even other drawings or specifications. If the plants' names, sizes, and locations are shown, it may convey sufficient information to the contractor for the proper installation of the interior landscape. The extensive or intricate interior landscape, garden-style or office, will require special attention for the planting plan.

The Garden-Style Planting Plan

The planting plan for the interior garden will be more complicated, if for no other reason than having so many plants in such close proximity (Fig. 3-17). As with the office landscape planting plan, graphic shortcuts are used to help make the information presented as clear as possible for the contractor. For massed ground cover plantings, drawing individual circles for each plant can be both visually confusing and time-consuming to draw. Sheets of various stick-on patterns are sold in architectural supply houses that can help differentiate between species, and can be applied in a matter of minutes (Fig. 3-18). Or, areas of one species of ground cover can be outlined with a distinctive line weight or pattern (Fig. 3-19). Barring that, showing just the centers of plants (with dots or plusses) rather than a circle for each one can save time and help clarify that portion of the plan.

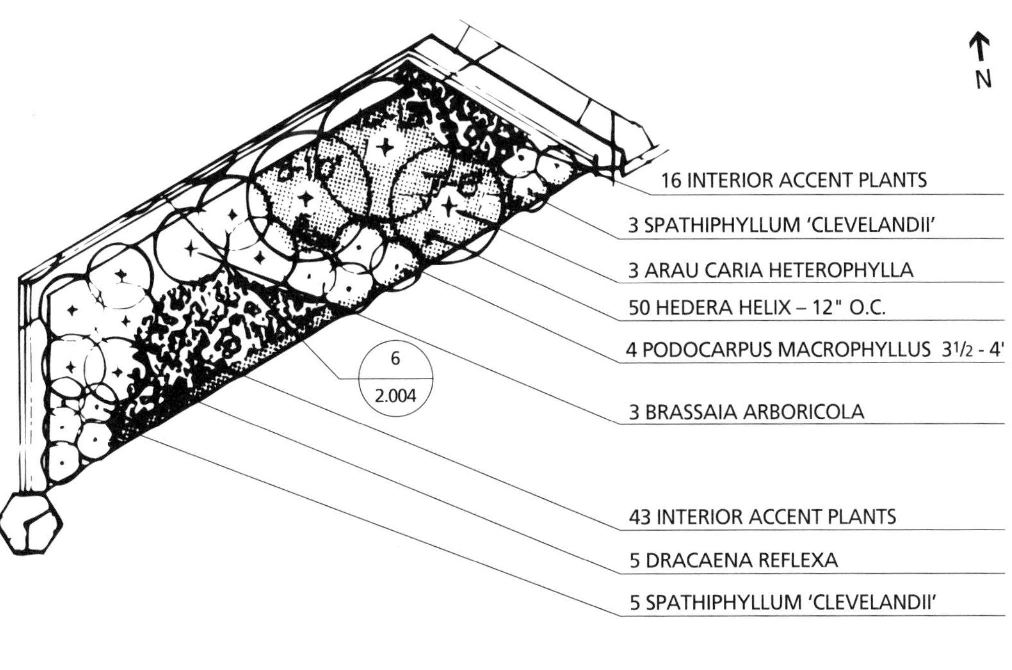

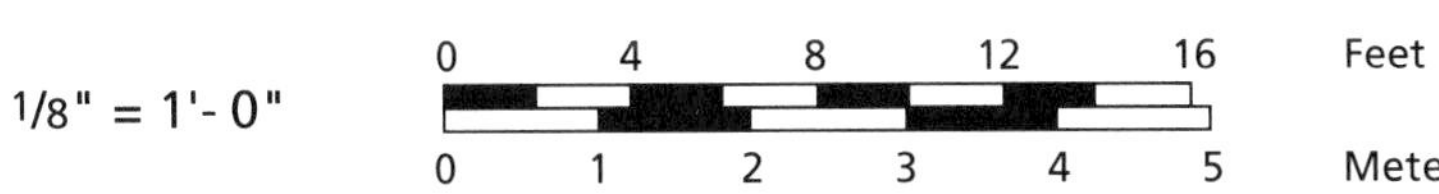

Fig. 3-18.
The final Huntington Avenue interior planting plan for the Westin Hotel at Copley Place. (Courtesy of The Architects Collaborative, Inc.)

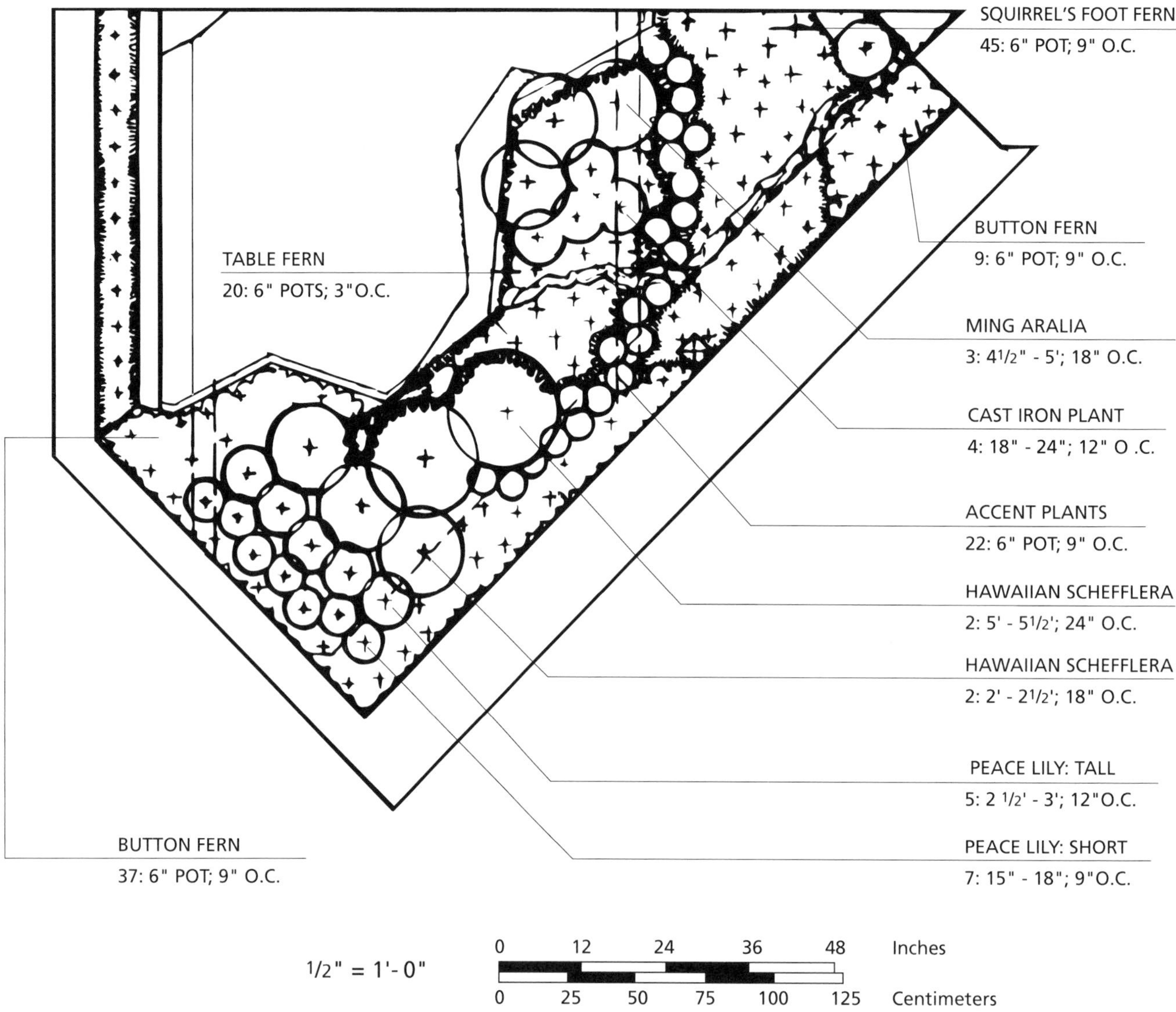

Fig. 3-19. Ground cover plants are delineated in this plan by outlining the perimeter with various patterns or line weights. Note how the plants' full names, sizes, and spacing requirements have been included in the plan. (Courtesy of The Architects Collaborative, Inc.)

The Office Landscape Planting Plan

The interior landscape designer is often provided with a reproducible copy of the furnishings plan (usually at a scale of 1/8 in = 1 ft 0 in) when asked to prepare an interior landscape planting plan for a commercial office space. Normally, this can be most beneficial to the designer, for it will show locations of not only furnishings, but interior and exterior walls, doors and windows as well. Occasionally, the furnishings plan itself can be very busy, making it difficult for the interior landscape contractor to read and determine locations for all plants. Besides showing walls and furnishings themselves, there may be an extensive network of coding to identify specific models of furniture, floor and wallcoverings, room identification, etc. An easy way to distinguish the plantings on a furnishings plan is to first "screen" the plan, creating a base drawing that reads as gray. This is a service commonly supplied by reprographic companies. All new data—the interior landscape information—then reads as black, or "full contrast", and will pop out to the contractor looking for this data (Figs. 3-20, 21).

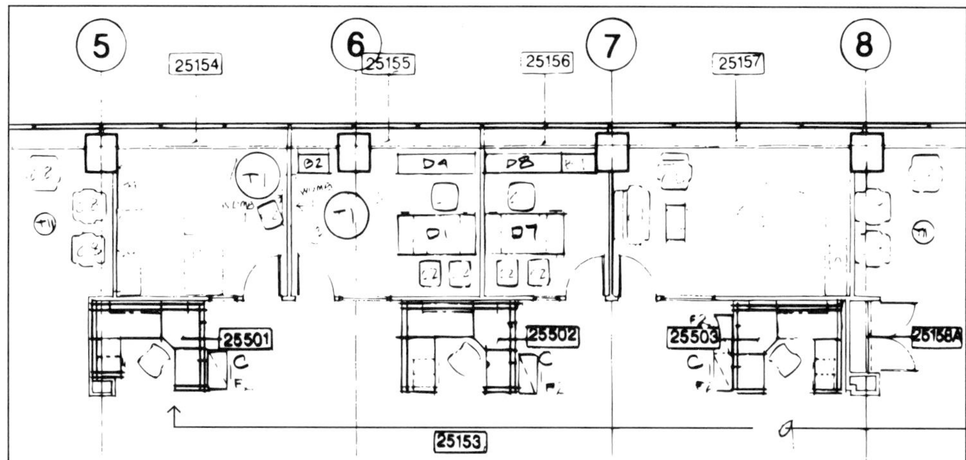

Fig. 3-20.
A typical furnishings plan, prior to being screened for use as a planting plan base sheet, already has a great deal of information on it. (Courtesy of Earl R. Flansburgh + Associates, Inc.)

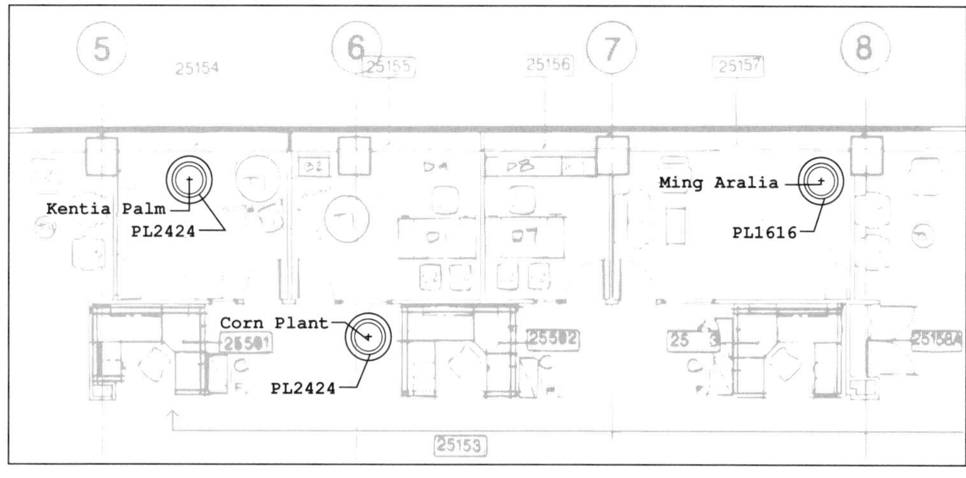

Fig. 3-21.
The same plan as shown in Fig. 3-20 after it has been screened, allowing the interior landscape information to be read quite easily despite the amount of furnishings data on it. (Courtesy of Earl R. Flansburgh + Associates, Inc.)

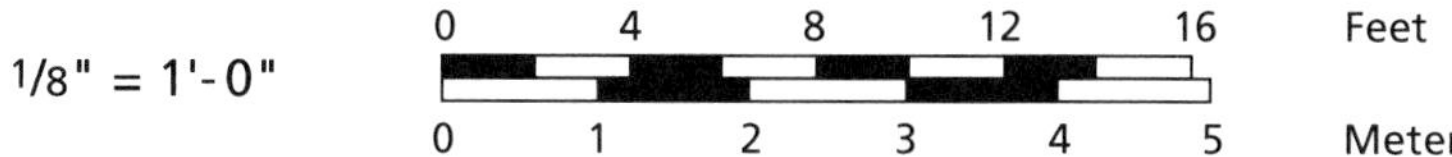

IRRIGATION PLAN

If the project is to have an irrigation system integral to the interior landscape, this plan will probably be required unless the scheme is simple enough to allow the irrigation design to be included on the planting or layout plan. (See Chapter Six: Irrigation)

DETAILS

Many interior landscapes are sufficiently straightforward that details are not even necessary, while others may require several drawings' worth. The most important detail of the interior landscape typically is the section showing the profile through the planting medium, from the floor of the planter to the surface of the planting medium (or mulch), in the case of garden-style plantings; or from the bottom of the decorative container to the top of the container, in the case of office landscape plantings. Subtle differences in the configuration of planter sections throughout a project may require a substantial number of different sections.

The "typical" **garden-style planter section** (Fig. 3-22), or "sandwich," consists of the following elements (in this hypothetical planter with cast-in-place concrete sides and bottom), from bottom to top:

The **Structural Slab.** This will be level unless specific provisions are made otherwise. A level bottom-of-planter is acceptable if a drainage stratum is provided to allow for the lateral flow of water once it passes below the planting medium.

Drains. These are placed at the low point of the planter to collect excess irrigation water. If the slab is level, drains can be placed anywhere, although there is an advantage to their being centrally located within a planter to afford flowing water the shortest distance from edge to drain. Although the water is filtered prior to reaching the drain, it is recommended that the drain be screened as a backup protection against clogging the drain pipe.

Waterproofing. Waterproofing is applied to the bottom and sides of the planter to prevent leakage. Materials for waterproofing can be either sheet membrane of various types, or liquid-applied elastomeric or asphalt-based products.

Protection board. This is placed atop the waterproofing to protect it first from work performed during construction, and afterward from sharp corners or edges of any materials placed atop it. Asphaltic fiber board is typically used for this purpose.

Drainage fill. This is placed atop the protection board to allow for a lateral flow of water through the fill material to a drain. Depending on cost and ease of installation, drainage fill can be either poorly graded (i.e., reasonably uniform in size) washed stone or styrofoam pellets such as is used in packing materials.

Filter fabric. This is a non-woven polypropylene matting that prevents the fine particles in the planting medium from infiltrating the drainage fill and clogging the drain. (*Note*: Several different manufacturers now market specialty products which serve as a combination of drainage fill and filter fabric: Enkadrain, Miradrain, Drainage Board, etc. Because the two latter products have flat, smooth bottoms, they may serve as protection board as well).

Planting medium. This is the growing medium used by plants for (a) storage of water and nutrients for the roots, (b) support of the root mass to keep the plants upright, and (c) circulation of air within the roots. For best results, planting medium should be installed in planters in lifts, or layers, not exceeding 12 in (30.5 cm), with each lift watered and compacted. Since bagged planting medium is delivered air dry, watering it during installation is essential, or the medium will draw moisture out of the root zone of the plant unless it is heavily watered.

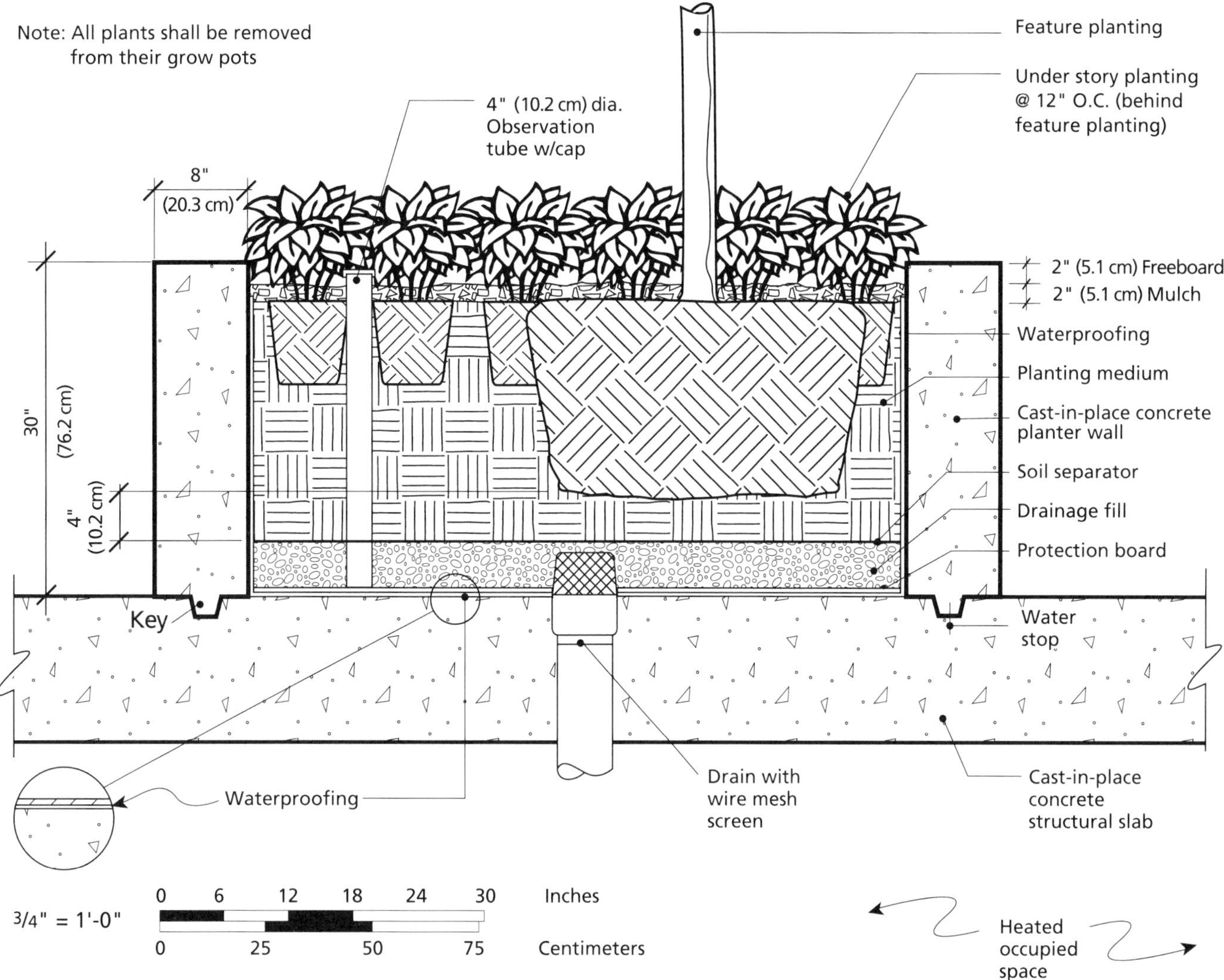

Fig. 3-22.
A this typical garden-style, built-in planter section—in this case, concrete—constructed directly atop a floor slab.

Decorative mulch is the topdressing placed atop the planting medium to improve appearance and provide a cleaner work surface on which maintenance technicians can walk, if necessary.

Other factors in this typical garden-style plant section are as follows:

The plants are **removed from their growing containers** prior to being planted into the planting medium. This system works well if plants are given good environmental conditions and can be expected to thrive. The growth of the roots into the planting medium will allow for extensive root development without the need to transplant. It does, however, make plant replacements more difficult.

The **planter wall** is shown as concrete, with a uniform thickness of 8 in (20.3 cm). Wall thickness will vary with wall height and material.

Freeboard. This is the vertical distance between the top of the planting "sandwich" and the top of the planter. It is provided to help contain the uppermost material (mulch or planting medium) within the planter walls without spillage.

Observation tubing. This is a corrugated, perforated polyethylene tubing placed through the planting section to enable maintenance technicians to observe, and if necessary extract, excess water from the bottom of the planter.

Note that unlike the typical exterior landscape detail, the tree is not **guyed**. Outdoors, trees are guyed or staked for the first growing season to prevent damage by vandals, wind, or driving rain until the root system grows sturdy enough to support itself. Indoors, trees need no protection from these problems. In addition, root systems grow so slowly by comparison that an indoor tree that is guyed when planted would have to be guyed virtually forever, for its roots may never attain the strength that outdoor tree roots gain in one growing season.

Similarly, **tree wrap** is not needed to protect bark as is done on exterior trees because of the limited effects of animals and vandals indoors.

Several variations on the standard section shown in Fig. 3-22 include the following: (Fig. 3-23)

The **structural slab** is sloped to allow a more positive flow of excess irrigation to the drain. This advantage can be included only when the planter design is executed prior to or conjunction with the structural design. It will increase the structural costs slightly.

The **planter wall** has been reconfigured near the top to appear to be narrower than what is required for standard concrete construction. If built at seating height, narrowing the planter wall width will help discourage people from sitting on it. This will also increase costs slightly for the added labor needed for the formwork.

A **specialty drainage product** has been used as a drainage stratum. This reduces the dimension required for the drainage fill from at least 4 in (10.2 cm) to less than 1 in (2.5 cm), and lessens the weight of the drainage material.

Mulch has been removed. In a planting whose design intent is to provide dense ground cover planting to the extent that the upper surface of the planting medium is not visible, mulch is an unnecessary addition to the landscape indoors. To avoid a maintenance technician's tracking planting medium across an indoor floorcovering after servicing plants, small pads of stone, wood, concrete or gravel could be stragetically placed within the ground cover planting for the technician to step on.

An **Uplight** has been added to the planter to dramatize the foliage of the tree above. Uplights serve no horticultural function; the botanical structure of leaves does not permit them to utilize light from below for photosynthesis. In addition, the heat generated from uplights placed in planting medium– particularly high wattage H.I.D. lamps– can raise planting medium temperature enough to damage the roots of nearby plants (I know a maintenance technician whose gum-soled shoes melted when she

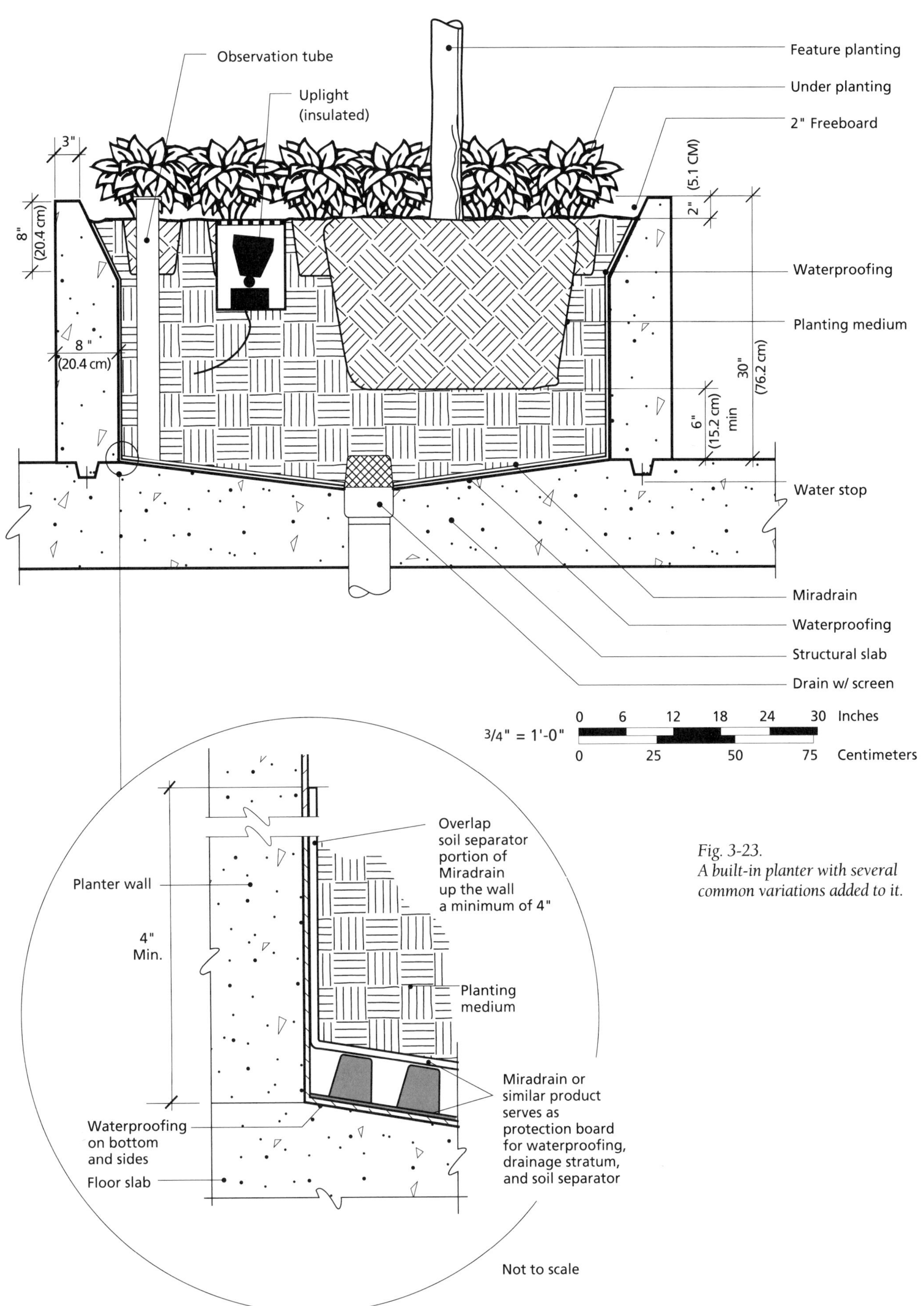

Fig. 3-23.
A built-in planter with several common variations added to it.

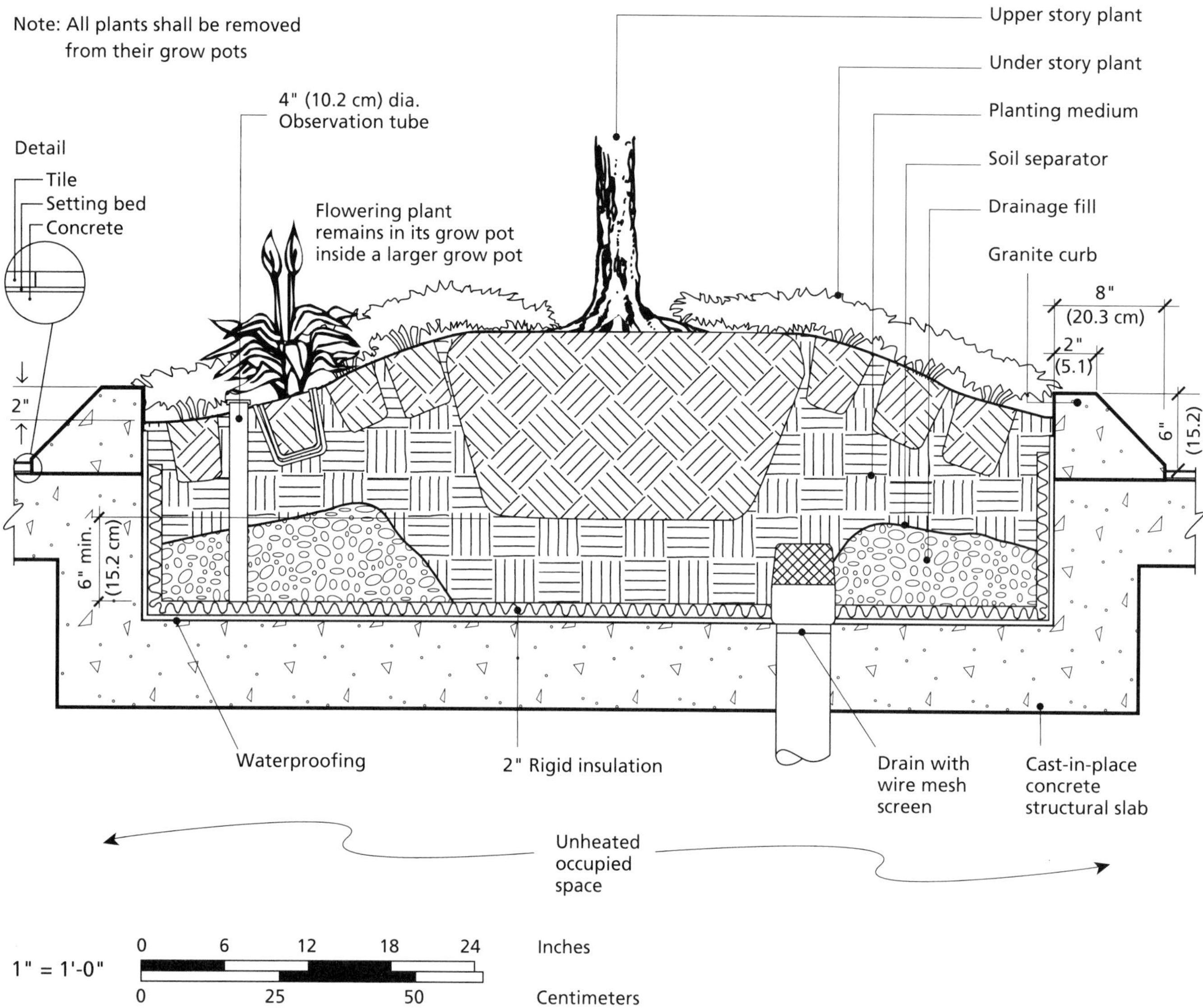

Fig. 3-24.
A planter whose bottom has been dropped can make an interior landscape look like a more integral part of the space in which it is located.

walked on an uplight in an interior landscape!). Uplights can be used effectively indoors as an aesthetic enhancement, but they must be properly insulated to avoid causing plant damage.

The "**depressed**" **planter** (Fig. 3-24) is one whose encasement has been dropped to provide a more open appearance to the interior landscape. The section shown is a planter whose bottom is dropped to enable the top of the planter to be approximately level with the surrounding pavement, an ideal relationship.

Curbing is added to raise the plant bed up several inches. Curbing can be a variety of materials that are aesthetically matched to the pavement and other finishes of the interior space. It is *necessary* to prevent floor cleaning liquids from infiltrating the planting medium. It also helps keep people from stepping into the plant bed. (See inset, Fig. 3-24, and photograph, Fig. 8-6)

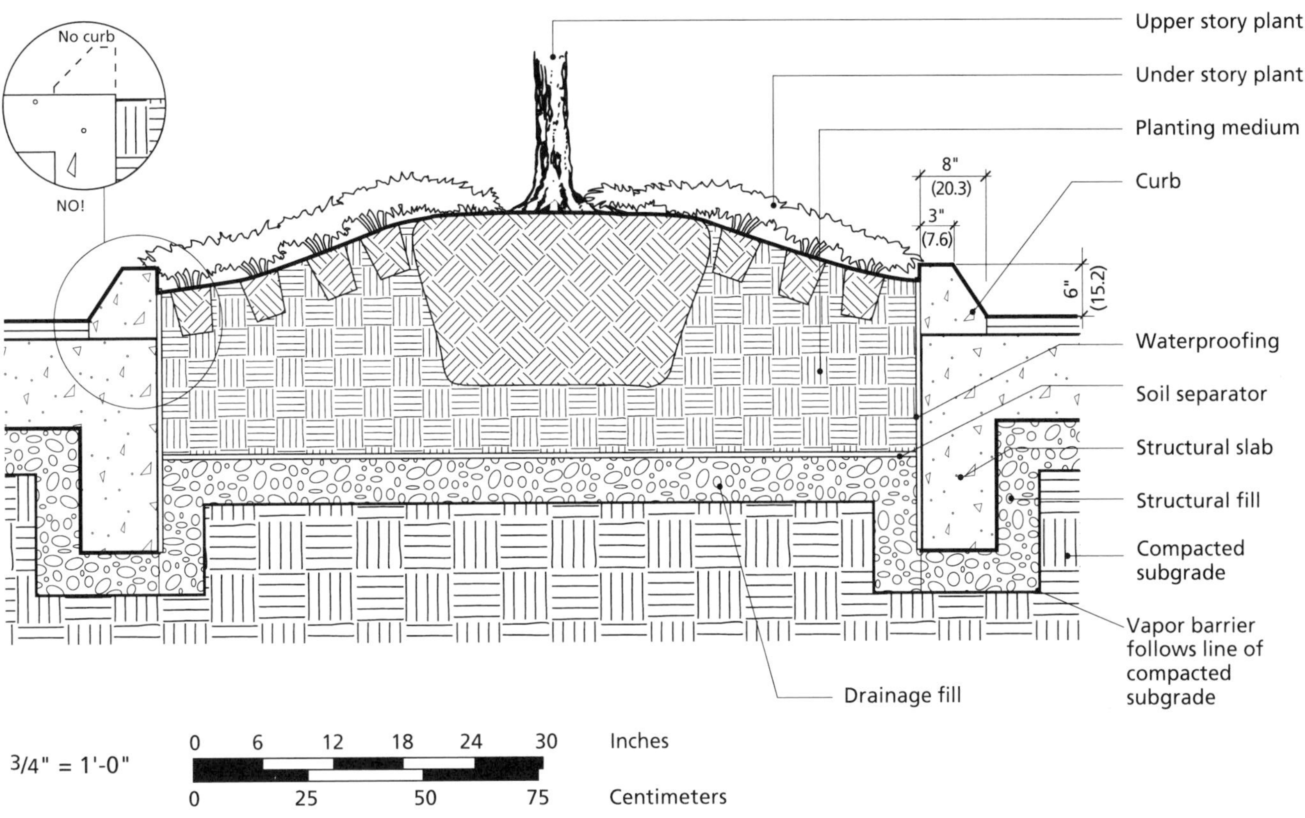

Fig. 3-25.
This "bottomless" planter can offer substantial cost savings if properly constructed.

When placed **over occupied space**, a depressed planter has major implications to the floor-to-ceiling height of the occupied space below. The structural configuration of a depressed planter also has considerable cost implications which must be addressed early in the design process.

The placement of plants directly above occupied space generates several special requirements. The accompanying detail shows plants on the first floor of an atrium built over an unheated parking garage in a northern temperate climate. Because the garage is unheated, the root zone of the plants must be protected from cold temperatures. This can be done either by warming the soil by placing electric cables through it, or by insulating the planter. Though less effective than soil warming, insulation is not prone to breakdown or on-going energy costs, and is more cost-effective to install. Insulation also serves in this instance as protection board for the waterproofing.

The **finish grade** of the planting medium undulates. The undulation allows the large specimen tree's root ball to fit in the planter while minimizing the magnitude of the slab depression (and thus maximizing the floor-to-ceiling height of the space below). It also allows the ground covers to become more visible when viewed from afar. Last, it creates a more natural appearance to the planting by establishing a noticeable "topography".

The **"bottomless" planter** (Fig. 3-25) is a slight variation to the "typical" cast-in-place concrete planter, in which the concrete planter walls are cast without a bottom.

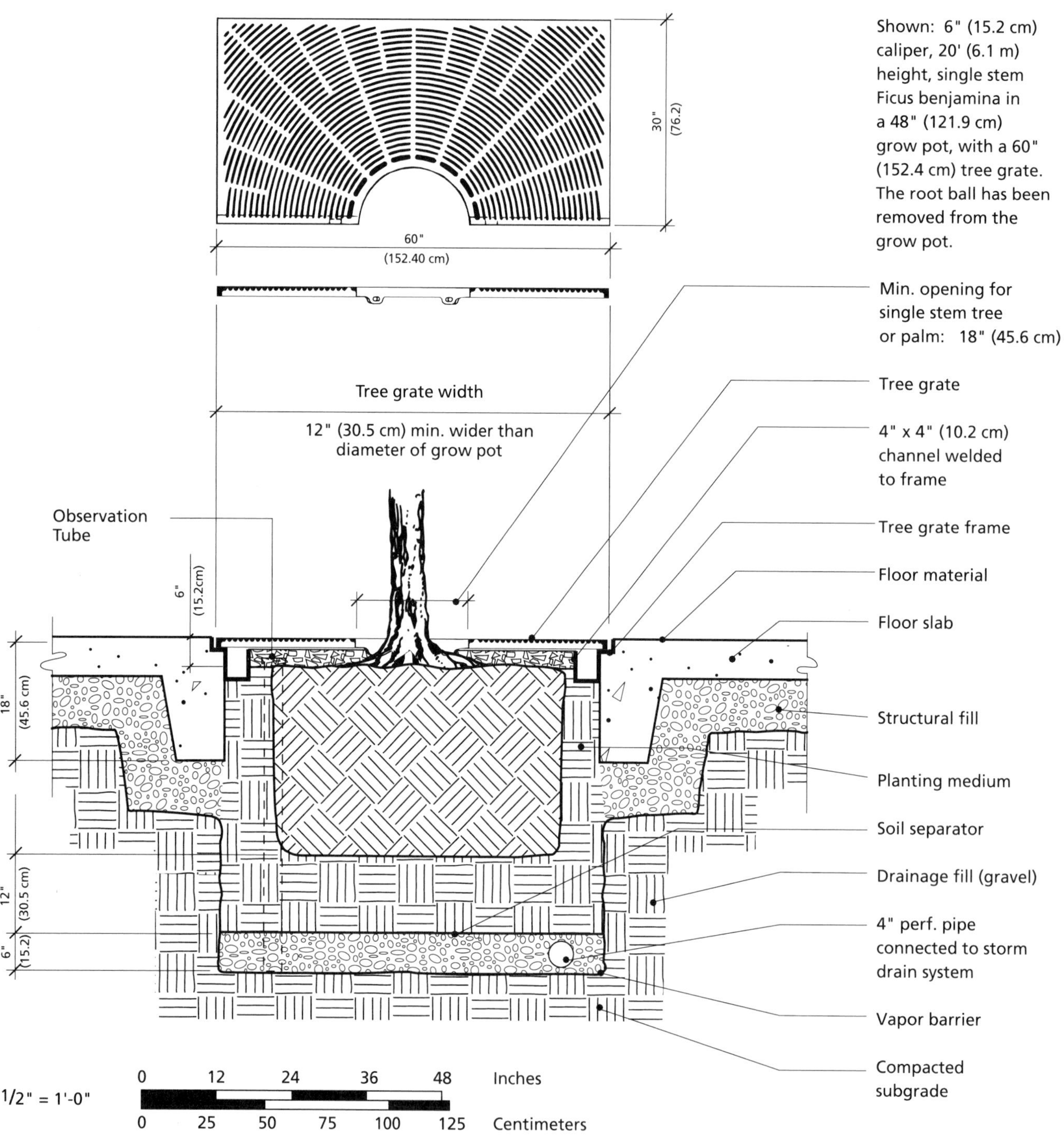

Fig. 3-26a.
The tree grate planting is an extremely effective way to display large trees or palms indoors, either with the trees removed from their grow pots as shown here in a "bottomless" configuration…

Advantages to this alternative are a slightly lowered cost due to less cast-in-place concrete and the elimination of the need for a drain. The bottomless planter is particularly useful when the planter is located at the lowest point on the bottom floor of a building, where a planter with a cast-in-place bottom and a drain might require a mechanical pump to rid the planter of excess water if the invert elevation of the pipe is lower than any other drain line in the building. The vapor barrier is installed to avoid the infiltration of soil-borne gases from the subgrade beneath the structural slab.

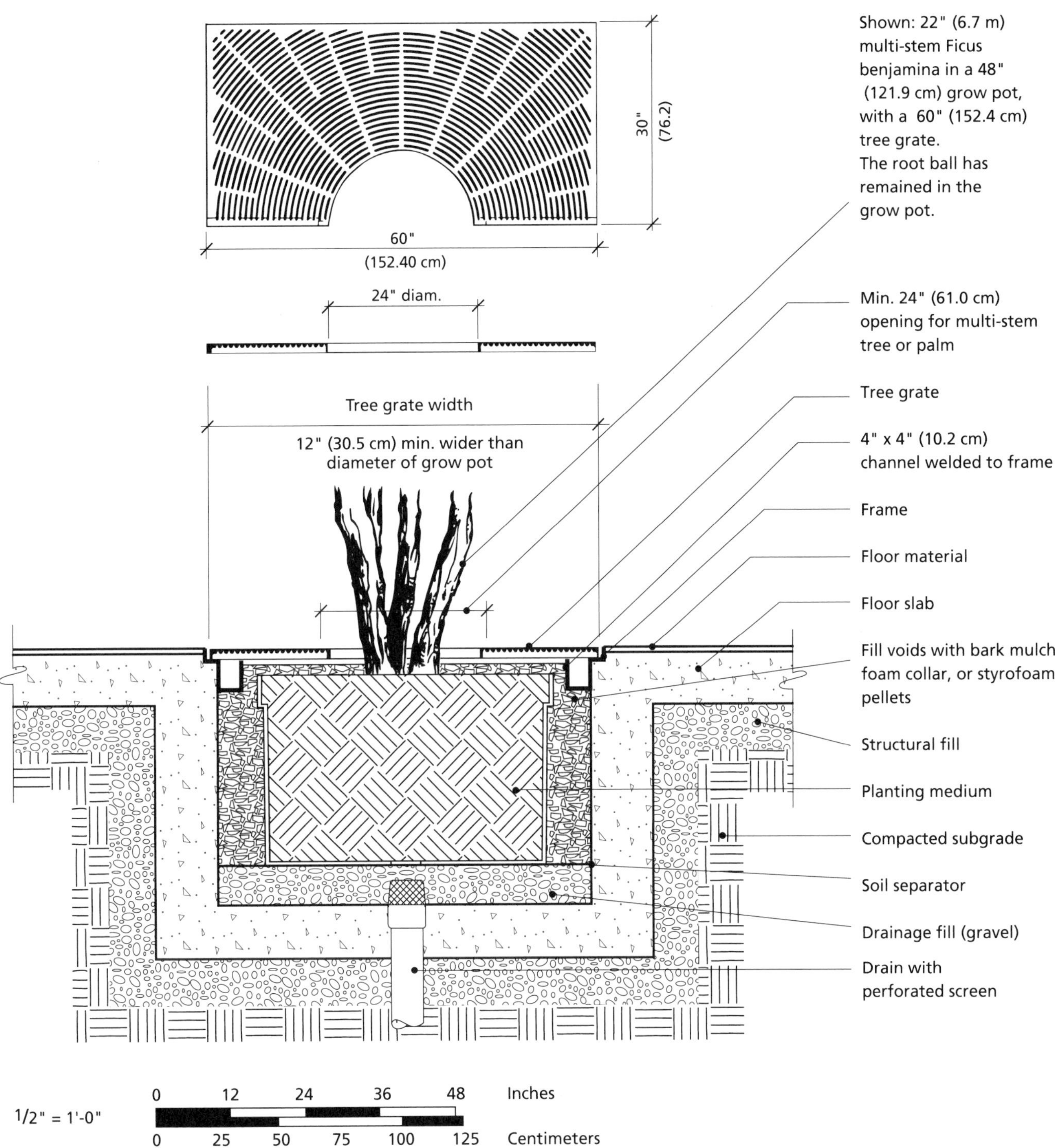

Fig. 3-26b.
...or with the trees kept in their grow pots, as shown here in a concrete bottomed pit.

The interior **tree grate** sections illustrated (Figs. 3-26a and 3-26b) are derivations of a popular method of planting trees outdoors. Chapter Two discussed the size of trees needed for interior tree grate-type installations to be effective: First branch height should be about 7 ft (2.1 m) to prevent tree branches from hitting pedestrians. The outdoor tree installation often ignores first branch height as a design factor when specifying tree size because the outdoor environment is generally so spacious that walking around tree crowns is not a problem. Indoors, spatial limitations may force pedestrians to have to walk directly under a tree's crown.

The specification of a tree grate design takes on more importance in the interior environment. With trees like *Ficus* that have multi-stem configurations or large trunk bases where roots begin to spread out, tree grates used indoors must either have a wider center opening or be expandable in its design to enable concentric portions of it to be removed as the tree grows.

Another major difference between the outdoor and indoor tree grate installation is the need to protect the indoor tree from the damaging effects of highly toxic floor waxes and cleaning chemicals. Tree grates are often placed within floors of polished concrete, granite, tile, brick, terrazzo, and other materials which are cleaned with harsh chemicals, products that are rarely used outdoors. Floor cleaning personnel will too often view a tree grate as a large floor drain and mop the cleaning fluids directly into the grate. To avoid the infiltration of these products into the planting medium of the tree, a channel should be welded to the frame of the tree grate as shown in Fig. 3-26a and Fig. 3-26b. This should pick up most of the material sent in its direction. Floors subject to frequent cleaning may generate a build-up of wax enough to warrant cleaning the channel out regularly, or connecting the channel of each tree grate to a floor drain (admittedly an expensive proposition). I have heard of interior landscape maintenance personnel who have scraped 2 in (5.1 cm) of dried wax out of a tree grate channel after only one year!

Balcony railings are among the most popular locations for designers to place interior plants. The large atrium space is well-served by ribbons of greenery to help mitigate the starkness of the architectural elements. Unfortunately, many designers detail balcony plantings in a manner that requires maintenance technicians to risk life and limb in order to execute even basic plant care tasks such as watering and grooming. In rarer cases, balcony plantings have been designed to be located outside glass windows or other configurations making them completely inaccessible to maintenance personnel, the theory being that balcony plantings can be fitted with automatic irrigation systems, and thus not need maintenance. Not true! Even with watering handled automatically, other tasks such as cleaning, pruning and insect control force the need for regular maintenance. Taken to its logical conclusion, the inaccessible balcony planter can be fitted with artificial plants, but even they must be dusted to look green instead of gray.

Balcony plantings can be adapted to manageable maintenance techniques and schedules in several different ways. The first is to mount the plantings atop a railing, so that maintenance technicians can readily handle the plants in situ. The planter itself can serve as the railing for a balcony (Fig. 3-27). Another is to fit the planter with a liner designed to be removed, either by hand or by special wires, so that the

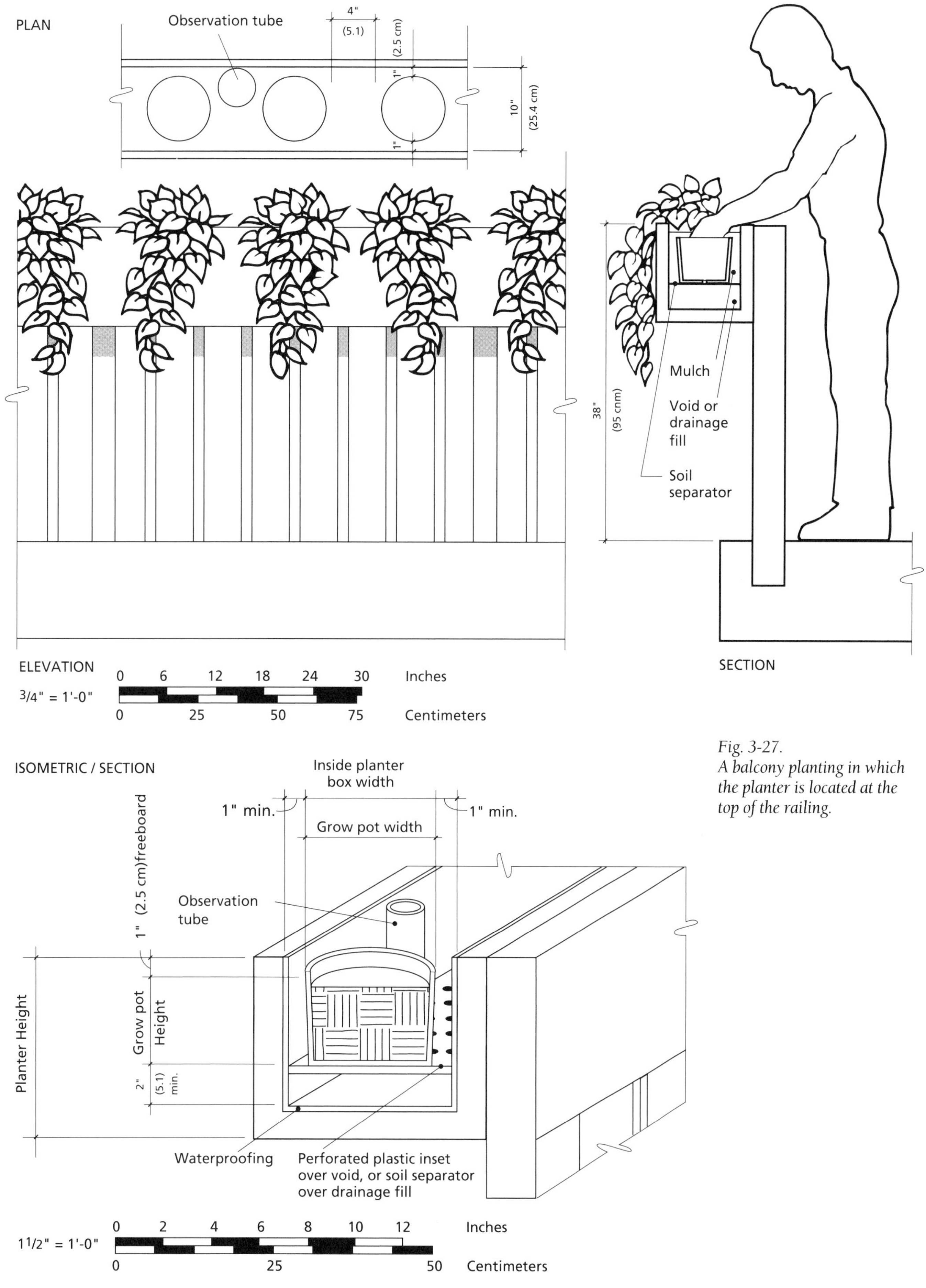

PLAN
Observation tube
4"
(5.1)
(2.5 cm)
1"
1"
10"
(25.4 cm)
38"
(95 cnm)
Mulch
Void or drainage fill
Soil separator
ELEVATION
3/4" = 1'-0"
0 6 12 18 24 30 Inches
0 25 50 75 Centimeters
SECTION
ISOMETRIC / SECTION
Inside planter box width
1" min.
1" min.
Grow pot width
1" (2.5 cm)freeboard
Observation tube
Planter Height
Grow pot Height
2" (5.1) min.
Waterproofing
Perforated plastic inset over void, or soil separator over drainage fill
1 1/2" = 1'-0"
0 2 4 6 8 10 12 Inches
0 25 50 Centimeters

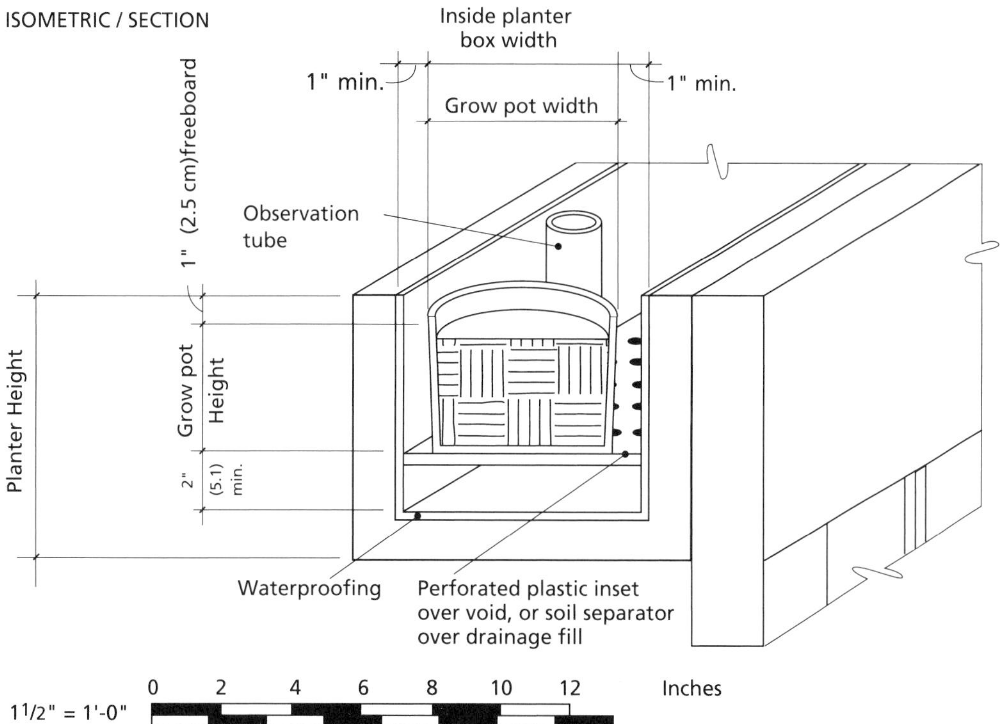

Fig. 3-27.
A balcony planting in which the planter is located at the top of the railing.

Fig. 3-28.
Balcony plantings in multi-story spaces can be maintenance hazards if they are difficult to access or are inaccessible. This design allows the technician to care for plants by removing a liner from the planter to provide maintenance in a safe place. The permanent part of the planter consists merely of a metal frame, securely attached to the floor slab, which supports the liner.

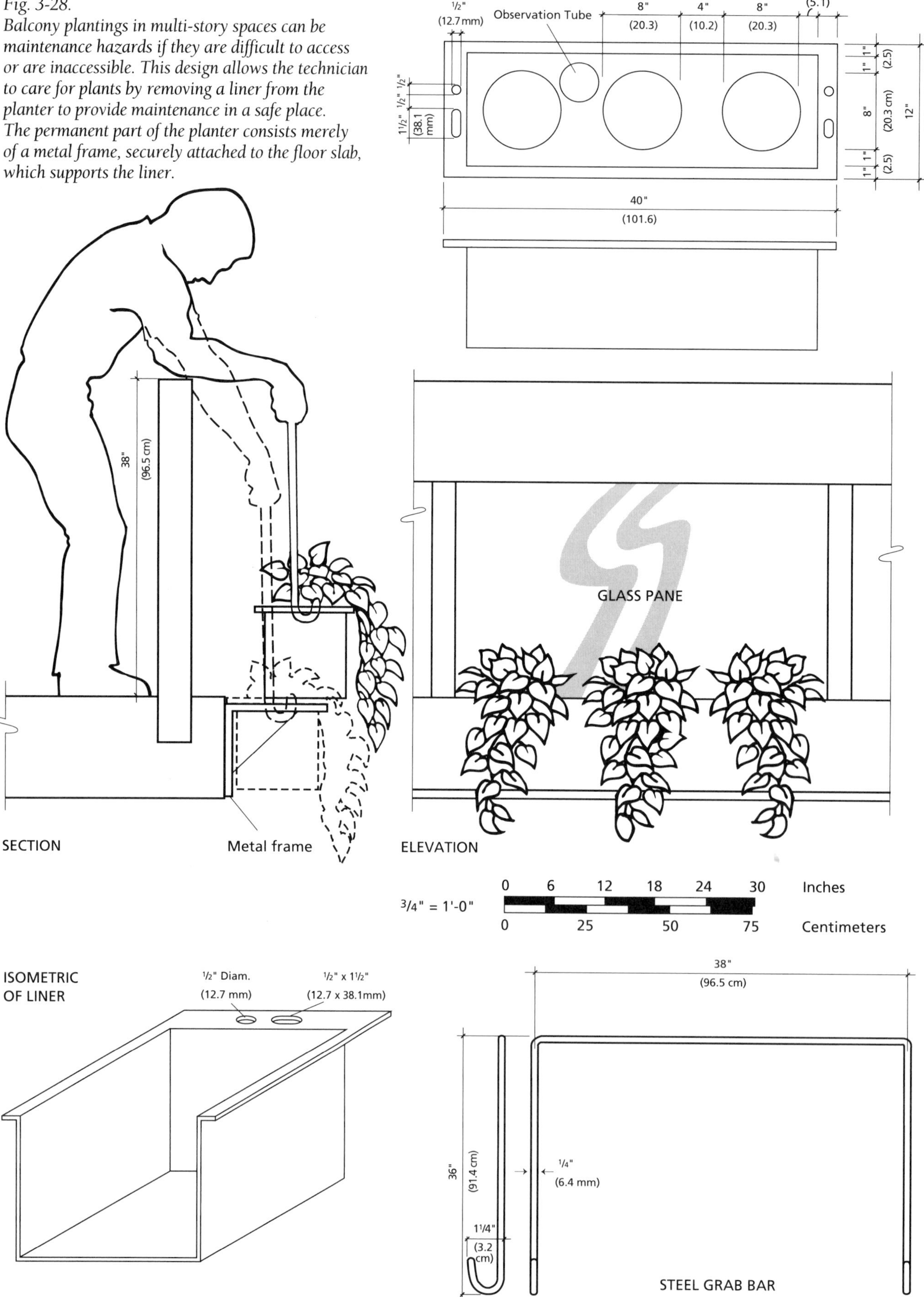

maintenance technician can lift the entire liner out of the built-in planter box and handle the plants in a safer location; the pedestrian side of the balcony railing (Fig. 3-28). A third option to be considered is to design railings whose pickets are spaced widely enough to allow access between them for plant care. Unfortunately, most building codes do not allow pickets to be spaced far enough apart to serve this purpose. The liner method also has the advantage of easily replacing individual or groups of plants in the event of plant loss, infestation, or simply the desire to rotate them.

Planting the decorative container

As has previously been stated, the majority of work performed by interior landscape contractors in this country is for commercial office accounts in which plants are placed in decorative, often portable containers. The proper planting profile of these containers is no less important to the success of the commercial account than the built-in section is to the atrium project.

The section through a typical decorative container with a live plant in it can be handled in three general ways. First, a "basic" installation consists of merely placing the grow pot into a decorative container, still the most common method of displaying plants in the commercial office; second, where the growing medium of the plant is used—in or out of its own grow pot—in conjunction with some type of subirrigation container, a solution rapidly becoming more popular in the interior landscape contracting business (and which is illustrated in Chapter Six, Irrigation); and last, as a miniature built-in, which is recommended in situations where good plant health (i.e., fewer anticipated replacements) can be expected and maximum space for root growth is needed (such as in bright light situations).

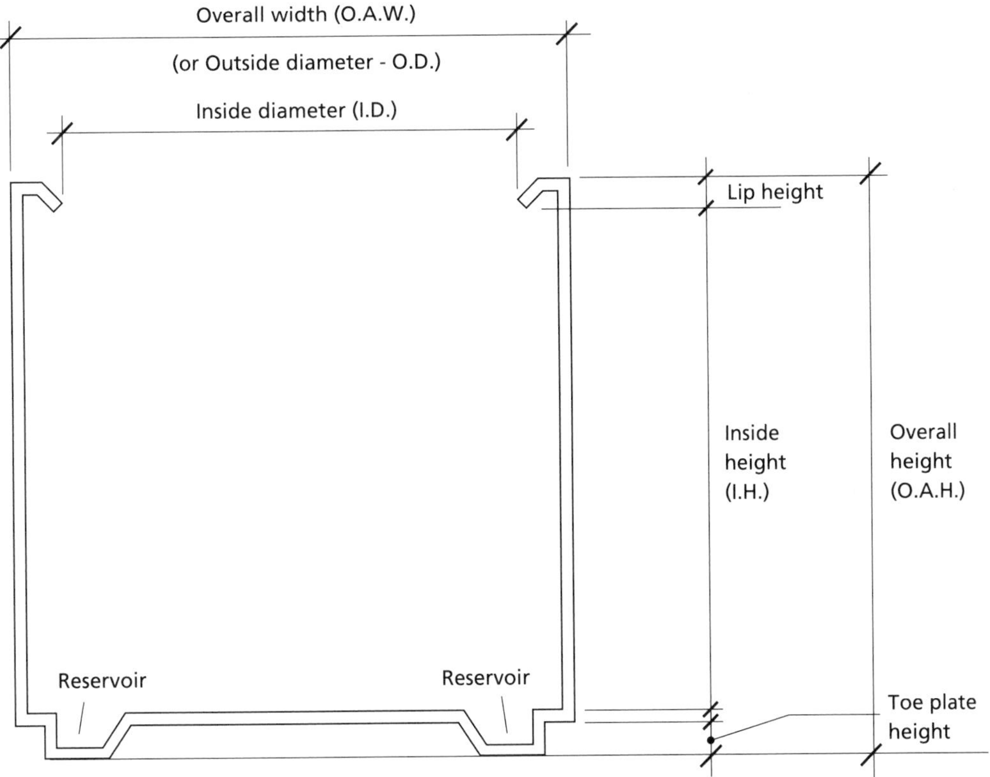

Fig. 3-29. Awareness of the inside height and width of decorative planters is essential to the proper specification of plants for them.

In the "basic" decorative container planting (Fig. 3-29), the plant placed within the container remains in its grow pot. The three key elements required of the designer in this solution are to ensure that the grow pot (1) will fit comfortably within the container; (2) is placed at the correct height relative to the top of the decorative container, and (3) is placed in a stable condition so that the plant won't tip over within the container.

Coordination of grow pot size with decorative container size may not be as straightforward as it looks. On first glance a designer, in looking at dimensions for grow pots and decorative containers, might be inclined to specify that the grow pot is 2 or 3 in (5.1 to 7.6 cm) narrower and an inch or two (2.5 to 5.1 cm) shorter than the decorative container in which it will be placed. This may be problematic. If the typical section shown in Fig. 3-29 displayed a 36 x 36 in (91.4 x 91.4 cm) fiberglass planter with a lip, the inside diameter would be fully 6 in (14.2 cm) narrower than the outside diameter, and the inside height would be 6 in shorter than the overall height.

The lip size of fiberglass containers will vary with each manufacturer, but will always increase with container size. A 12 in (30.5 cm) container might have a 1 in (2.5 cm) lip, but a similarly designed 60 in (152.4 cm) container from the same manufacturer might have a 4 in (10.2 cm) lip. Increasing lip size on fiberglass containers is done both to keep an aesthetic likeness to a container line and to provide additional rigidity to the container. Similarly, the toeplate at the bottom will increase with container size as well. Because of these variances, the specifying of fiberglass container manufacturers whose inside heights and widths are printed right in their catalogs is recommended. If the catalog does not have the information, the local sales representative or manufacturer will be able to provide it.

The toeplate configuration also serves multiple functions. The primary purpose is to allow a recess near the ground to hide wear from feet, vacuum cleaners, floor polishers, etc. It also adds structural rigidity to the fiberglass, contributes to the uniformity of a container line, and, in combination with the formwork for the container bottom, allows for the existence of a reservoir at the bottom of the container to collect excess irrigation water. Without this reservoir, grow pots placed directly onto the flat bottom of a container might sit in excess water.

The ideal placement of a plant in a container with a lip would have the top of the mulch at a level equal to one-half the height of the lip, as shown in the right inset of Fig. 3-30. Determination of mulch depth for a decorative container planting is a little trickier than for a garden-style installation, where a fixed dimension can be readily specified. Mulch should not come over the top of the decorative container, nor should it come up to below the bottom of the lip (see left and center insets, Fig. 3-29). Yet it

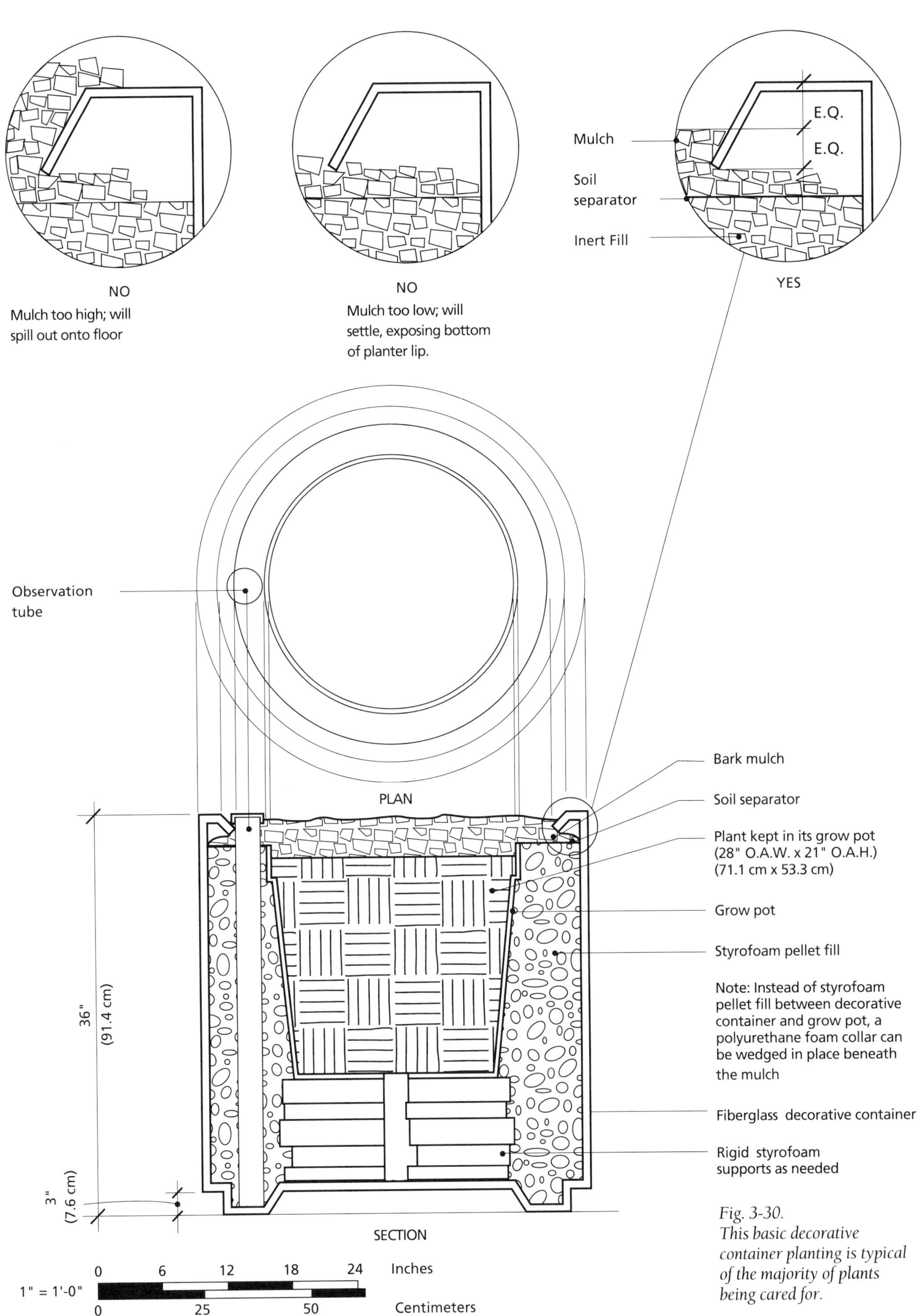

Fig. 3-30.
This basic decorative container planting is typical of the majority of plants being cared for.

must cover the rim of the grow pot. Mulch depth will therefore vary depending on the depth of the growing medium in the grow pot. Placement of the grow pot within the container at the proper height may require supports beneath the grow pot. Rigid insulation is an excellent material for support in that it is lightweight, inert, and easy to cut to fit. If additional weight inside the container is desired to discourage moving it or because the weight is needed to counterbalance the weight of a tall specimen, bricks can be used as the supports, provided they can be placed at the bottom of the container in a stable fashion without shifting, and provided that the bricks used don't raise the grow pot too high.

To prevent mulch placed outside the area of the plants' own growing medium from settling to the bottom of the decorative container, the void between the container wall and the grow pot wall must be infilled with a lightweight, inert material such as styrofoam pellets. To avoid infiltration of mulch with the styrofoam pellets, a layer of soil separator can be cut to cover the pellets. An even better alternative to mulch or pellets is to compress a urethane foam collar between the grow pot and the decorative container. The void areas remain open, and no soil separator is needed.

Bark nugget mulch is also used to fill voids, because it reduces the number of products the contractor must supply to the site and eliminates the possibility of the white styrofoam pellets becoming visible. However, the organic nature of bark can cause odors if water remains at the bottom of the decorative container. As with the built-in planters, an observation tube will allow monitoring of irrigation.

The miniature "built-in" planting (Fig. 3-30), uses the decorative container as if it were permanent construction, and is intended for plants which can anticipate relatively good health. This solution will generally be more costly, heavier, and more time-consuming to install, but it should provide plants with a more natural environment that is easier to maintain and will allow plants to grow in place for a much longer time before they need repotting.

As with the built-in planter, the bottom of the planter is covered with drainage fill and then a soil separator. While permanent built-in planters can often benefit from a specialty drainage product at the bottom that is only a ½ in (1.3 cm) deep, the lack of a drain in a decorative "built-in" generates the need for a "safety" drainage fill stratum (again, styrofoam pellets or gravel), perhaps 4 to 6 in (10.4 to 15.2 cm) in depth, covered with soil separator to prevent the planting medium from infiltrating into the drainage fill. The planting medium is then placed atop the soil separator to a depth of about one-quarter the height of the root ball, to give the plant's roots room to grow down. The plant is removed from its grow pot and placed on the planting medium, which has been watered and compacted. More planting medium is then

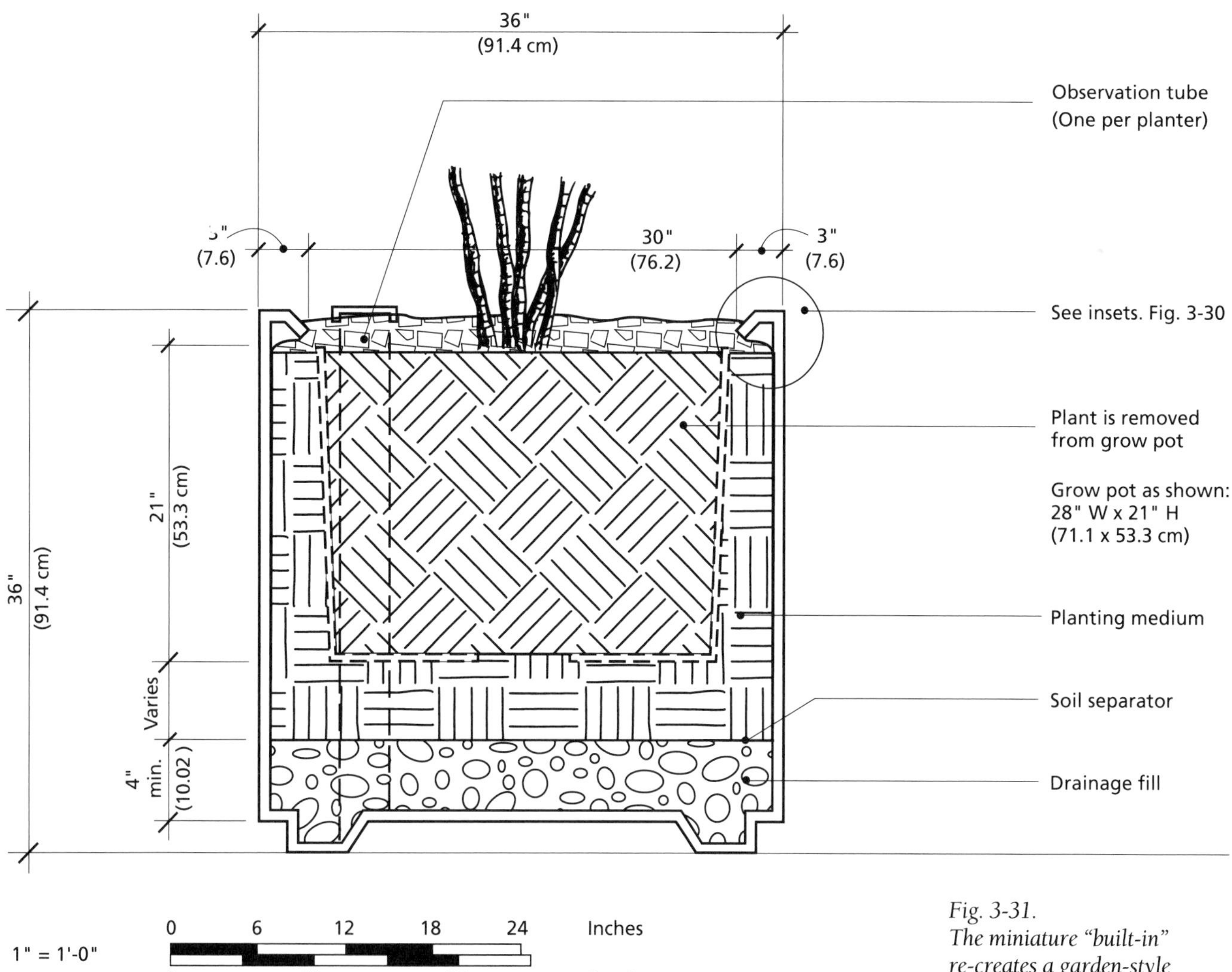

Fig. 3-31.
The miniature "built-in" re-creates a garden-style planting section in a decorative container.

watered in and compacted around the sides up to the top of the plant's root ball. With the addition of an observation tube (especially important because there is no drain) and a topdressing of mulch, the planted decorative container will very much resemble the "sandwich" of a built-in planter.

PLANT LIST

The plant list of the contract documents is as integral to the final product as the planting plan, and should be included on the planting plan if at all possible. It can also be included on a detail sheet or in the set of specifications.

The basic data provided by all plant lists should include at least the following: The common name, the botanical name, the size of the plant, and the quantity specified, as in Table 3-1

Table 3-1

Quantity	Botanical Name	Common Name	Size
10	Ficus benjamina	Weeping Java Fig Tree	16–18 ft ht

QUANTITIES: There are two points of interest regarding the quantities column of the plant list. First, the number of specimens indicated in the quantities column for each listed plant should match the number found on the planting plan. They often do not. (We design professionals, alas, sometimes fail to rank counting—or spelling—high on our list of skills.) In such discrepancies, the numbers on the *plan* should govern rather than the numbers in the quantity column of the *plant list*. A good accompanying specification will make this priority clear to the contractor. The reason for this is that the numbers on the plan show the design intent, while the numbers in the plant list are a compilation of that intent prepared as a convenience to the contractor.

Second, many interior landscape projects have plants in many different locations within a building, often on many different floors. It can be most helpful to the contractor when pricing a project or planning an installation to know how many plants of a certain species are in each area. This can be accomplished by having a "Quantities by Area" subset to the "Quantities" column of the plant list, as shown in Table 3-2.

Table 3-2

Quantities by Area*						Total	
A	B	C	D	E	F	Quantity	Botanical Name
2			1	3	4	10	Aglaonema 'Silver Queen'
12	3	2		5		22	Brassaia arboricola
4						4	Ficus benjamina
28	2	1	2	2	12	47	Dracaena reflexa
6		1		2	3	12	Polyscias fruticosa
141		21	20	32	114	328	Epipremnum aureum
109	120	12			25	266	Hedera Helix

*"Quantities by area" key:

A—Central Atrium B—First Floor C—Mezzanine

D—Entrance Lobby E—Pool F—Penthouse

PLANT NAMES: The reason for indicating both botanical *and* common name is that while the use of common names is, in fact, more widespread, the same plant may be known by different common names in different parts of the country, making the specification by common name alone too imprecise. While used less frequently, the botanical name is only rarely misinterpreted when identifying a plant.

The plant list, in combination with the specifications, must be able to provide whatever specific information about the selection of plants is needed so the contractor can furnish precisely what the designer has specified. Conversely, the designer should use enough flexibility to enable a contractor to find the specimen in question at several sources in order to provide the client with a competitive price. If the designer wishes to specify a particular cultivar of plant, the cultivar *must* be identified in the botanical name of the plant.

PLANT SIZES: The proper specification of size for a plant is essential in that too loose a specification provides too much leeway to the contractor, and too strict a specification makes a plant too difficult to locate, or even impossible to provide. Difficulty in locating a plant will cause the price to increase, while specification of the nonexistent plant will require a substitution during bidding or construction. As an example, 10 matched 18-ft (5.5 m) *Ficus benjamina* are desired. If the plant list calls for 15 to 20 ft (4.6 to 6.1 m) specimens as a height range, the contractor could justifiably—in that it meets the specifications—provide all the specimens at 15 ft, almost 20 percent shorter than what the designer intended. If, on the other hand, the contractor provided some at 15 ft and some at 20 ft, also justifiable, they would not be matched. But if the plant list called for "15-ft" *Ficus benjamina*, without a size *range*, the designer could justifiably claim that the plant does not meet proper specifications if the plant delivered were as little as one inch below the specified size! The most problematic plant specification for contractors is the specimen that doesn't exist, such as the 15- ft (4.6 m) *Spathiphyllum* 'Mauna Loa', or the 20-ft (6.1 m) *Ficus benjamina* in a 14-in (36 cm) pot.

Size ranges for the specifications of interior plant materials should be based on the *American Standard for Nursery Stock*, published by the American Association of Nurserymen (1990). As with many other aspects of the foliage plant industry, nurseries in Florida and elsewhere which deal in plants for interior use have not standardized their size listings, and do not abide by this reference. It is, however, the most equitable means of specifying plant material. Its recommendations, and some of mine, are as listed in table 3-3.

Table 3-3

Maximum height (or spread) of plant		Size range series
≤18 in (45.7 cm)		3 in (7.6 cm)
	Example: 15–18 in (38.1–45.7 cm)	
18 in–4 ft (45.7 cm–1.2 m)		6 in (15.2 cm)
	Example: 3 1/2–4 ft (1.1–1.2 m)	
4–10 ft (1.2–3.0 m)		1 ft (30 cm)
	Example: 5–6 ft (1.5–1.8 m)	
10–24 ft (3.0–7.3 m)		2 ft (61 cm)
	Example: 16–18 ft (4.9–5.5 m)	
>24 ft (7.3 m)		4 ft (1.2 m)
	Example: 28–32 ft (8.5–9.8 m)	

For trees measured by caliper rather than by height or spread, the gradations given in Table 3-4 are recommended.

Table 3-4

Maximum caliper of trunk	Size range series
≤2 in (5.1 cm) Example: 1 1/4–1 1/2 in (3.2–3.8 cm)	1/4 in (0.6 cm)
2–6 in (5.1–15.2 cm) Example: 4 1/2–5 in (11.4–12.7 cm)	1/2 in (1.3 cm)
6–10 in (15.2–25.4 cm) Example: 7– 8 in (17.8–20.3 cm)	1 in (2.5 cm)
>10 in (25.4 cm) Example: 10–12 in (25.430.5 cm)	2 in (5.1 cm)

These size gradations allow both specifier and supplier to agree on the size range for any given species of plant.

Many occasions will require the specification of two or more different sizes of the same species. In such cases, two details must be addressed. First, the plant list must carry each size designation separately. Second, the planting plan must indicate not only the species of plant but the size for each species wherever it is located (Fig. 3-19).

KEY: For plans in which there is little room to write out either the common name or botanical name next to its location, a key should be added. A key can be as simple as a letter designation, as shown in Table 3-5.

Table 3-5

Key	Botanical name	Common Name	Size
A	Bucida buceras	Black Olive	18–20 ft (5.5–6.1 m)
B	Ficus benjamina	Weeping Java Fig Tree	12–14 ft (3.7–4.3 m)
C	Ficus benjamina	Weeping Java Fig Tree	18–20 ft (5.5–6.1 m)

Such a key can be confusing, particularly if the plant list is not on the same sheet as the planting plan. It is generally easier to reference back and forth between plant list and planting plan if the key contains some correlation to either the botanical name or the common name, as shown in Table 3-6 a and b.

Table 3-6a

Key	Botanical name	Common Name	Size
Bb	Bucida buceras	Black Olive	18–20 ft (5.5–6.1 m)
Fb1	Ficus benjamina	Weeping Java Fig Tree	12–14 ft (3.7–4.3 m)
Fb2	Ficus benjamina	Weeping Java Fig Tree	18–20 ft (5.5–6.1 m)

or,

Table 3-6b

Key	Botanical name	Common Name	Size
BO	Bucida buceras	Black Olive	18–20 ft (5.5–6.1 m)
WJFTa	Ficus benjamina	Weeping Java Fig Tree	12–14 ft (3.7–4.3 m)
WJFTb	Ficus benjamina	Weeping Java Fig Tree	18–20 ft (5.5–6.1 m)

Not all plants are specified by height. The spread takes precedence over height in some cases, and the container size governs in still others. Because specimens of the same height or spread might be supplied in two different sized pots, it is good practice to specify pot size *in addition* to plant size in all cases. The "Size" column should reflect those distinctions when necessary; see Table 3-7.

Table 3-7

		Size	
Botanical name	Common Name	Height or Spread	Pot Size
Brassaia arboricola	Hawaiian Schefflera	2.5–3 ft sprd	14 in
Bucida buceras	Black Olive	18–20 ft ht	48 in
Ficus pumila	Creeping Fig	Trailing	8 in

Identification of height, spread, and pot size is *still* insufficient to properly specify many interior plants because of the wide variety of growth habits offered of like species. Additional specificity of plants must be listed in a "Remarks" column, or, if highly descriptive, in footnotes to the plant list. Unlike temperate climate plants which are generally grown only in their natural state (topiary and bonsai are two exceptions), tropical foliage plants can and often are grown in contrived shapes. The specifier has the option, depending on species, of selecting plants "with character", braided, shaped, narrow, full, with aerial roots, and so on. Large trees can be specified with tall crowns or low ones, in which case the "first branch height" is added to the specification. This is especially important in dealing with trees planted in tree grates, because first branch height will determine whether a person can walk under the canopy of the tree after its root ball is placed beneath a tree grate. Many tropical foliage shrubs, trees and palms are available as single- or multi-stem specimens. Some multi-stem plants are available either as several branches emanating from one trunk (a true multi-stem), or can have two or more trunks planted in one pot. This is normally handled by indicating in the "Remarks" column the number of plants per pot, as in "3 ppp". A prototypical plant list dealing with all the intricacies found in the interior landscape is shown in Table 3-8.

Table 3-8

INTERIOR PLANT LIST

Key	Quantities by Area* A	B	C	Total	Botanical Name	Common Name	Height or Spread	Size Pot Size	Planter**	Remarks
Trees										
Fb1	—	3	5	8	Ficus benjamina	Weeping Java Fig Tree	8–9 ft ht	21 in	PL2424	Single stem
Fb2	—	11	—	11	Ficus benjamina	Weeping Java Fig Tree	14–16 ft ht	32 in	PL3636	multi-stem
FB3	10	—	—	10	Ficus benjamina	Weeping Java Fig Tree	24–26 ft ht	60 in	—	See note 1
Shrubs										
ASQ	—	18	24	42	Aglaonema 'Silver Queen'	Silver Queen Chinese Evergreen	24–30 in ht	14 in	PL1616	—
Ba1	—	4	6	10	Brassaia arboricola	Hawaiian Schefflera	4–4.5 ft ht	14 in	PL1616	Bush form
Ba2	—	5	2	7	Brassaia arboricola	Hawaiian Schefflera	5.5–6 ft ht	17 in	PL2020	Braided standard
DdJC	—	6	8	14	Dracaena deremensis 'Janet Craig'	Janet Craig Dracaena	3.5–4 ft ht	14 in	PL1616	4 ppp
Ground Covers										
Ea	—	26	12	38	Epipremnum aureum	Golden Pothos	—	8 in	PL1616	See note #2

* Area Key: A—Central Atrium; B—Entrance Lobby; C—Pool

** Refer to Furnishings Section of specifications for complete planter information

Notes:

1. Ficus in central atrium shall be matched specimens; true multi-stem; first branch height shall be 8 ft from finish grade; crown width shall be 16–18 ft, minimum.
2. Golden Pothos shall be underplanting for Janet Craig Dracaena. Runner length shall be 2 ft 0 in, minimum.

Table 3-8: A hypothetical plant list for a reasonably intricate project.

The process of documenting the design of the interior landscape is evolutionary. The first steps in the process are meant to familiarize first the designer with the client's scope of work, and later to familiarize the client with the designer's output. Lastly, the final documentation enables the contractor to construct the design according to the designer's and client's wishes.

The ideal set of contract documents will be sufficiently detailed, clear, and comprehensive that they could be issued to a contractor who would use them to purchase and install all the products specified, with no further changes needed to the drawings or specifications, with no need for any substitutions during construction, with no need to ask any questions of the designer, and create an installation which is the precise intent of the designer.

CHAPTER FOUR
SPECIFICATIONS

The working drawings portrayed in Chapter Three represent only a part of the package a designer must prepare for an interior landscape design to be properly bid and constructed. The drawings indicate how things go together. They often, depending on the size or complexity of the project, must be accompanied by specifications—written instructions—which tell the contractor precisely what it is that is being put together and the sequencing of procedures needed perform the tasks at hand. Specifications serve the important function of helping to ensure that the products and procedures requested by the designer are adhered to by the contractor. Drawings alone cannot usually provide the amount of detail needed to adequately describe all of the contractor's responsibilities. A specifications "book" (specifications are typically provided in an 8 1/2 x 11 in (21.6 x 27.9 cm) format, but can also be provided directly on the drawings) for the construction of a medium-sized office building might be 5 or 6 in (12.7 or 15.2 cm) thick, and will contain information under as many as 16 separate major divisions, as per the format of the Construction Specifications Institute (CSI). For our purpose, we will be dealing with the one technical section on interior landscaping, whose CSI designation is 12800, and which is located under CSI Division 12, furnishings. Specifications following the CSI format divide all technical sections into three subsections, regardless of which technical section it is.

The subsections are:

General, which provides general information about the work of the section, and coordinates this work with the work of other sections and the requirements of the General Conditions.

Products, which provides a list of the various materials to be used by that trade, including detailed descriptions of the required quality level of the materials, trade names of products and manufacturers, and minimum standards of performance the materials must meet.

Execution, which indicates the preparation, sequences, methods and procedures to be used by the contractor during the course of the work.

The scope of each technical section of specifications is usually set by the ability of a certain trade to perform the work described within that section. Trade agreements, custom, and convenience also affect the scope. The interior landscaping section, then, would be written to describe as comprehensively as possible all the work for which the interior landscape contractor (or subcontractor) will be responsible. In many projects, interior landscaping is an integral part of a greater scope of work, as with the atrium garden containing not only plants but walkways, seating, lighting, masonry walls, and so on. The interior landscaping technical sections should be written to include only the tasks to be performed by the interior landscape contractor. Other technical sections will be written to describe work to be performed by other trades as shown on the drawings.

GENERAL

This subsection outlines general requirements for the work of this trade, and asks the contractor to review the work (i.e., the technical sections) of other trades to ensure that all work is properly coordinated. It briefly defines the scope of work to be performed and lists all work associated with the interior landscape which is to be performed by others. Even though the drawings may show an overlap in scope between responsibilities, Section 12800 will provide interior landscape contractors with a clear indication of what they are responsible for completing; this subsection will also identify the related work of other trades.

The General subsection also references the standards of quality to which the work must conform, to the extent this information is available. For the interior landscape, the standards of quality used are published by organizations like the Associated Landscape Contractors of America, the Florida Foliage Association, and the Florida Department of Agriculture and Consumer Services. Specific references to (parts of) documents of these organizations are frequently made in the Products subsection.

The General subsection asks contractors to prove their competence to perform the required work by demonstrating their experience and financial stability commensurate with the scope of work of the project. This subsection states the policy for submission of samples and indicates what, if any, guarantees are required. If substitutions are to be allowed on the project, the procedure for a substitution request appears in this subsection.

PRODUCTS

The Products subsection identifies all the materials to be provided by the interior landscape contractor and does so in sufficient detail to eliminate doubt about the correctness of the materials to be supplied. The products always identified in this subsection of 12800 include: (if they are to be supplied and installed by the interior landscape contractor) planting medium, anti-desiccant, insecticide, leaf cleaner, mulch, drainage fill, plant containers (those in which the plants are grown and shipped) and, of course, the plants themselves. Products sometimes included in this section are decorative containers (which are often included elsewhere in the furnishings section) and irrigation equipment (such as subirrigation containers) that are installed by this contractor rather than the plumbing contractor.

In describing the required materials, the specifier has three options. First, brand name products can be specified, which leave no room for misinterpretation. This is called a "proprietary" specification. Such specificity is helpful, but it does not allow the contractor the option of providing "generic" equivalents that could possibly give the owner a comparable product at a lower cost.

Second, the specifier can request brand-name products "or equal to be approved by the landscape architect" (or architect, interior designer, etc.) This allows the possibility of a competitive brand or generic equivalent. In naming products by brand, it is good practice to name three (3) where available, to maximize competitive choice and lower prices, even where not specifically required by the Owner.

Third, the specifier can write "performance" specifications that do not mention brands, yet define the products in sufficient detail by their appearance, color, weight, density, composition, or testing results so that the contractor will be able to furnish only products that are acceptable to the owner/designer. Performance specifications are often required by law, particularly when public funds are used for construction. They are the most difficult to write and the type most subjected to misinterpretation.

Accessory materials

PLANTING MEDIUM: Section 12800 covers many different products to be supplied by the contractor. Next to the plants themselves, the most important material to specify is the medium used to support the growth of plants. Out of doors, planting medium is normally either topsoil or topsoil mixed with other materials such as peat moss. In the interior landscape, the use of topsoil without other additives as a growing medium can be problematic. Soil-borne insect pests and fungi which can normally be controlled outdoors by wind, rain, or chemical applications will not have such benefits indoors. Sterilizing topsoil can solve that problem– at a substantial cost– but other problems occur. Topsoil is extremely heavy. At 100 to 120 pounds per cubic foot (1600 to 1920 kg/CM), topsoil can be difficult to get to many indoor job sites, and its density can require special structural reinforcing if placed over an occupied space. Lastly, topsoil will compact more readily that a planting medium with peat and other organic materials in it, to the point where the plants' root systems can be deprived of air and moisture.

A sterilized planting medium consisting of peat, bark mulch, sand, and perlite will offer optimal growth characteristics in a light weight, pest-free mix. Many variations of these ingredients, with some left out and with others left in, are available pre-mixed by many different manufacturers, and come in bags for easy handling. Accepting one of these pre-mixed products "or equal" is a reasonable specification in that it provides the specificity to purchase a product of a certain quality, yet allows the contractor the option of obtaining a similar product for which a lesser price can be offered. If the plants for a particular project have special requirements that cannot be met by one of these pre-mixed products, the planting medium requirements must be amended and spelled out in greater detail.

MULCH: Mulch serves both horticultural and aesthetic functions out of doors. It helps moderate soil moisture and temperature by acting as a buffer from the sun, it helps prevent erosion of the soil from wind and rain, and it provides an attractive surface on the ground plane to contrast with neighboring lawn or hardscape elements. In the interior landscape, the need to serve the horticultural function is diminished by the lack of bright, hot light, wind, and rain.

As an aesthetic addition to the ground plane, mulch will be just as important indoors as out of doors. Large size mulch is often selected for outdoor use because smaller sized mulch can be blown away, and because the scale of the exterior landscape requires a coarser texture. Indoors, smaller mulch size should be considered. The "neatness" of the interior space will also normally generate the need for a more decorative mulch-bark nuggets versus shredded bark, which is less expensive than nuggets. The long strips typical of shredded bark help hold the exterior landscape in place; but indoors, its lack of aesthetic appeal will render it less desirable. The large expanses of area requiring mulch out of doors are normally relegated to shredded bark or wood chips of some sort due to cost considerations. The smaller areas of the interior landscape can often take advantage of a variety of more colorful and decorative possibilities, such as colored cork, stone chips (marble, granite), river cobbles, etc. Wood or cork products as an indoor mulch should (in some areas must) be used in conjunction with a fire retardant. Some fire codes preclude their use altogether.

DRAINAGE FILL: Once the waterproof membrane is installed at the bottom of a planter, the lowest portion of the planting medium profile to be placed by the contractor will be the drainage fill, a stratum of porous material through which water can flow to a drain. It can consist of either a loose material (gravel or styrofoam pellets) at least four to six inches in depth, or it can be a specialty product specifically designed for this use such as Enkadrain, Miradrain, or Drainage Board. These specialty products all have the advantage of combining not only drainage fill but the soil separator which must be placed above it to filter fine particles from the water as it passes through the planting medium.

Plant materials

A good interior landscape specification should go into considerable detail in describing the plant materials, a necessity borne out of the great variety of plant quality levels found for any given species at various foliage nurseries in Florida, California or wherever else indoor plants are grown; a much greater variety than is normally found for temperate climate plant materials.

For example, a 20-ft Pin Oak (Quercus palustris) is pretty much the same looking specimen regardless of where it is cultivated; it might vary slightly in density or spread from one nursery to another. But one 20-ft Weeping Java Fig tree (Ficus benjamina) could be two or three times the cost of another, depending on caliper, number of trunks or major limbs, crown spread, crown density, first branch height, "character" (aerial roots), etc. Certain nurseries will grow plants with an distinct "look".

Whatever is not identified in the plant list for plant species descriptions must be carried in the specifications. This is done by asking that plants conform to the following standards:

For nomenclature: *Hortus Third*, Macmillan Publishing Company, 1976. It is important that plant names used by the designer be the same ones understood by the contractor. Use of a standard reference such as *Hortus Third* helps solve that problem. I use *Hortus Third* because it is a standard of the industry which lists a substantial number of the tropical species grown in the United States for interior use. For the many plants introduced since *Hortus'* publication in 1976, I try to reference them as varieties of genera listed in *Hortus*.

For size: *Guide to Interior Landscape Specifications*, published by the Associated Landscape Contractors of America, Fourth Edition, 1988 (The "ALCA Guide"). The specification of sizes for ornamental plants is done in size ranges to allow for reasonable variation in their growth. If a designer were to specify a plant to be "15 ft in height", with no height or spread range, a strict interpretation of the specification would allow the designer to reject a plant that was 14 ft 11 in (4.5 m) (too small) or 15 ft 1 in (4.6 m) (too big). The size range of temperate climate plants is governed by the American Association of Nurserymen's *"American Standard for Nursery Stock"*, 1990, which calls out the size categories of most types of plants, and determines whether the size refers to height or spread. It also indicates the required relationship between the plant's height or spread and its root ball diameter. The ALCA Guide best serves this purpose for most of the more popular interior plants.

For cultural requirements: *Guidelines to Foliage Plant Specifications for Interior Use*, published by the Florida Foliage Association, 1978. This document will recommend how much light intensity is recommended for optimal growth of various interior species, and how long plants should be acclimatized in their containers before shipment.

For quality standards: *Grades and Standards for Nursery Plants, Part I* (1973) *and Part II (Palms and Trees*, 1975) published by the Florida Department of Agriculture and Consumer Services, 1975. These companion volumes describe in detail how plants grown in Florida nurseries are categorized by four levels of quality: "Florida Fancy", denoting "exceptional" quality; "Florida No. 1", denoting "good, satisfactory" plants considered acceptable for general use; "Florida No. 2", "fair" plants with only possibilities of living and thriving, and "Florida No. 3", which are culls, poor plants unsuitable for landscape use. Limiting the allowable plant material to "Florida Fancy" alone will result in a high level of plant quality, but strict interpretation of the standards set by the Florida Department of Agriculture and Consumer Services will be costly for the owner. As a compromise, I would recommend allowing either "Florida Fancy" or "Florida No. 1" as a general rule, and perhaps requiring specimens of special interest to be "Florida Fancy".

EXECUTION

The third part of the three part format deals with procedures of the installation process, which begin at the nurseries supplying the plants. The designer must have the right to inspect plants at the place of growth, for doing so will give an insight as to how well cultivated the plants are. It also avoids having the contractor ship plants considerable distances only to have them rejected after they are delivered.

Since the majority of indoor plants originate from nurseries in Florida or other subtropical climates, such inspection often means sending the designer those same considerable distances. Only projects with substantial interior landscapes, or with interior landscapes whose specimens are instrumental to the success of the project, can afford that luxury.

Depending on the relationship of the designer to the owner, the designer may wish to specify only that the designer *shall have the right* to make a nursery inspection. It should be stated so as to be clearly understood by owner and contractor that the cost of the designer's trip will not be borne by the contractor. Transportation costs will either be assumed by the owner, or by the designer under the terms of the designer's contract with the owner. A second option is to require the contractor to assume the cost of the designer's trip (transportation, hotel, transfers, meals, etc.) as part of the cost of the interior landscape contract. A third option is for the specifications to require that the contractor pay not only for the transportation costs of the designer, but the designer's time as well. Since the specifications are normally written by the designer *after* the design contract with the owner is signed, but *before* the contractor's contract is signed, this third option is generally invoked when the designer no longer has money in the design budget to cover a nursery trip which may last several days and cost several thousand dollars in time alone.

Acclimatization

When plants are inspected, it may be difficult for the designer to determine if the plants have been properly acclimatized. By establishing minimum periods of acclimatization, the specifications are confirming the requirements of the ALCA *Guide to Interior Landscape Specifications*. This will help avoid the spectre of placing apparently healthy plants in an interior environment, only to perform poorly in the lower light levels because they have not been properly acclimatized.

Planting Operations

A key to the success of the interior landscape installation is the proper coordination of work between the interior landscape contractor and other tradespeople working on the project. Unlike many trades who can perform their work whenever the general contractor requests that they do so, the interior landscape subcontractor must first assess the project site's acceptability for plants to be installed. In order for plants to flourish:

- The space to receive plants must be completely enclosed, with no missing doors or windows to let in outside air.
- Waterproofing must be in place and sufficiently cured.
- Plant growth lighting must be in place, aimed properly, and working.
- The mechanical systems of the space must be in place, balanced properly, and operating on a 24 hour-a-day basis.
- Other work which creates either dust or fumes (drywall, paint, etc.) must be completed.

Once assured that the space is ready to receive plants, the interior landscape subcontractor must confirm through the general contractor that the work of other trades still on-site will avoid conflict during the installation process. The specifications must place the burden of this coordination on the general contractor rather than the interior landscape subcontractor.

The sequencing of construction is then listed, step by step. Prior to the actual planting, the specifications should require that the contractor stake out the location of the plants, or place the plants where they are to be planted, and secure the designer's approval.

Maintenance of the plants must begin *as soon as plants are planted,* not when planting operations are completed. In order to establish continuity between the installation and the maintenance of the plants, the installation contractor should be made responsible for maintaining the plants for a reasonable time afterward; at least 6 months, or preferably 1 year (to coincide—in new construction—with the general contractor's maintenance or guarantee period for the building's construction).

The specifications of an interior landscape will be written for the idiosyncrasies of that specific project. What follows is a "master" specification, prepared as a generic guide for any interior landscape, but which must be "customized" for every new project.

SECTION 12800
INTERIOR PLANTING

PART 1 - GENERAL

1.01 GENERAL REQUIREMENTS

A. Include the GENERAL DOCUMENTS and applicable parts of Division 1 as part of this Section.

B. Examine all other Sections of the Specifications for requirements which affect work of this Section whether or not such work is specifically mentioned in this Section.

C. Coordinate work with that of all other trades affecting, or affected by work of this Section. Cooperate with such trades to assure the steady progress of all work under the Contract.

1.02 SCOPE

A. Provide all labor, materials, equipment, services and transportation required to complete all interior planting work as indicated on Drawings, as specified herein, or both.

B. The subcontractor performing the work under this Section shall be a qualified interior planting specialist, normally engaged in interior planting work acceptable to the Landscape Architect.

1.03 ALTERNATES

A. Refer to ALTERNATES Section for alternates affecting the scope of work under this Section.

B. Work done under ALTERNATES Section shall fully comply with applicable requirements for similar work under this Section.

1.04 RELATED WORK UNDER OTHER SECTIONS

A. Exterior planting, specified under EXTERIOR PLANTING Section.

B. Plant growth lighting, specified under ELECTRICAL Section.

C. Planters, except as otherwise specified herein, specified under PLANTERS Section.

D. Waterproofing and waterproofing protection, specified under WATERPROOFING Section.

E. Tree grates, specified under SITE IMPROVEMENTS Section.

1.05 REFERENCE STANDARDS

A. The work shall conform to the codes and standards of the following agencies as further cited herein:

Associated Landscape Contractors of America,
405 North Washington Street, Falls Church, Virginia 22046.

Florida Foliage Association, Apopka, Florida.

Florida Department of Agriculture and Consumer Services,
Division of Plant Industry, Post Office Box 1269, Gainesville, Florida 32602.

1.06 SAMPLES

A. Submit available samples as requested by the Landscape Architect of all materials (except live plant materials) specified herein in accordance with requirements of the GENERAL CONDITIONS and/or Division 1, and before ordering materials, obtain written approval from the Landscape Architect.

B. Provide 3 x 5 in or larger high quality, 35 MM color print photographs of the actual specimens proposed for this project (as opposed to typical samples) upon Landscape Architect's request.

C. Include samples for testing as requested by the Landscape Architect.

1.07 QUALITY ASSURANCE

A. Subcontractor for work under this section shall provide evidence of having successfully completed, installed and maintained interior landscape projects of scope and size similar to this project with regard to quantities of plants involved, sizes of plants involved, anticipated cost, and architectural complexity.

B. Minimum acceptable experience is five (5) years in practice and two (2) completed projects.

1.08 GUARANTEES

A. Attention is directed to provisions of the GENERAL CONDITIONS regarding guarantees and warranties for work under this Contract.

B. The health and appearance of all plants specified herein shall be guaranteed by this subcontractor during the period specified herein. Any plant which fails to retain its health and appearance as installed and approved shall be replaced in like size and kind under this section at no additional cost to the Owner.

C. Guarantee period: The guarantee for plant health shall be for a period of 12 months from the date of acceptance of the plantings.

PART 2 - PRODUCTS

2.01 PLANTING MEDIUM

A. Planting medium shall be a sterilized, soilless growing medium specifically formulated for the culture of plants. It shall contain sphagnum peat, composted bark, and nutrient package, and may also contain one or more of the following: clean, washed, granite sand; perlite; vermiculite; styrofoam pellets; and wetting agent. Acceptable products are Metro-Mix 500, as manufactured by W.R. Grace & Company; Fafard Mix No. 3, as manufactured by Fafard; Pro-Mix BX, as manufactured by; Pro-Gro 300, as manufactured by Pro-Gro Products; or equal as approved by the Landscape Architect.

B. Submit to the Landscape Architect a list of ingredients and approximate percentage of each by volume for any product submitted as an "equal".

2.02 ACCESSORY MATERIALS

A. Anti-Desiccant: Shall be "Wilt-Pruf", available from Nursery Specialty Products, Inc., New York, NY, or approved equal, delivered in manufacturer's containers and used according to manufacturer's instructions. Apply during shipment and as required.

B. Peat: Shall be domestic brown sphagnum peat, free of woody materials and of mineral matter such as sulphur and iron, and shall have a pH value between 4 and 5. Deliver air dry.

C. Mulch: Shall be 1. (Small) (Medium) (Large) sized (Redwood) (Pine) bark nuggets, treated with a non-toxic, fire retardant substance, or 2. (Granite) (Marble) chips with color approved by the Landscape Architect, or 3. River cobbles, or 4. Pulverized brick, or 5. Expanded aggregate nuggets such as "Leca", or equal as approved by the Landscape Architect.

D. Soil Separator: Shall be 1. Enka Filter, as manufactured by Akzo Industrial Systems Company, Asheville, North Carolina, or 2. Mirafi 6000, as manufactured by Mirafi, Inc., Charlotte, North Carolina, or equal as approved by the Landscape Architect. Stabilenka Type 100 and Mirafi 6000 shall consist of a single layer of polyester non-woven filter fabric, or 3. Enkadrain, as manufactured by Akzo Industrial Systems Company, Asheville, North Carolina. Enkadrain shall consist of a two layer composition of polyester non-woven filter fabric, heat bonded to a matting of compression-resistant nylon monofilament fiber of open three dimensional construction. 4. Miradrain, as manufactured by Mirafi, Inc., Charlotte, North Carolina. 5. Drainage Board, as manufactured by Geo Tech Systems Corporation, McLean, Virginia.

E. Drainage Fill: Shall be 1. Poorly graded, washed aggregate varying from 3/8 to 3/4 in (0.95 to 1.91 cm) in diameter, or 2. Styrofoam pellets, as manufactured by E.I. DuPont de Nemours, Wilmington, Delaware, or equal as approved by the Landscape Architect.

F. Containers: Each plant shall be supplied in a lightweight container that will resist tearing and ripping and that contains drainage holes.

G. Inspection Tube: Shall be black, dark brown, or dark green, perforated polyethylene tubing of diameter and length shown on the Drawings and as manufactured by Advanced Drainage Systems or equal approved by the Landscape Architect. Each tube shall be equipped with a cap of matching color.

H. Brick: Brick used as support beneath plantings shall be 3,000 psi (minimum) face or paving brick with smooth, straight surfaces which provide for maximum stability against shifting of grow pot above.

I. Foam Collar: Shall be urethane foam, with a density of 1.1–1.2 lbs/CF (17.6–19.2 kg/CM), supplied in a 3 1/2 x 3 1/2 in (8.9 x 8.9 cm) cross section, 108 in (274.3 cm) in length, ASTM D-3574, as manufactured by M.H. Stallman Co., Providence, R.I.

2.03 PLANT MATERIALS

A. All plants shall be nursery grown unless specifically authorized to be collected.

B. Standards: Plant materials shall be true to names and sizes and shall conform to the following standards:

1. For Nomenclature: *Hortus Third*: Macmillan Publishing, 1976.
2. For Sizes: *"Guide To Interior Landscape Specifications"*, The Associated Landscape Contractors of America, Fourth Edition, 1988.
3. For Cultural Requirements: *"Guidelines to Foliage Plant Specifications For Interior Use"*, Florida Foliage Association, 1978.
4. For Quality Standards: Florida Fancy or Florida No. 1, as per *"Grades and Standards For Nursery Plants"*, Parts I and II, Florida Department of Agriculture and Consumer Services, 1975.

C. All plant material shall be of the type, species and caliper indicated, true to species and variety, and shall be sound, healthy, vigorous, acclimatized plants, free from defects, disfiguring knots, sun-scald injuries, chlorosis, insect pests and eggs, bores, and all other forms of infection. They shall have normal, well-developed branch systems and fibrous root systems.

D. Container-Grown Stock: Shall have been grown in a container long enough for the root system to have developed sufficiently to hold its soil together, firm and whole. No plants shall be loose in their containers.

E. Foliage: The foliage of all plants shall be free of dust, dirt and any chemical sprays and liquids which would have a deleterious effect on the plants' appearance or health. This shall include products specifically formulated as leaf polish. Combination foliage cleansers and polishes are acceptable.

F. Trunks: Trunks of trees shall have a shape normal to their species, and all old abrasions and cuts shall be completely callused over.

G. Major trees shall have been transplanted or roots pruned at least once during the previous three years. No trees shall have cuts of limbs over 1 1/2 in (3.8 cm) in diameter.

H. Substitution of plant materials will not be permitted unless authorized in writing by the Landscape Architect. If claim is submitted that any plant specified is not obtainable, a proposal will be considered for use of the nearest equivalent size or variety with a corresponding adjustment of contract price. Such claim shall be substantiated and submitted in writing.

I. Plant material labels shall be durable, legible labels stating the correct plant name and size in weather-resistant ink or embossed process. Attach labels securely to all plants, bundles, and containers of plant material delivered, being careful that labels attached directly to plants will not restrict growth.

J. All trees and plants shall show individual certificates of inspection by the State Agricultural Department of the state of origin. In the event of boxed material, each box shall have its own certificate.

2.04 PLANT SIZES

A. Measurements: All trees and shrubs shall be measured when their branches are in their normal position. Height dimensions specified are from bottom of container to the normal top of plant (See ALCA *Guide*, fourth edition, p. 49). Number of canes specified shall be the minimum acceptable. A cane is defined as a primary stem which starts from or close to the ground, or at a point not higher than one-fourth the height of the plant. Trees which have had their leaders cut, or so damaged that cutting is necessary, will be unacceptable.

B. All plants shall conform to the measurements specified in the plant list.

C. Plants larger than those specified in the plant list may be used if approved by the Landscape Architect, but use of such plants shall not increase the Contract Price. If the use of larger plants is approved, the spread of roots or ball of earth shall be increased in proportion to the size of the plant.

D. Up to 10 percent of undersized plants of any one variety or grade may be used, provided that there are sufficient plants above size to make the average equal to or above specified size and provided that undersized plants are larger than the average size of the next smaller grade.

PART 3 - EXECUTION

3.01 INSPECTION (OF PLANTS) AND ACCEPTANCE (OF AREAS TO RECEIVE PLANTING)

A. Plants shall be subject to inspection and approval by the Landscape Architect at the nursery, upon shipment to the site, and during installation for conformity to Specification requirements as to quality, size and variety. Such approval shall not impair the right of inspection and rejection upon delivery to the site or during the progress of the Work, for size and condition of containers or roots, diseases, insects and latent defects or injuries. Rejected plants shall be removed immediately from the site.

B. A written request for inspection of plant materials at their place of growth shall be submitted to the Landscape Architect at least ten calendar days prior to digging. This written request shall state the place(s) of growth and quantity of plants to be inspected. The Landscape Architect reserves the right to refuse inspection at this time if, in the Landscape Architect's judgment, a sufficient quantity of plants are not available for inspection. The material shall have been inspected and tagged by the interior landscape subcontractor or his/her authorized representative, prior to the Landscape Architect's inspection.

C. Inspection of plants before digging shall be at the option of the Landscape Architect. The interior landscape subcontractor or his/her representative shall be present during the Landscape Architect's inspection of plants at the nursery.

3.02 CERTIFICATES OF INSPECTION FOR PLANT MATERIAL

A. File with the Landscape Architect all necessary State, Federal and other inspection certificates, as may be required by law.

B. Certify and guarantee that all plant materials are true to name and in conformance with these Specifications.

C. The invoice, or a written statement, shall show the size and grade of materials received or shipped, together with the source of origin and the health of the plant materials.

D. At the time of bidding, the interior landscape subcontractor shall specify which plant material was furnished from his/her own stock and which plant material was obtained from other growers, along with the source of origin.

3.03 DELIVERY AND HANDLING

A. Delivery: Notify the Landscape Architect five working days prior to delivery of plant materials stating the proposed delivery date and manner of shipment. Furnish an itemized list of the actual quantity and size of plant material in each delivery. Unlisted plants will be unacceptable. Typical samples of each variety and size of plant shall be submitted for approval. These samples, if approved, shall be planted and maintained as standards of comparison with plants furnished. All plants shall be adequately protected at all times from the sun, cold, heat, and from drying winds during shipment and during movement from the delivery vehicle to the site.

B. In loading, unloading and handling plants, exercise utmost care to prevent injuries to the branches or roots of the plants.

C. All plant material shall be shipped in enclosed and environmentally controlled trailers by carriers experienced in handling live plants. Throughout shipment and delivery, all material shall be protected against adverse environmental conditions.

D. Delivery of plants shall be scheduled carefully to arrive at the job site only after planting areas have been prepared.

3.04 DIGGING, HANDLING AND PROTECTION OF PLANTS

A. Plants shall have roots covered with firm natural earth, of sufficient diameter and depth to include most of the fibrous roots. Plants, including their containers and containerization, shall conform to the Standards of the Florida Department of Agriculture and Consumer Services. No plant moved will be accepted if the planting soil is cracked or broken before or during planting operations except upon special approval of the Landscape Architect.

B. Bundles of plants shall be opened and the plants separated before the roots are covered. Care shall be taken to prevent air pockets among the roots. No plant shall be bound with wire at any time. Prevent damage to bark and breaking of branches.

C. All plants shall be thoroughly sprayed with a general insecticide acceptable to the Landscape Architect before being transported to the site. The insecticide shall be used in strict accordance with the manufacturer's directions and all applicable local, state, and Federal regulations.

3.05 ACCLIMATIZATION

A. All plant materials shall be acclimatized at the nursery or at a designated storage area not less than two months prior to installation if originally grown under shade conditions. If grown under full sun, the acclimatization period shall be not less than twelve months. During this acclimatization period, the light levels made available to the plant materials shall be gradually diminished from light levels present at the nursery to approximately 250 footcandles.

B. The storage area shall consist of any permanent or temporary structure which can control light levels as indicated, and protect the plant materials from any endanger ing physical or environmental factors during the acclimatization process. The acclimatization process shall include control of temperature, humidity, watering intervals and fertilization schedule.

3.06 PLANTING OPERATIONS

A. Make a thorough examination of all planters and areas receiving the work of this Section, and before starting the installation, notify the Landscape Architect, in writing, of any defects or obstructions which would affect the satisfactory completion of the work. Commencement of work will be construed as acceptance of preparatory work by others.

B. Coordinate the work to assure availability of on-site staging areas and other facilities required for efficient installation.

C. Ensure that all plant material which requires application of restricted insecticides and fungicides are thoroughly treated off the site before installation and that no residue of such materials remain in the soil at the time of delivery.

D. Verify that planter beds have been properly waterproofed, and that the waterproof ing has been water-tested prior to the commencement of planting operations.

E. Install (a stratum of) drainage fill as shown on the Drawings in all planter areas.

F. Install soil separator over drainage fill to prevent planting medium from infiltrating the drainage fill layer.

G. Place planting medium over drainage beds to dimensions indicated on Drawings. There shall be a minimum of 6 in (15.2 cm) of planting medium under each plant, or as shown on the Drawings. Planting medium shall be placed in lifts not exceeding 12 in (30.5 cm). Each lift shall be thoroughly watered and compacted prior to the placement of the succeeding lift.

H. Install all plant material as soon as possible after delivery, using workers trained and familiar with plant material of this type, under the direct supervision of a competent planting foreman. All areas shall be kept free of accumulation of debris at all times.

I. Stake out locations of all plants and secure the Landscape Architect's approval prior to installation. The Owner and the Landscape Architect reserve the right to make final adjustments at the job site.

J. Plants shall be installed only at times when environmental conditions are not detrimental to the plant's health. All building areas to receive plants shall be permanently enclosed. All heavy construction in the vicinity shall be completed so that dust in the air is at a very minimum and all water supply, lighting, heating, ventilating, and air conditioning systems shall be tested, aimed (lighting) and fully operational prior to plant installation.

K. Furnish and install all plants shown on the Drawings and as specified on the plant list. The quantities indicated on the plant list are included for convenience only. Furnish under this Section all individual plants in quantities and locations indicated on the Drawings.

L. All plants shall be inspected for injury to trunks, evidence of insect infestation and improper pruning after planting.

M. No plant will be accepted that requires staking to keep the plant in an upright position.

N. Protect all other work from damage by work under this Section.

3.07 PRUNING AND (MULCHING)

A. Each tree and shrub shall be pruned to preserve the natural character of the plant, as directed by or in the presence of the Landscape Architect.

B. Pruning shall be done with clean, sharp tools.

C. All plants shall be placed in such a way as to match the manner in which they were grown in the greenhouse or nursery. All dead foliage and damaged branches of plants which are nevertheless still acceptable to the Landscape Architect shall be trimmed under the direction of the Landscape Architect in an acceptable manner after installation to present a healthy appearance. Pruning or trimming done without such direction shall be cause for replacement of any plant without additional cost to the Owner.

D. After completion of planting installation, a layer of mulch shall be spread uniformly across the planting bed to the depths indicated on the Drawings.

3.08 MAINTENANCE

A. Be responsible for maintaining all plants for a period of one year from the date of acceptance. Maintenance shall include watering, pruning, trimming, fertilizing, cleaning, disease and insect control, and foliage care. Maintenance shall begin immediately after each plant is installed.

B. Submit to the Landscape Architect for approval a maintenance schedule listing all materials and procedures and the intervals at which they are to be provided.

C. Maintenance following one year from the date of (1) project opening (2) acceptance shall be available through a separate Contract between interior landscape subcont ractor and Owner. Such maintenance agreement shall be renewed after one year by agreement.

D. Rotate as necessary all plants in movable jardinieres if possible, to evenly expose all sides to natural light, at least once per month.

E. The Owner agrees that plants will not be moved without the interior landscape subcontractor's consent and that the interior landscape subcontractor shall not be responsible for damage to the plants caused by the Owner's agents or others, or resulting from extreme changes in temperature or prolonged absence of light. Should either circumstance arise, by accident or by intent, the interior landscape subcontractor will be notified and proper arrangements to protect the plants will be negotiated between interior landscape subcontractor and Owner.

F. Water: Suitable water for planting and maintenance will be made available by the Owner prior to planting operations by the Owner. All hose extensions and the like required for watering shall be provided by the interior landscape subcontractor.

3.09 CLEAN UP

A. Upon completion of planting and prior to acceptance, remove from the site all excess soil and debris, and repair all damage resulting from planting operations.

3.10 INSPECTION AND ACCEPTANCE

A. The Landscape Architect will inspect all work for acceptance upon the written request of this trade received at least ten calendar days before the anticipated date of inspection.

B. At the time of the Landscape Architect's inspection, any plant that is missing, dead, not true to name or size as specified, or not in satisfactory growth, as determined by the Landscape Architect, shall be replaced. In case of any question regarding the condition and satisfactory establishment of a rejected plant, the Landscape Architect may allow such a plant to remain through another month, at which time the rejected plant, if found to be dead, in an unhealthy or badly impaired condition, shall be replaced at once.

C. All replacements shall be plants of the same kind and size as specified in the plant list. They shall be furnished and planted as specified herein. The cost of such replacement shall be borne by the interior landscape subcontractor.

D. After all necessary corrective work has been completed, the Landscape Architect will certify in writing the acceptance of the planting, beginning the guarantee period.

CHAPTER FIVE

PLANT GROWTH LIGHTING

One of the reasons for the expanded appeal and use of interior plants during the half of the twentieth century has been the improved ability of modern technology to provide plants with adequate light. This has, in turn, been the result of advances in two broad areas: Natural light—the development of glazing systems which help create bright and dynamic, yet environmentally controllable, skylighted spaces; and electric light—the continued refinement of a wide variety of efficient lamps and fixtures capable of providing high intensities of properly balanced light from light sources relatively distant from the plants at a continually decreasing cost per kilowatt hour.

Whether lighting is provided by natural or electric sources, three characteristics of light must be considered in their ability to help keep plants healthy: intensity, duration, and quality. Intensity is the brightness—how much light is provided—and is measured in footcandles. Duration is the amount of time each day plants are exposed to the light, and is measured in hours. Quality, or spectral energy, is the wave length of light, and is measured in nanometers.

The three factors are interrelated to a very great extent. High intensity and long duration will not be beneficial if the quality of the light source is poor; long duration of appropriate light quality won't work under low intensity, etc. Reasonable levels of each must occur, depending on the individual species. Unfortunately, the field of interior landscaping is sufficiently young that the levels of intensity, duration, and quality needed to properly support the health and maintenance of interior plants are still very much debated even by experts in the field.

The debate is made that much worse by the factionalization of the experts. Interior landscape contractors—those directly responsible for the continued health of plants—tend to claim higher levels of light and longer duration are needed. Design professionals who, in representing the financial wishes of clients in the development community, tend to claim that lower—and less expensive to install and to operate—levels of light and duration are needed. The most appropriate levels of each factor can be assessed by taking stock of successfully completed projects to determine what light intensity, duration, and quality has worked for each species.

Characteristics of Light

INTENSITY

A common misconception within the interior landscape community regarding light intensity is the subtle distinction between light tolerance and light requirement. Many have characterized interior plants as "low", "medium", and "high" light species, and in so doing assert that a "low light" plant *requires* low light, etc. This is virtually never the case. Such categorizing is more properly identified as a light *tolerance*, for the plants generally considered as "low light" species are those tolerant of perhaps 50 fc or less (given, of course, appropriate duration and quality of light), but which will thrive on much higher intensities, perhaps even levels worthy of "high light" plants.

To get an idea of how tolerant plants must be of the lower light availability indoors, the intensity produced by sunlight should be addressed. Full sunlight in Florida during the summer may typically be as a high as 12,000 fc. For plants used to these intensities, the typical amount of light available to interior plants will be substantially less, even when direct sunlight can reach the floor of an interior space. It is rare that an interior landscape, especially in a commercial setting, will receive more than 2 or 3,000 fc of light for more than two or three hours per day.

Plant Lighting vs. People Lighting

The vast majority of interior spaces in which plants are placed rarely receive more than 50 to 75 fc of light, for that is an amount deemed appropriate for human living and working comfort. Task lighting in typical work spaces is generally specified at 70 fc at desk height. Effect lighting (lighting for appearance, as opposed to functional, or task lighting) can be considerably less. Convincing an client to increase light intensity beyond these baseline levels solely for plant health can be difficult. The convincing and understanding of intensity levels is realized when the client has to replace plants that have deteriorated due to low light levels.

Moreover, energy codes in many cities or states are written to prevent the excessive consumption of electricity by limiting the number of watts per square foot which can be consumed by electric lighting. Unless the interior landscape designer is able to have input to the design process at an early stage, the chances are good that ambient lighting in an interior space will not be sufficient for plant sustenance unless plants are located near windows.

It thus becomes crucial for interior landscape designers to evaluate the need for plant growth lighting as early in the design process as possible. Adding lighting in the schematic design stage is both easier and less costly than at any time thereafter, especially after construction has begun.

DURATION

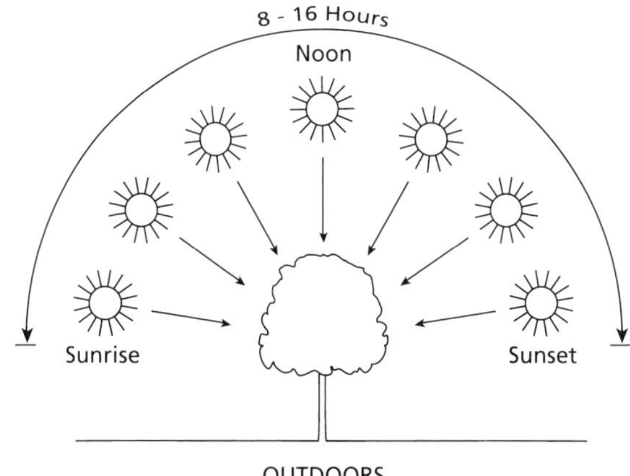

Fig.5-1.
Exterior plant material receives the benefit of sunlight from sunrise to sunset, unless obstructed by other plants, buildings, mountains, etc.

The intensity of light plants receive is tempered by the duration of that intensity. Plants in nature receive durations of light which vary with the season, with latitude, with weather, and with their immediate surroundings (relative location of larger plants, buildings, mountains, etc.). A typical day of June daylight in a northern or southern temperate climate will be about 16 hours, while a December day will contain only 8 hours. This yields a yearly average of 12 hours of daily daylight, weather permitting. Logic tells us that plants used to receiving 12 hours of light per day out of doors will do best if they were to receive at least the same duration of light indoors, or, preferably, more to compensate for the lesser intensities available indoors.

But the human factor conspires to limit the duration of light availability indoors, as it limits intensity. Electric lighting in commercial spaces is normally operated only during human occupation of the space, typically from 8 AM to 6 PM daily, a 10-hour day at best. Worse, lights are often not turned on at all on weekends. Once the hurdle of designing sufficient electric lighting into a space is achieved by the interior landscape designer, it can become difficult to get owners or tenants to operate the lights long enough during the day for optimal plant health. If the issue of the cost of electrical consumption can be eliminated, the schedule of electric light duration can be resolved through the use of automatic timing systems.

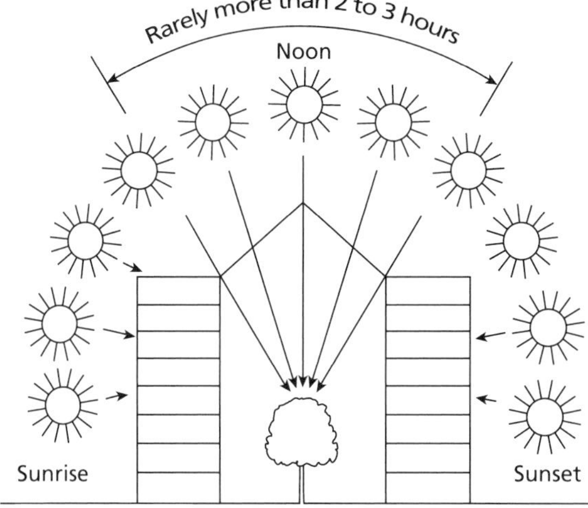

Fig.5-2.
Interior plants which receive light from skylights rarely get the benefit of more than 2 or 3 hours of direct sunlight per day.

The ability to provide sufficient duration of daylighting suffers as well, for the physical confines of a daylighted interior space will provide meaningful intensities of light for a much shorter portion of the day than is actually available outside a building. While outdoor plants often reap the benefits of sunlight for most of the daylight hours, direct sun rarely penetrates to the floor of most skylighted spaces for more than an hour or two during the day (Fig. 5-1 and 5-2).

There is a direct correlation between intensity and duration. A plant receiving an average of 300 fc of light over an eight hour span receives a total of 2400 fc hours of light. Similarly, a plant receiving an average of 800 fc of light for three hours will also receive 2400 fc-hours of light, a like amount, and to an extent, of like use to plants. Taken to the extreme, this does not mean that 4800 fc for 30 minutes, or 9600 fc for 15 minutes, will be as useful. In fact, there is evidence that high intensities at short duration periods will create stresses that will produce chlorophyll destruction of foliage and nutritional disorders. But it is the amount of footcandle-hours—intensity x duration—that determines how much light energy will be available to plants.

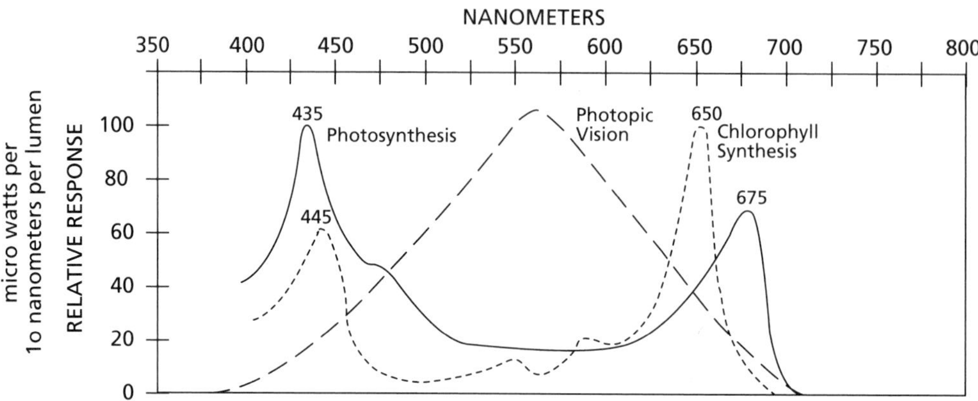

Fig. 5-3.
This chart compares the peaks of spectral energy for visible light with those for photosynthesis and chlorophyll synthesis. Note that while visible light peaks at the 550 to 600 range (green), photosynthesis peaks at 435 and 675, while chlorophyll synthesis peaks similarly at the 445 and 650 range.

QUALITY

One of the prime advantages of daylight over electric light as a source for plant growth has been the quality of light which daylight provides. The spectral energy required for photosynthesis and for chlorophyll synthesis shown in the chart (Fig. 5-3) indicates peaks in the 650 nanometer (red) and 450 nanometer (blue) wavelengths. Clear glass, as used in nineteenth century glasshouses, transmitted light evenly throughout the visible light spectrum, producing optimal spectral energy. The use of tinted glazing causes higher proportions of incoming light to be absorbed by the glazing material, while reflective glazing causes higher proportions to be reflected back into the atmosphere (Fig. 5-4). Thus, the remaining light is of both a lesser intensity, and, depending on the composition of the glazing, more restrictive with respect to certain light wavelengths. The effects of greatly altered spectral energy will be addressed later in this chapter, in the discussion of electric light sources for plant growth.

Fig.5-4.
With tinted or reflective glass, a certain percentage of light is absorbed and a certain percentage is reflected.

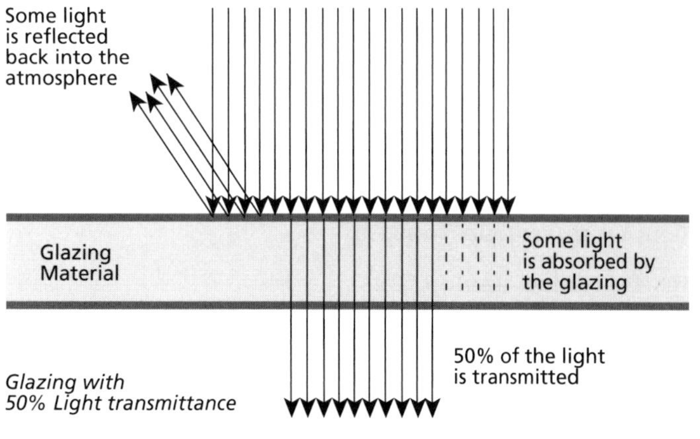

Types of Light

NATURAL LIGHT

Natural light entering an interior space through some type of glazing system consists of three types of light: The first is "sunlight", or the direct rays of the sun. The second is "daylight", or "skylight", the indirect light present during overcast weather or whenever solar orientation prevents direct sunlight from penetrating to the interior space. Daylight is also present on clear days, the result of reflectance off moisture or particulate matter in the atmosphere.

The third is "reflected" light, and can be either direct sunlight or daylight which has reflected off exterior or interior surfaces before or after it passes through the glass. The combination of direct sunlight, skylight, and reflected light is the total available light (Fig. 5-5).

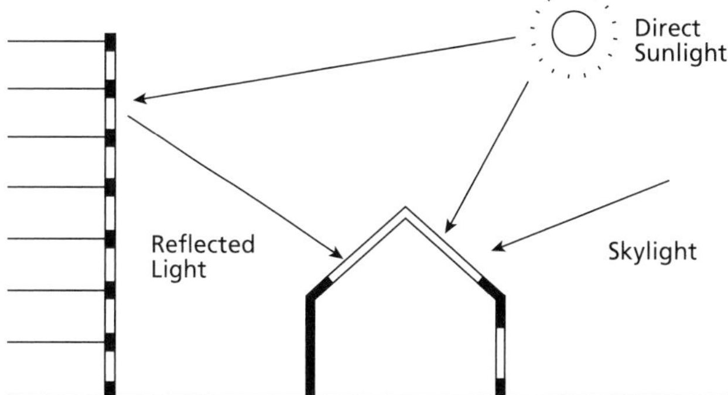

Fig.5-5.
The three categories of natural light—direct sunlight, daylight, and reflected light—all combine to become the total available light passing through glazing.

As a result of the drastic increase in oil prices due to the oil embargo following the Arab-Israeli war of 1973, developers impressed upon architectural firms the need to reduce fossil fuel operating costs in the buildings they designed. By the late 1970s, electric lighting had overtaken heating, ventilating, and air conditioning as the largest consumer of energy in commercial structures (Fig. 5-6). Designers found that one way to reduce electrical consumption for lighting was to increase the availability of natural light to interior spaces, thereby decreasing the dependence on electric lamps for illumination during daylight hours.

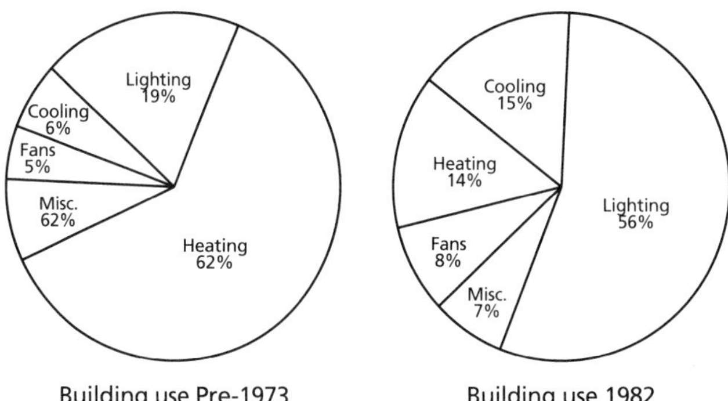

Fig. 5-6.
The rising cost of fossil fuels in the 1970s generated a move to more efficient methods of heating buildings. By 1982, lighting had become the prime consumer of energy of all building operating systems.

Prior to this time, there were no alternatives to the use of clear glass in skylights or glasshouses. The quality of light that clear glass allowed through it was excellent for plant growth, but severely compromised the comfort of interior spaces beneath it during the warmer months of the year, particularly before the advent of air conditioning. Even afterward, modern technology had still not been able to provide adequate, cost-effective cooling capacity for spaces with copious amounts of clear-glassed skylight.

The economics of the 1970s accelerated the desire to fill this technological gap. Architectural glazing systems with tinted or reflective glass first developed in the 60s were finally "brought out of the closet" and used to help create dramatic interior spaces by permitting the transmittance of daylight without the accompanying excessive buildup of heat from solar gain. Reflective and tinted glass became key elements in atrium and skylight design.

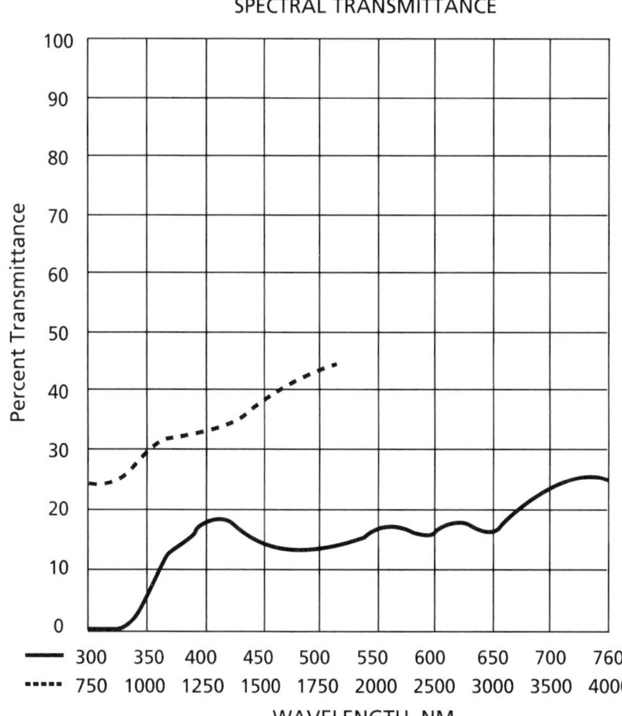

Fig. 5-7.
A spectral energy distribution curve for reflective glass indicates how the glazing composition can alter the relative percentages of transmittance for the light spectrum. (Courtesy of PPG Industries)

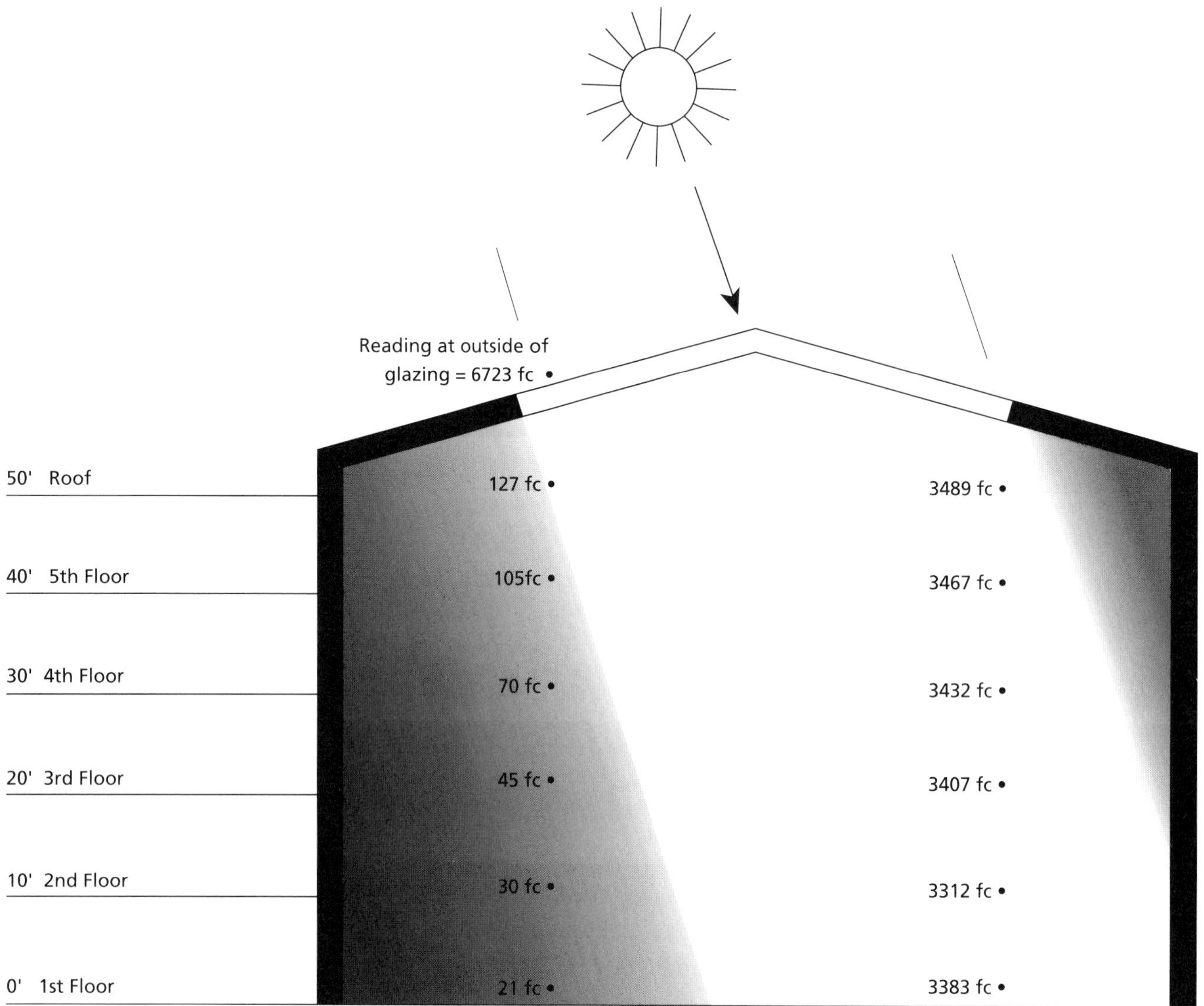

Fig. 5-8.
A computer model indicating relative light level readings for direct sunlight and indirect light as it passes through glazing into an atrium space. The model uses the latitude of Detroit, Michigan (42°- 20' N) at noon on March 21. Note that the direct sunlight has lost only 3 percent of its intensity since being transmitted through the glass; but the reading on the atrium floor in indirect light has lost 83 percent of its intensity from its corresponding location just inside the glazing, and is no longer bright enough to sustain plant growth of any kind. (Courtesy of Leonard Kersch)

The very qualities which make reflective and tinted glass appealing to the architectural community adversely impact the effect light which passes through it has on plant growth. In addition to reducing the intensity of light, sometimes significantly, reflective and tinted glass alters the spectral energy of the light. Figure 5-7 illustrates how drastically reflective and tinted glass can alter the spectral energy of light passing through it.

Unless skylighted areas are extremely generous, the amount of time a plant can receive direct sunlight is limited. This relegates plants, in many cases, to obtain a majority of their light energy from daylight, the maximum intensity of which will be considerably lower than can be provided by direct sunlight. The capacity of daylight to provide proper levels of plant growth lighting is related to the area of glazing available, the proximity of the plants to the glazing and the percentage of light transmittance of the glazing. Direct sunlight has the ability to maintain virtually all its intensity as it passes through glazing and down into an atrium space. Daylight does not have that attribute. As the distance between skylight and atrium floor increases, daylight intensity decreases markedly (Fig. 5-8). Similarly, as plants are moved farther away from windows, intensity will decrease.

Interior landscape designers often make the mistake of presuming that if the ceiling above an interior landscape is skylighted, it will provide adequate light for plant growth, which is all too often not the case. With architectural glazing having the ability to reduce light transmittance by more than 90 percent, skylighted spaces can often have light level readings below 20 fc in the middle of a bright, sunny day.

Transparent vs. Translucent Light

In addition to reflective and tinted glass, a third type of glazing has made its mark on contemporary architecture since the mid-twentieth century: Fiberglass and other glass compositions which create translucent, rather than transparent, glazing. Translucent glazing systems offer tremendous benefits to interior spaces containing plants, yet they have not been used extensively. In addition to their limited use potential as window glazing (the outdoors cannot be seen through them), their use as skylight glazing has likewise been limited; many architects prefer to see the sky (and any cloud formations) through them from within, and prefer the light dynamics of sun and shadow created by transparent glazing.

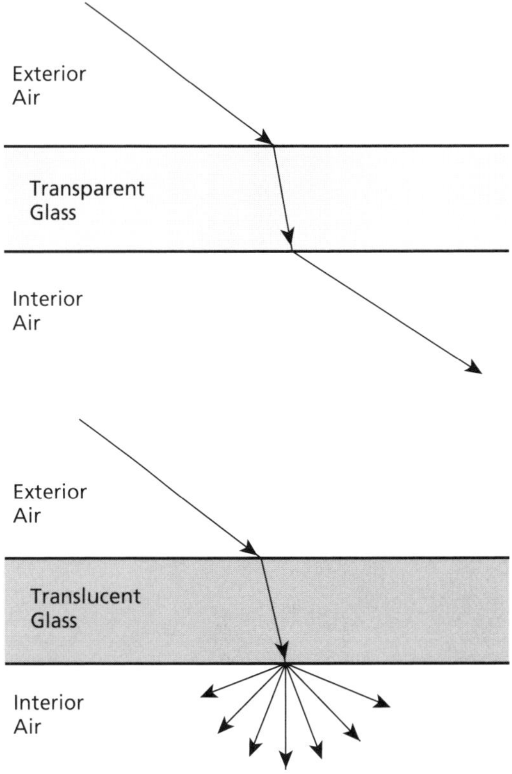

Fig. 5-9.
The differing effects of an individual ray of visible light passing through transparent and translucent glazing. (Courtesy of Leonard Kersch)

The benefit offered to plants is that the dispersion of light by translucent glazing (Fig. 5-9) systems allows significantly brighter light levels to enter interior spaces than the same percentage of light transmittance by transparent glass. For example, if the transmittance of both translucent and transparent glazing systems were 50 percent, and an incoming ray of light had an intensity of 1,000 fc, the ray exiting the glazing (i.e., coming into the interior space) would have an intensity of 500 fc for both systems. But the amount of light on the floor of the atrium space below would be four to five times brighter for the translucent system.

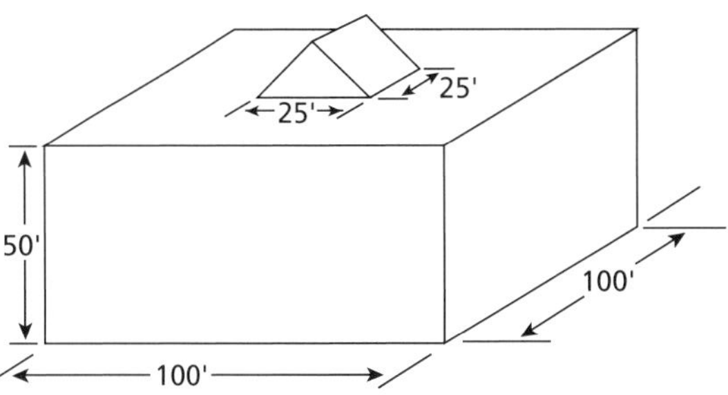

Fig. 5-10.
The hypothetical atrium used for comparing the light transmittance of transparent and translucent glazing. The atrium measures 100 ft (30.5 m) square, with a 25 ft (7.6 m) square skylight at 50 ft (15.2 m) above the atrium floor (Courtesy of Leonard Kersch).

This impact is demonstrated in the accompanying computer simulation which illustrates footcandle readings of identical atrium spaces provided with translucent and transparent glazing systems (Fig. 5-10, 5-11). This means that the translucent system can supply more useful light for plant growth without adversely affecting heat

Fig. 5-11.
These six computer models demonstrate the differing lighting effects created by clear glazing (left side) and translucent glazing (right side), using identical atrium configurations and light availability. The dotted square in the center of each "atrium" is the location of the skylight. Numbers in each plan represent light level readings in footcandles. All light levels are taken at an elevation of 2 ft 6 in (0.76 m) above the atrium floor. (Courtesy of Leonard Kersch)

TRANSPARENT

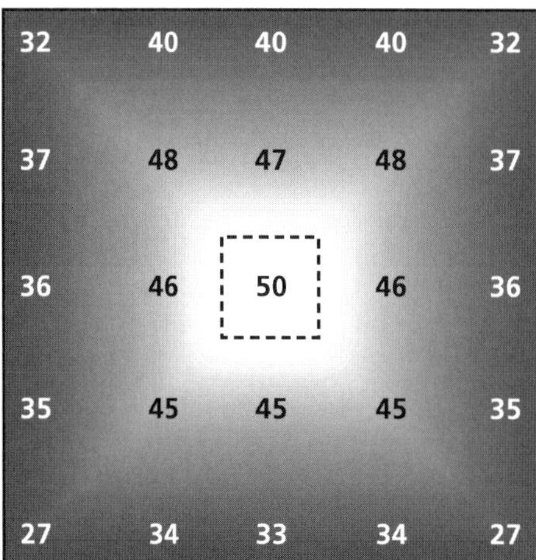

Fig. 5-11a. Noon, December 21

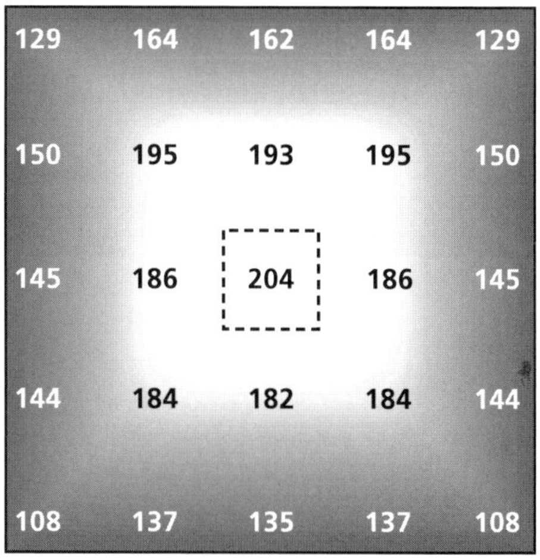

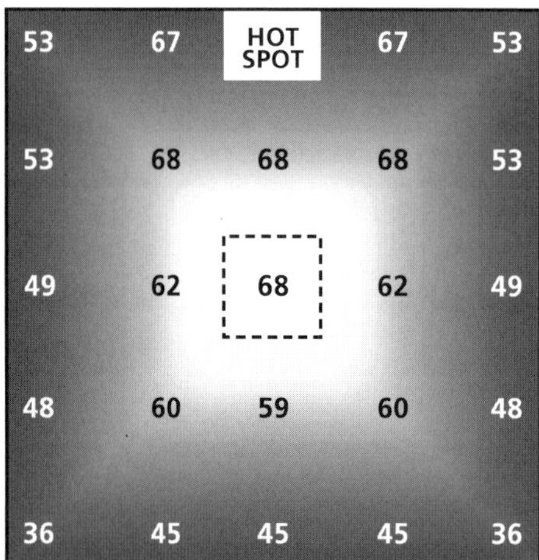

Fig. 5-11c. Noon, March 21. Note the "hot spot" where the clear glazing has allowed direct sunlight to penetrate to the baseline elevation at 2 ft 6 in above the atrium floor.

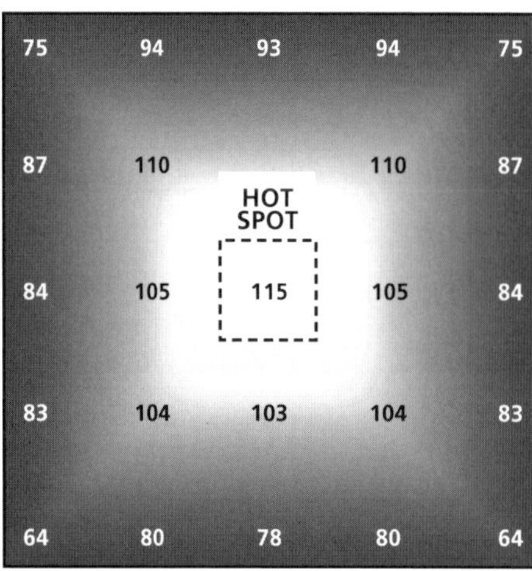

Fig. 5-11e. Noon, June 21. Note again the "hot spot" of direct sunlight.

TRANSLUCENT

129	164	162	164	129
150	195	193	195	150
145	186	204	186	145
144	184	182	184	144
108	137	135	137	108

Fig. 5-11b. Noon, December 21

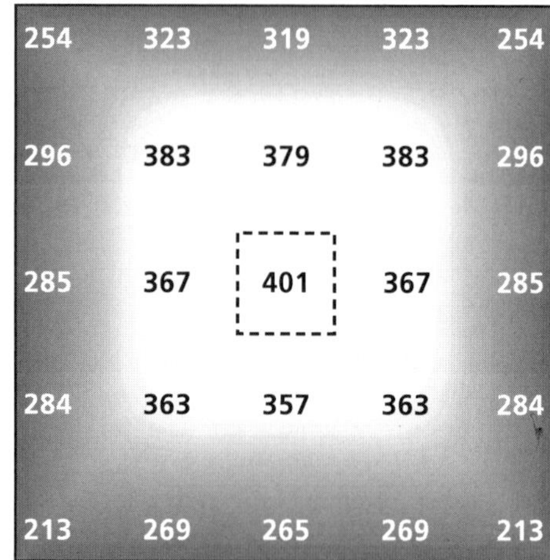

Fig. 5-11d. Noon, March 21

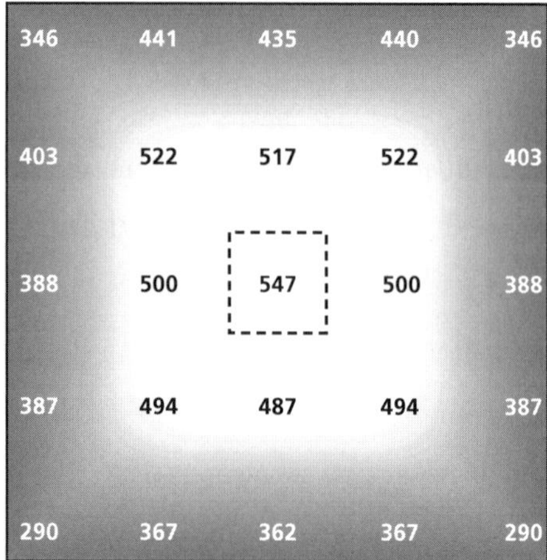

Fig. 5-11f. Noon, June 21

Transparent Glazing

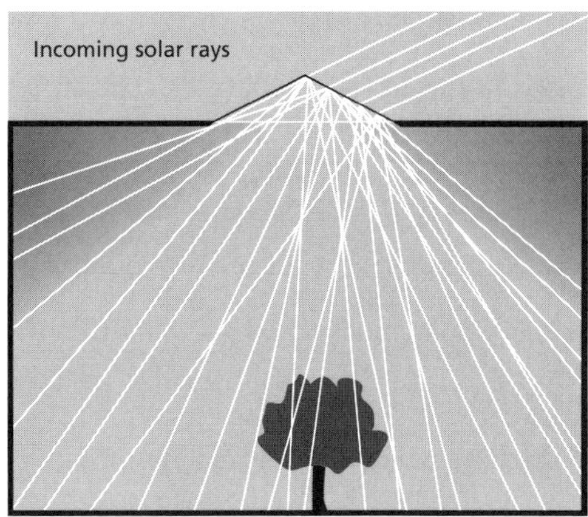

Translucent Glazing

Fig. 5-12.
In winter, the low angles of the sun—or even at mid-day—may preclude direct sunlight passing through clear glazing from reaching an atrium floor. Translucent glazing has the ability to disperse even low-angle, early morning and late afternoon sunlight into useful plant growth lighting. (Courtesy of Leonard Kersch)

gain during warm weather. Increasing light availability without increasing air conditioning costs is a substantial benefit offered by this system. Some translucent glazing manufacturers, such as Kalwall Corporation, offer a composite system consisting of two outer faces of reinforced glass fibers containing a center of insulation, adding energy conservation attributes as well. Translucent glazing can also direct the low angle rays of the early morning and late afternoon sun into an interior space, which a transparent glazing system cannot do (Fig. 5-12), giving plants longer durations of usable growth lighting.

SKYLIGHT ORIENTATION

Another factor in skylighting design and its effect on plant growth is the relationship of plant location to skylight, and the orientation of the skylight itself. It is a common fallacy that the optimal plant location is always directly beneath a skylight. If there is a desire for plantings to receive direct sunlight through a skylight, the positioning of the glazing must be a function of the angle, or altitude, of the sun to the location of the foliage. (Fig. 5-13)

Fig. 5-13.
The most appropriate skylight location is often not directly above plantings if the design intent is for the plants to capture some direct sunlight.

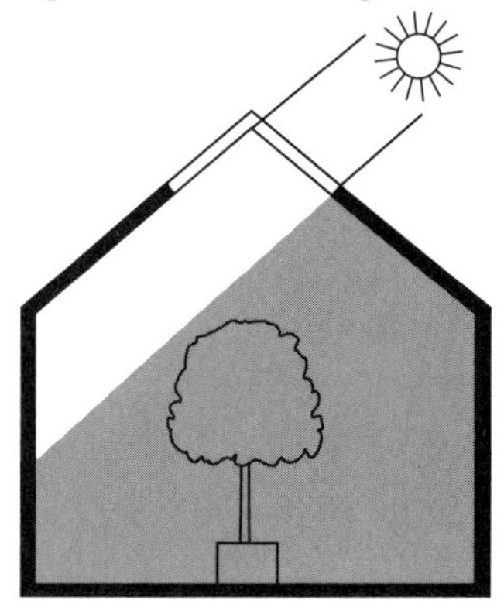

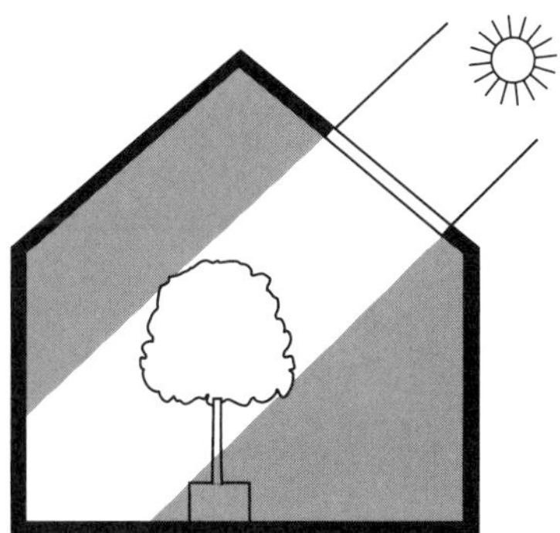

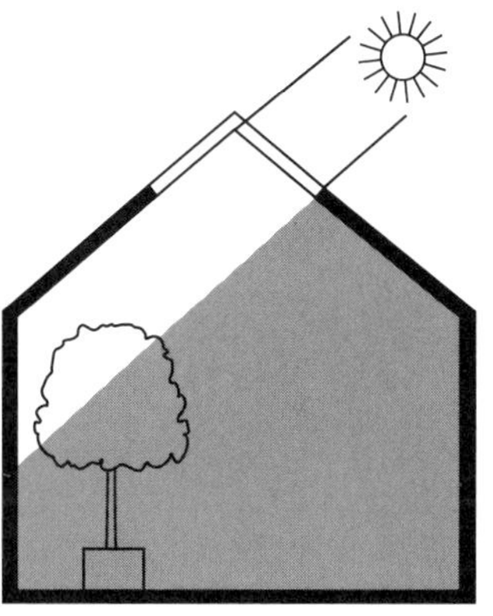

ELECTRIC LIGHT

After the invention of the incandescent lamp by Edison, the advent of fluorescent lighting in 1938 was the next major step in the development of electric plant growth lighting, for it marked the introduction of the first electric light source whose spectral energy was compatible with the horticultural needs of plants. But the nature of fluorescent lighting prohibits it from providing intensities of light suitable for plant growth in many applications. Since it was not a point source of light, its energy was too diffused to be able to be focused and directed, regardless of the reflectors in which it was housed.

The newer High Intensity Discharge (HID) sources (mercury vapor, high pressure sodium, and metal halide) are, like incandescent, point sources of light. As such, they can be placed within fixtures whose reflectors can direct a significant portion of their light output to specific targets. The ability to aim their light output allows HID lamps to be mounted at considerable distances from the plants they are lighting, giving architects, space planners, and interior landscape designers much greater flexibility in the design of spaces with living plants in them.

A second major advantage to HID lamps as a plant growth light source is their increased efficiency, i.e., their ability to produce more light for the same electrical consumption than a less efficient lamp. Incandescent lamps, the least efficient electric light source, expend a greater percentage of their electrical energy as heat, leaving much less energy for light output. The following chart illustrates the comparative characteristics of the six most popular plant growth light sources according to efficiency, wattage availability, and lamp life for the commonly available lamps of each type: *(Refer to Table 5-1)*.

The higher efficiencies and aimability of HID lamps would make them appear to be perfect solutions to the problem of plant growth lighting, but they do have their down sides. HID lamps are considerably more expensive than incandescent and fluorescent lamps. They are larger, and require special fixtures and base configurations which are not as readily available as standard incandescent or fluorescent fixtures. They require ballasts (as do many fluorescent fixtures) to regulate voltage or limit current, which often emit almost as much heat as the lamps themselves. The ballasts are heavy and unwieldy, making their fixtures correspondingly larger than an incandescent fixture. They have electrical characteristics that warrant consideration: Unlike incandescent, fluorescent, and quartz lamps, they require some time (often a few minutes) to reach full output. After being shut off, they must be cooled (again, several minutes) before their arcs will restrike.

Lamp life

The lamp life of all electric light sources is an important factor in the proper maintenance of plants. This is particularly critical with HID lights mounted at the top of multi-story atrium spaces whose locations render them difficult to access for lamp replacement. Maintenance personnel responsible for changing light fixtures must make regular surveys of fixtures to ensure than burned out lamps are replaced within a few days. However, the need to replace lamps is only obvious when a lamp has actually burned out, not when the useful "lamp life" of the bulb has been reached. "Lamp life" is considered by electric light manufacturers to be the point at which 50 percent of the test lamps have burned out. No electric lights burn at full brightness for their entire life until burnout. Incandescents, more than any other light source, retain most of their brightness until burnout, but most other light sources suffer a decrease

Table. 5-1. Comparison of electric light source characteristics.

Lamp Type	Wattage	Efficiency (mean lumens per watt)	Lamp Life (hours)
HIGH INTENSITY DISCHARGE			
High Pressure Sodium (clear)	70	77	24,000 +
	150	96	24,000 +
	250	99	24,000 +
	400	112	24,000 +
	1,000	126	24,000 +
Metal Halide (clear)	100	68	10,000
	175	59	10,000
	250	68	10,000
	400	72	10,000
	1,000	88	10,000
Mercury Vapor ("Deluxe White")	75	30	16,000
	100	32	24,000 +
	175	41	24,000 +
	250	39	24,000 +
	400	44	24,000
	700	43	24,000 +
	1,000	47	24,000 +
FLUORESCENT			
Cool White	40	67	20,000 +
Warm White	40	69	20,000 +
Daylight	40	56	20,000 +
TUNGSTEN-HALOGEN ("clear")			
	100	14	2,000
	250	19	2,000
	500	21.5	2,000
	1,000	21	2,000
INCANDESCENT ("Standard" color)			
A-19	75	14	750
A-19	100	15	750
A-21	150	17	750
R-40 Reflector Spot	150	11	2,000
R-40 Reflector Spot	300	12	2,000
R-40 Reflector Spot	500	11	2,000

in light output over the course of their lamp life. Fluorescents will typically lose more than 50 percent of their light output prior to burnout, as can HID sources. With drops in output of that magnitude, it then becomes essential for maintenance personnel to establish a lamp replacement program based not on burnout but on hours of operation, if light output is critical to plant growth.

Because the spectral energy of electric lamps is so drastically different from daylight, and from one source to another, the varying effects of each type of electric lamp source on plants (and on the human eye) can be dramatic.

Electric Light Sources

INCANDESCENT

The oldest electric light source has undergone surprisingly few changes since Edison first popularized it in 1879. It still consists, as it did then, of a glass envelope filled with inert gas, and a filament which glows when energized by electrical current. Because the filament (Edison first tried carbon, but tungsten is now used) uses electrical energy inefficiently, incandescent lamps produce more heat than light, and require high wattages to provide meaningful illumination for plant growth. But even with higher wattages, the spectral energy emitted by incandescent has too high a ratio of red to blue wavelengths, and produces excessive internodal growth. The result can be spindly, weak stalks or shoots with sparse foliage. The high concentration of infrared output in incandescent also causes the transpiration rate of foliage to increase. On the positive side, the colors they render are pleasing to the human eye, they are inexpensive and they are easy to use.

FLUORESCENT

Currently the most popular electric light source worldwide because of its ubiquitous commercial usage, fluorescent lamps come in a variety of slightly different color outputs (with names like Cool-White, Warm-White, Deluxe-White, Daylight-White, etc.). Fluorescent lamps are glass tubes containing mercury vapor under low pressure through which an arc is struck when the lamp is energized. Fluorescents are superior to incandescent for plant growth, but none of the fluorescent lamps typically used commercially offer the full spectrum of light energy that plants need. Cool-White and Warm-White, the two most popular standard fluorescents, are somewhat deficient in the longer wavelengths (red and far red). Their shortcomings are not sufficient to create abnormal plant growth, as with incandescent, but as previously stated, their photometrics dictate that they must be relatively close to the plants to provide adequate intensity. Fluorescent lamps specially formulated for plant growth (so called "grow lights") emit either full spectrum light or light in wavelengths needed specifically for photosynthesis and chlorophyll synthesis (Fig. 5-14). These lights, however, are not properly balanced for human vision, and should not be used in commercial interior situations. They are best relegated to strictly horticultural applications in which the light source is within 18 in (45.7 cm) to 4 ft (1.2 m) of the foliage to be illuminated, such as light benches in warehouse space or in light gardens.

MERCURY VAPOR

The first of the high intensity discharge lamps to be introduced is similar to fluorescent in emphasizing the blue over the red wavelengths. Mercury vapor lamps have two glass envelopes. The inner one contains mercury vapor under higher pressure than fluorescent lamps which is ionized by the arc passing through the vapor when the lamp is energized. These lamps are available with clear or phosphor coated outer envelopes. (Fig. 5-15) The phosphor coatings help compensate for the emphasis in the blue and blue-green wavelengths, providing better color rendition for human vision and for plant growth than the clear lamps, especially with regard to their effect on green foliage. Mercury vapor lamps have the longest life span of all electric light sources, about 24,000 hours for most wattages. While more efficient that incandescent or fluorescent, mercury vapor lamps are the least efficient of the HID lamps, as indicated in Table. 5-1.

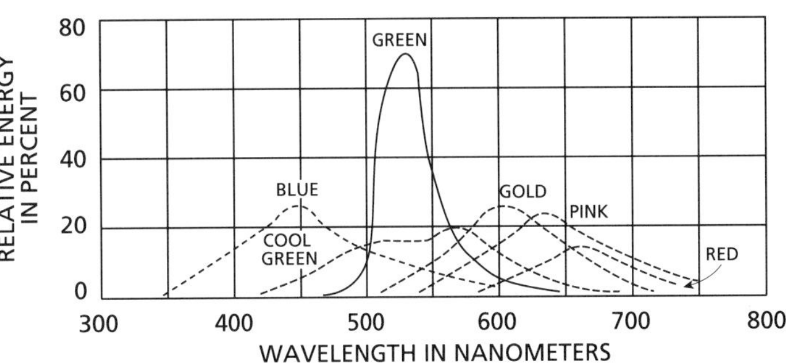

Fig. 5-14. Spectral distribution curves of typical fluorescent lamp colors shown without mercury line emission. (Courtesy of GTE Sylvania)

METAL HALIDE

These lamps use various combinations of halogens and rare earth salts to create a color rendition considered to be the best for plant growth, and also quite pleasing to the human eye. With excellent color and improved efficiency over mercury, fluorescent, and incandescent, they have become extremely popular in recent years despite two drawbacks: First, their lamp life is less than mercury vapor, about 15,000 to 20,000 hours; and second, their fixtures must have protective lenses to guard against ultraviolet light generation. (Fig. 5-16) An added benefit to interior landscape designers is that reasonably well balanced color photography of interior landscapes lighted only by metal halide lamps can be achieved with standard daylight-biased film.

HIGH PRESSURE SODIUM

Other than low pressure sodium, which is not suited to plant growth lighting because of its monochromatic light output, this is the most efficient electric lamp source in general use, and is in considerable demand for street and parking area lighting, where color rendition is less important that cost-effectiveness. High pressure sodium uses a

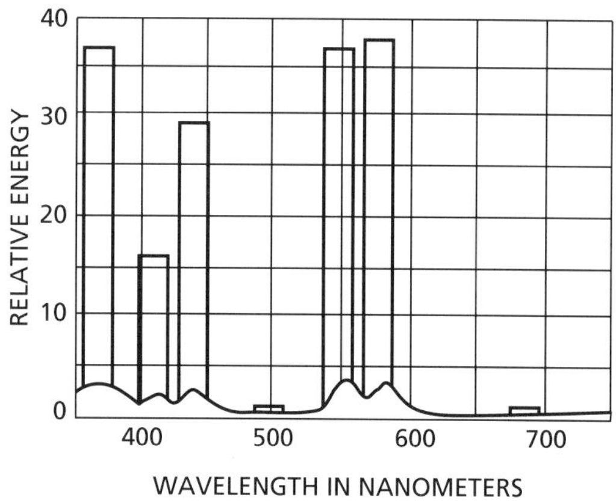

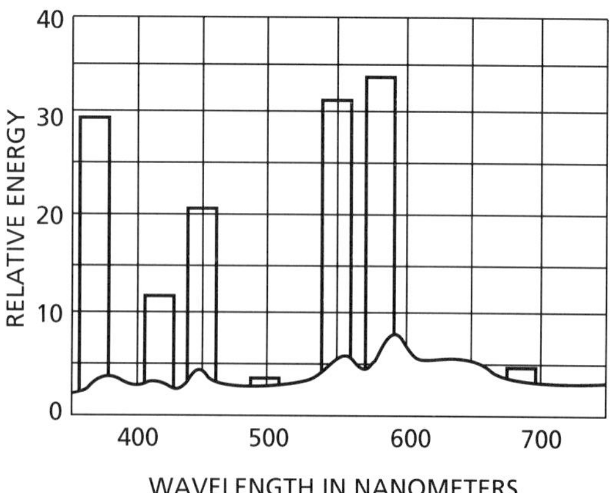

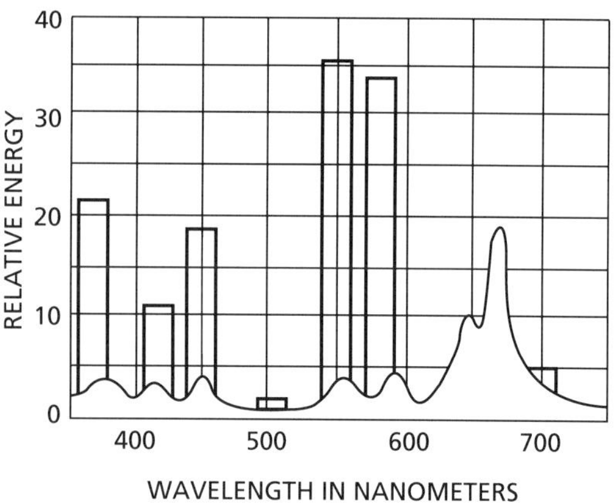

Fig. 5-15. Spectral energy distribution typical of most mercury lamps. (top) Clear mercury, (middle) Increased-efficacy phosphor-coated mercury, and (bottom) improved-color phosphor-coated mercury. (Courtesy of GTE Sylvania)

double glass envelope like the other HID sources, but employs an arc tube made from polycrystalline alumina for chemical and heat resistance. This source produces a general spectrum of light, but greatly emphasizes the yellow wavelengths. The new "white" high pressure sodium lamp looks more like incandescent than any other HID lamp source to the human eye, but are available in limited wattages. In addition to causing extended internodal growth like incandescents, they also display plants very poorly, giving them an unhealthful appearance. Prior to the advent of metal halide, high pressure sodium was used successfully in conjunction with mercury vapor lamps to provide a balanced light spectrum for plant growth lighting, but the ability of metal halide to serve this function with one light source has diminished the use of high pressure sodium in commercial plant growth applications.

DIFFUSED VS. POINT SOURCE

One of the advantages of using high pressure sodium in conjunction with mercury vapor was that plants growing under both types of lights benefited from a broad spectral range and from two separate light sources. As effective as metal halide can be in promoting plant growth from a spectral energy standpoint, a single point source of light over a plant can be horticulturally detrimental. While the light dynamics of a point source allow its energy to be focused and directed, a single point source cannot penetrate to the interior foliage of most plant species. Inner leaves of specimens like Ficus trees will never receive any light and will eventually drop, creating an "umbrella effect"—a thin canopy of leaves at the outer shell of the plant's crown. The diffused light supplied by daylight, fluorescent light, or multiple sources of HID lights will eliminate this umbrella effect and help grow fully foliated, healthy plants. A minimum of three or four luminaires placed to provide light at up to 45° angles works well. It must be remembered, though, that glare becomes a factor when electric light sources are angled towards a target, and the greater the angle from the vertical plane, the higher the potential for glare to be an issue.

The present thinking is that light energy emitted from two light sources, such as high pressure sodium and mercury lamps, makes it difficult for plants to absorb the proper ratios of the spectral energy for their various photo-responses. The main reason for this phenomenon is that the lamps have different light deterioration factors in their spectral emission and different replacement periods.

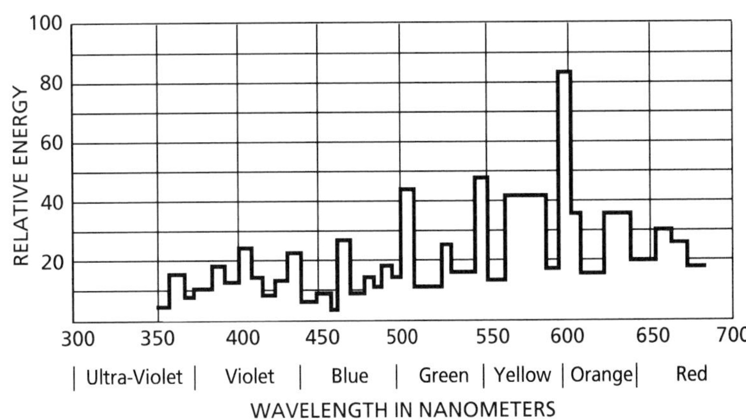

Fig. 5-16.
Spectral energy distribution of a 400-W phosphor-coated metal halide lamp. (Courtesy of GTE Sylvania)

To ensure good diffusion of light in the atrium, the lighting must be designed to maintain approximately 70 percent on a vertical, and 30 percent on a horizontal orientation. This will provide good light penetration to the center of trees, as well as maintaining proper intensities on the surface.

PHOTOPERIOD

Electric lighting offers great flexibility in determining the duration of lighting for plants. Unlike daylight, both the number of hours and the time of day when electric lighting is available can be controlled by switches or time clock. Plants can be grown successfully under daylight, electric light, or combinations of both. The most viable solution to an interior plant lighting problem will take into account many factors: The location of the interior space within the building (i.e., whether windows or skylights are feasible); the architectural configuration of the space itself; the lighting design of the remainder of the building; the use of the space; the density, size, and species of plants to be lighted; and the budget. The keys to the right solution are to address the issue as early in the design process as possible and to keep the lines of communication open between client, architect, interior designer, lighting designer, and interior landscape designer.

The flexibility afforded the design community by recent technological advances in electric lighting and glazing enable plants to thrive in spaces where it would not have been possible only a decade or two ago. As the efficiency of HID lamps continues to increase, and the ability of tinted, reflective and translucent glass and other glazing system materials continues to improve its light transmittance while insulating heat and cold, still other applications for interior landscaping will become apparent in the future.

CHAPTER 6
IRRIGATION

The most important—and costly—task in the maintenance of interior plants is providing them with proper amounts of water. Unfortunately, it is often not given much consideration by designers, many of whom believe that watering, and maintenance in general, are responsibilities of the contractor and need not be dealt with as part of the design process. But the efficiency of watering plants can be improved by designers regardless of whether plantings are placed in decorative containers or planted directly into an interior garden.

As advances in technology have improved our ability to provide adequate light and proper environmental conditions for plants, similar advances in technology have enabled maintenance technicians to better control the flow of water to plants and helping to reduce over- and under-watering. Still other advances lay ahead of us. In fact, until recently, the ability to irrigate plants indoors both effectively and cost-effectively lagged far behind the ability to do so for outdoor plants.

The reasons for this are evident in the manner in which plants utilize water for irrigation, and in the environmental differences between indoor and outdoor plants. Lawn grass, the most commonly irrigated outdoor plant, has a very shallow root system (which is why it benefits so much from irrigation in the first place), extending only a few inches into the soil. Water will stay within the root zone only for a short time before it percolates down below the root zone. The rate at which lawn and other outdoor plants utilize water is subject to the health, size, and species of the plant; local weather (sun, clouds, wind and temperature) conditions; and the composition of the surrounding growing medium and substrate. These actions cause water to evaporate on impact, transpire from foliage, be absorbed by roots, or pass down through the root zone (Fig. 6-1) quickly enough that irrigation supplied artificially can be provided on a regular basis without fear of overwatering, once a reasonable application rate has been established. Regardless of the type of irrigation system—manual or automatic; spray, drip or mist—an outdoor plant can be irrigated at a rate at which plants will absorb what they need and the remainder will be removed from the root zone quickly enough to avoid the debilitating effects of overwatering.

Fig. 6-1.
The hydrologic cycle as it affects exterior plants.

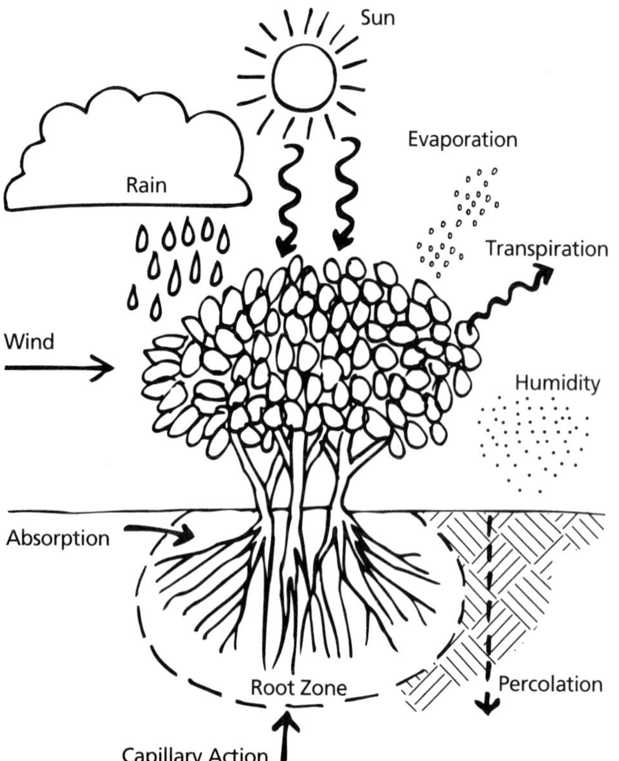

The "artificial" indoor environment has several substantive differences from this pattern. With no wind and fewer hours and lower intensities of bright light available, the ability of water to evaporate from foliage and the surrounding soil is greatly diminished. Generally lower light levels promote slower growth, resulting in slower rates of transpiration from the leaves and absorption of water by the roots. And the ability of water to percolate down through and out of the root zone is often hampered by the need to use a planting medium with high water retention capability, enabling watering intervals to be extended and service visits to be reduced.

In short, indoor plants need less water than outdoor plants, and the technology is just now emerging to be able to supply this decreased demand within the parameters of a totally automated irrigation system, one in which water is supplied to plants without any intervention by humans. Water in a totally automated system is brought to the plantings through a building's plumbing system, and once delivered to a nearby location, is given to the plants at a controlled rate for a controlled time interval set by a clock, or by sensors.

In addition to a generally diminished usage of water, interior plants have markedly different water requirements, a situation exacerbated by the often close proximity of species with diverse watering needs to one another.

MANUAL WATERING

Until recently, manual irrigation of individual plants by a service technician with a watering can or hose—provided the most reasonable method of keeping plants properly moistened. Manual watering of plants is still the most popular method of irrigation indoors, and even though manual watering would clearly be the contractors' responsibility, the interior landscape designer can favorably affect the ability of the service technician to perform this time-consuming function and to provide improved plant care.

Provision of a water source

The designer can first play a vital role in ensuring that a suitable water source is close by. The technician maintaining plants in an office building must sometimes travel to other floors to fill a watering can or cart because of the absence of a hose bib or sink, or because the standard sink in a washroom may not be designed to permit a fill-up of a bulky watering can. A request by the interior landscape designer to the architect or mechanical engineer early in the design process to provide a maintenance storage/ work area, or at the least a washroom sink with appropriate fittings, can do the trick (Fig. 6-2). It should include a source of hot and cold running water with fittings and sink size adaptable to accommodate hose connections or bulky watering cans; a work bench and work area to allow for repotting of small and large specimens; a floor drain to allow for hosing down the work area; and a storage room to house the tools and supplies needed for normal plant care.

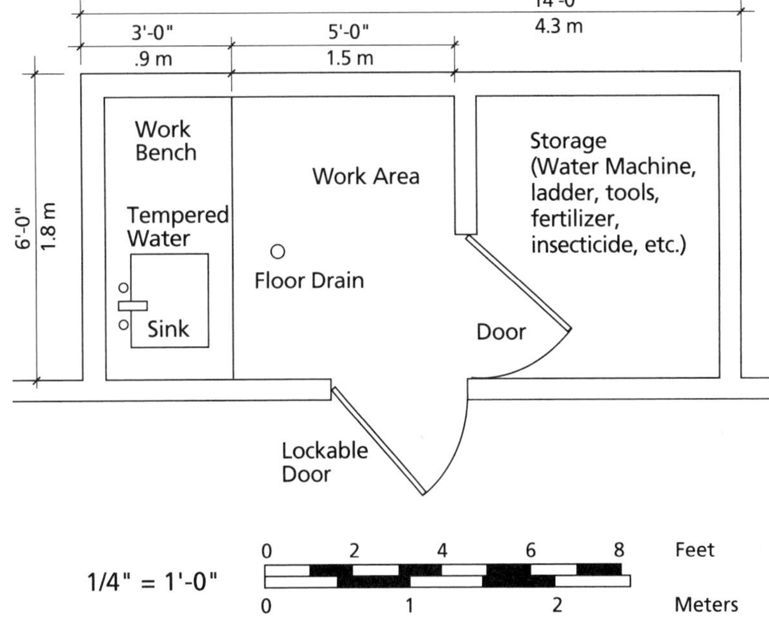

Fig. 6-2. A prototypical maintenance storage/ work area designed to accommodate the needs of the interior landscape service technician.

Fig. 6-3a.
A section through a typical box hydrant.. (Courtesy of Zurn Industries, Inc.)

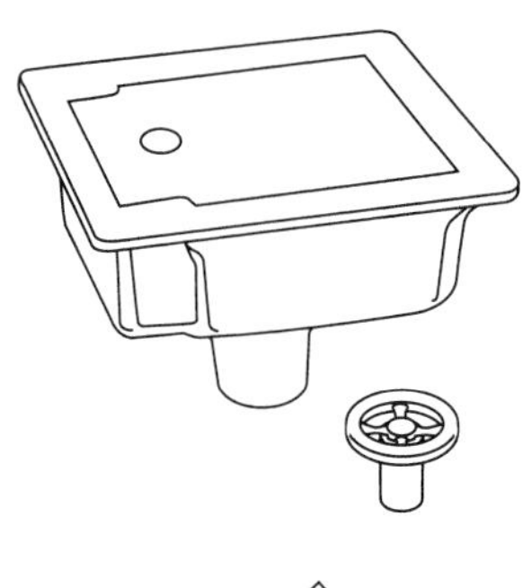

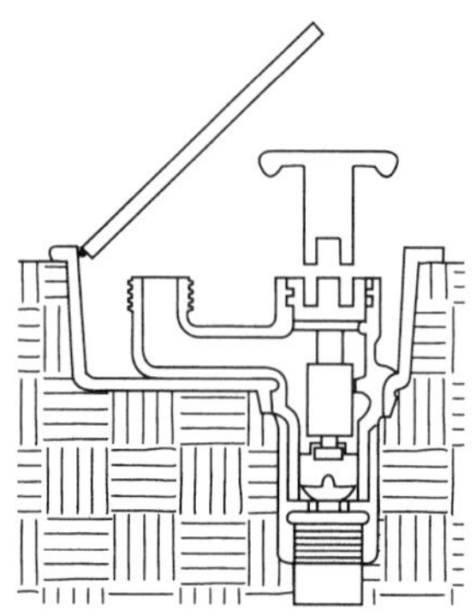

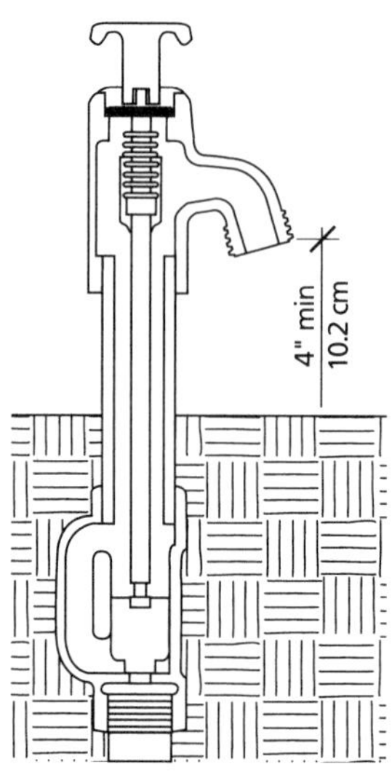

Fig. 6-3b.
The ubiquitous hose bib can greatly benefit the ability to manually irrigate a large interior planting . (Courtesy Zurn Industries, Inc.)

In garden-type settings, even a maintenance closet close to the plantings will not adequately support the service technician; a water source must be available within the garden area so the technician may use a hose to provide water manually, but as efficiently as possible. A flush-mounted box hydrant can be supplied with tamper-proof hardware to avoid unwarranted use (Fig. 6-3a). It is a visually unobtrusive method of installing a water source in a garden-style planter. It would be ideally located at the level of the mulch or planting medium, at the edge of a plant bed. Quick-coupler fittings allow for rapid connections to hoses. The more common hose bib, usually more visible, can also be fitted with tamper-proof hardware (Fig. 6-3b).

Tempered water

It is also important to be able to provide tempered (i.e., mixed hot and cold) water for irrigation. Most interior plants are tropical or sub-tropical, and prefer a water temperature range from 60° to 80° F (12° to 24° C). Cold water from a faucet in a northern temperate climate during mid-winter might be as low as 40° F (5° C). If tempered water is not possible, another solution would be to heat-trace the water (wrapping the water supply line in electric wire that heats up when energized, warming the pipe and the water within it. This solution is effective only if the movement of water through the pipe is relatively slow). A less expensive solution, in both installation and on-going operational cost terms, is to wrap the water supply pipe in insulation.

With watering recognized as the most important aspect of plant maintenance, the potential ability to increase watering effectiveness is seen as a key factor in controlling maintenance costs and further promoting the effectiveness of plants indoors. Several alternatives to manual watering are increasing in popularity.

SUBIRRIGATION

Subirrigation has been responsible for enormous strides in improving the capability of the service technician to apply water to plants. It is also widely considered to be a superior water delivery system to manual watering, for it allows plants to draw water from the planting medium by capillarity at a more measured pace than manual top-watering, eliminating the extreme dry-wet-dry cycles which can result from manual watering. Begun in Europe during the 1970s, subirrigation consists of a reservoir of water beneath or next to the planting medium of the plant's root zone.

There are three basic methods used by subirrigation devices for drawing water from the reservoir: Wick, capillary leg, and vacuum sensor. Success has been achieved by manufacturers using each of the three methods.

One example of the wick system is Water Disc, which uses a fabric wick extending from the bottom of the reservoir up into the planting medium (Fig. 6-4). This system adapts both the typical grow pot and the decorative container to subirrigation by adding a reservoir of water beneath the grow pot. A fabric wick is threaded through the bottom of the grow pot, with both its ends resting at the bottom of the reservoir. In addition to new plantings, this type of system is ideal for retrofitting standard grow pots for subirrigation if the decorative container is water-tight. If the container is not water-tight, a water-tight saucer must be placed beneath the Water Disc unit.

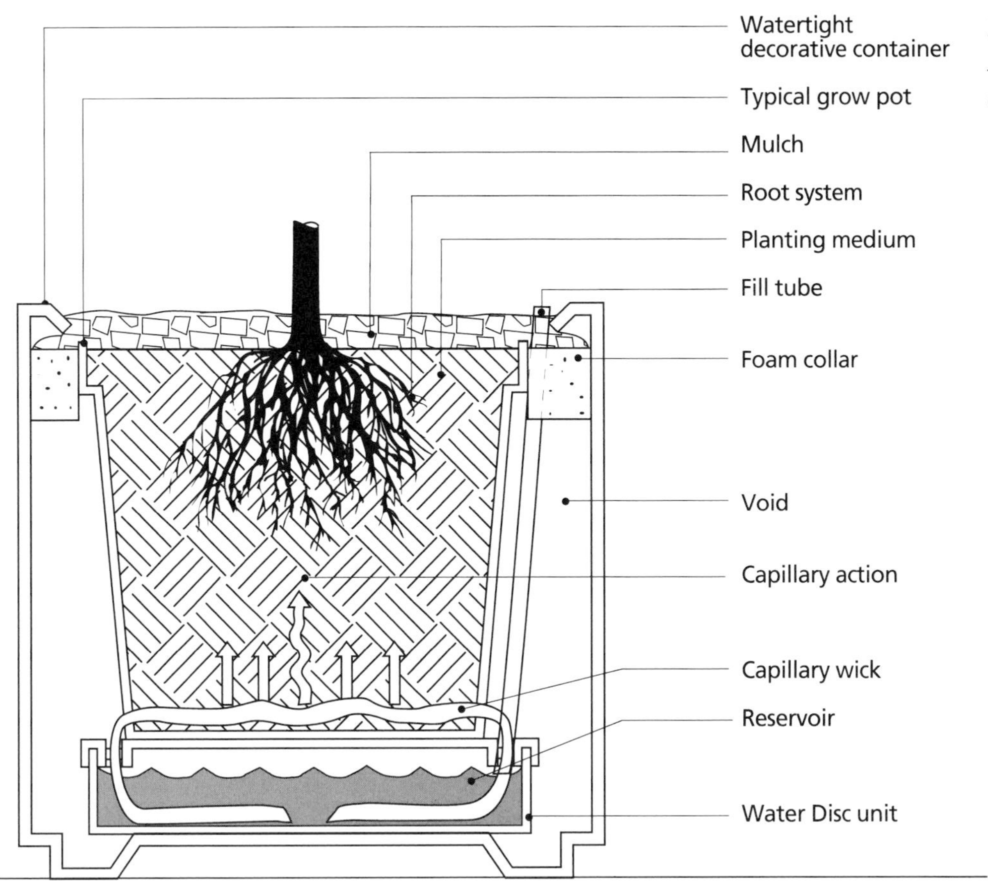

Fig. 6-4.
A fabric wick system as designed by Water Disc. (Courtesy of Water Disc)

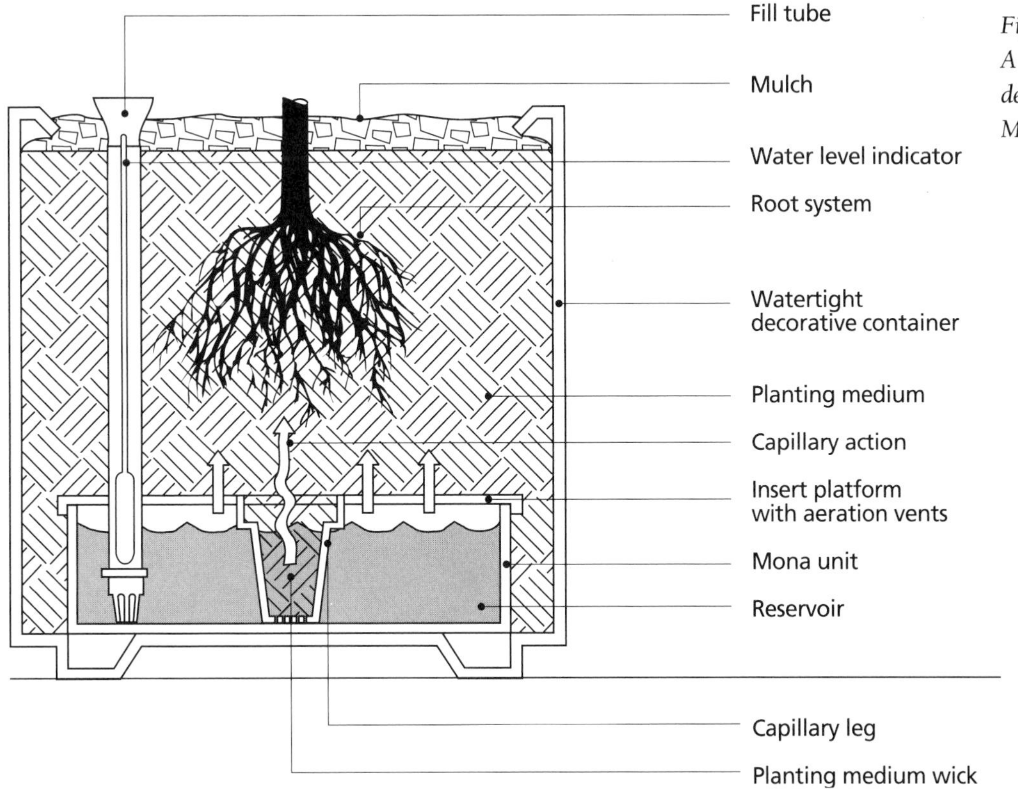

Fig. 6-5.
A capillary leg system as designed by MPS. (Courtesy of MPS-Scandinavia-USA)

One example of the capillary leg concept, the Mona Plant System (MPS), uses a capillary leg of planting medium (Fig. 6-5). It is also designed for use with any watertight decorative container. The Mona uses one or more legs of planting medium (depending on reservoir size) that are located within in the reservoir. Water in the reservoir reaches a similar level in the planting medium wick, which then distributes the water upward into the root zone by capillary action. This system requires the removal of the plant from its original grow pot, and direct planting into a planting medium providing optimum capillarity, drainage, and aeration.

Jardinier, another capillary leg type, recommends the use of perlite in their capillary moat (Fig. 6-6) to serve as an aerator and drainage medium. It replaces the typical grow pot with an integrated grow pot/water reservoir that can be placed inside a decorative container. Plants can be grown from inception in this system, eliminating the need to transplant or retrofit plants previously grown in typical grow pots. As of this writing, more than 30 foliage nurseries in Florida, California, and Hawaii are marketing specimens that are grown directly in Jardinier subirrigation systems. Jardinier is offered with or without drainage/aeration holes at the top of the reservoir. The system with drainage holes should be used with a water-tight saucer inside the decorative container.

Unlike the first three, which all must be placed within decorative containers, other wick systems like Grosfillex and Decor America (Figs. 6-7, 6-8) are built into their own decorative containers. With all these systems, water will continue to be drawn into the planting medium by capillary action until the planting medium has become saturated. It is therefore essential that the planting medium used with subirrigation systems use a formulation with a low saturation point; that is, one which contains enough perlite and/or sand to provide reasonable drainage.

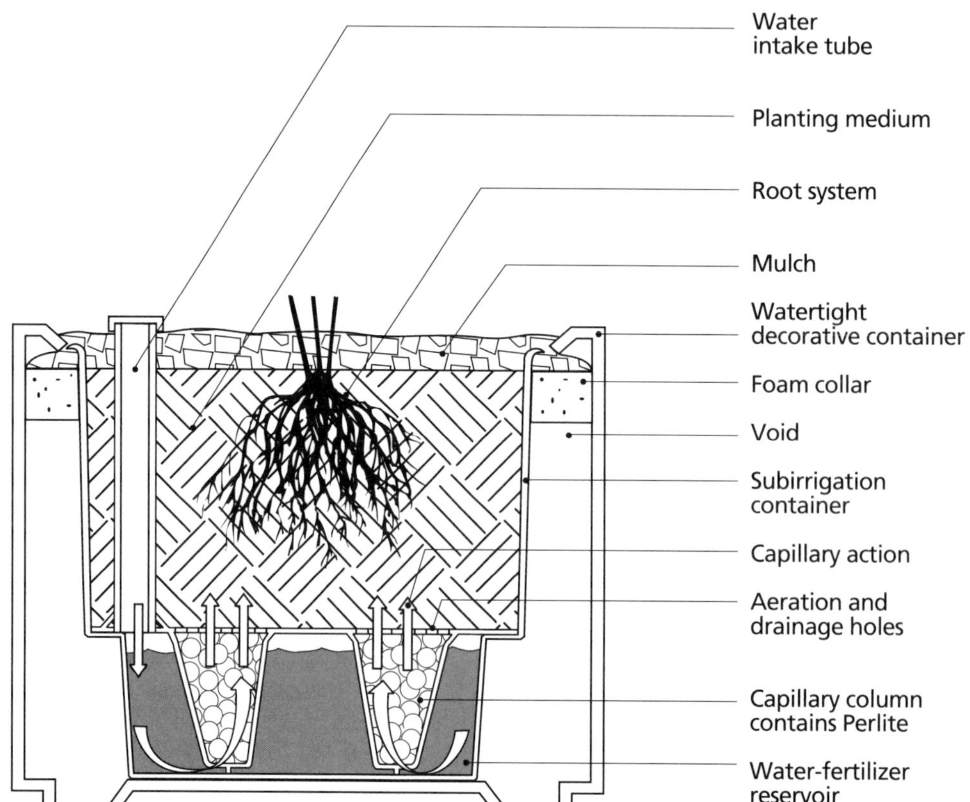

Fig. 6-6.
A capillary leg system as designed for the Jardinier System. (Courtesy of Jardinier Systems, Inc.)

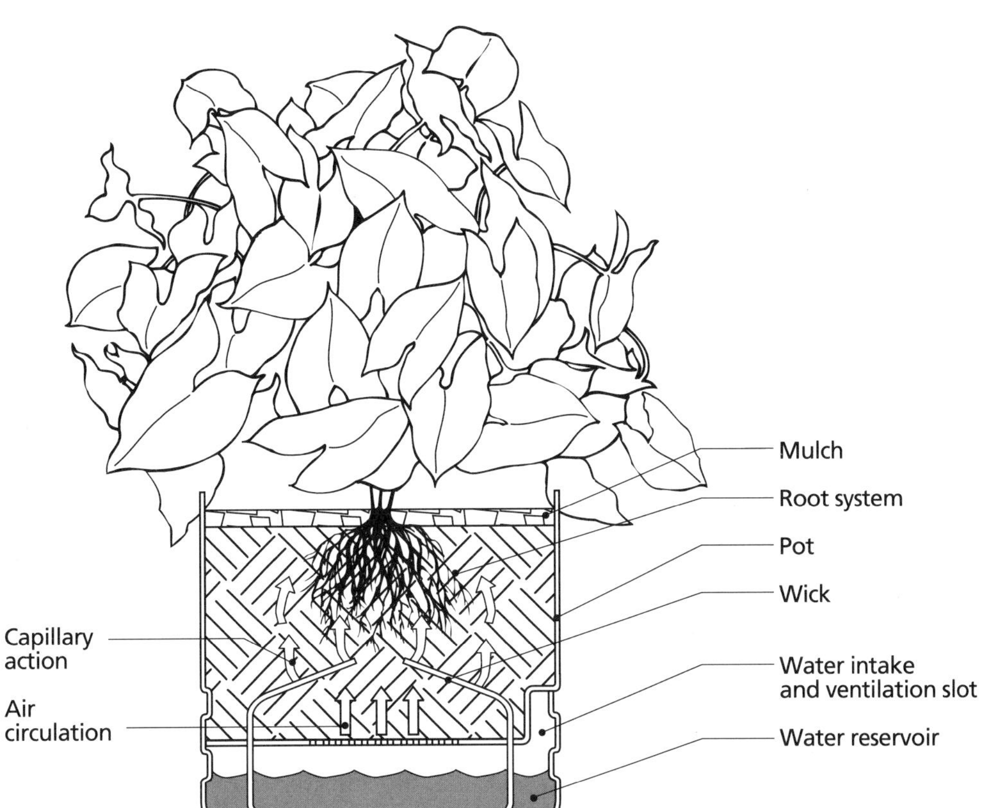

Fig. 6-7.
A wick system as designed for the Grosfillex planter. (Courtesy of Grosfillex, Inc.)

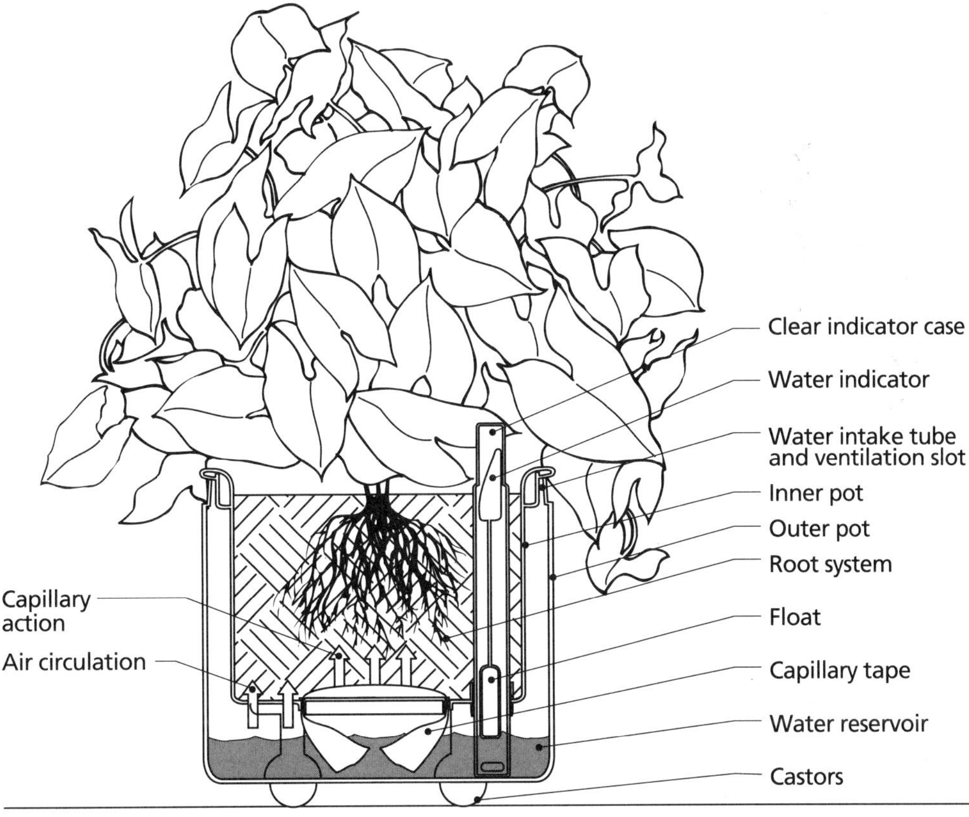

Fig. 6-8.
A wick system as designed for the Decor America planter. (Courtesy of Decor America, Inc.)

Another popular subirrigation system concept is the vacuum sensor system exemplified by the Natural Springs planter line by Planter Technology (Fig. 6-9), which uses the vacuum sensor system to allow water to infiltrate the planting medium In this system, a sensor is primed (dipped in water to fill all air voids) and inserted into the upper stratum of planting medium. After the reservoir is filled, air pressure in the sensor allows water to be released from the reservoir into the planting medium. When voids in the medium are filled with water, the air pressure in the sensor decreases and the flow of water stops. Unlike other subirrigation systems, the Natural Springs concept can theoretically be kept filled without the fear of overwatering, for the vacuum sensor will automatically cut off the flow of water when the soil reaches a point of saturation.

Subirrigation in containerized plantings

The adaptation of subirrigation to plants displayed in a decorative container is fairly straightforward. If the decorative container is watertight, the subirrigation component (depending on the brand) can simply be placed at the bottom of the container and planted as usual (Fig. 6-10). If, however, the decorative container is porous (e.g., a wicker basket), some types of subirrigation would still work (such as the Jardinier) with a impermeable saucer, while others would require the addition of a watertight liner within the decorative container (Fig. 6-11).

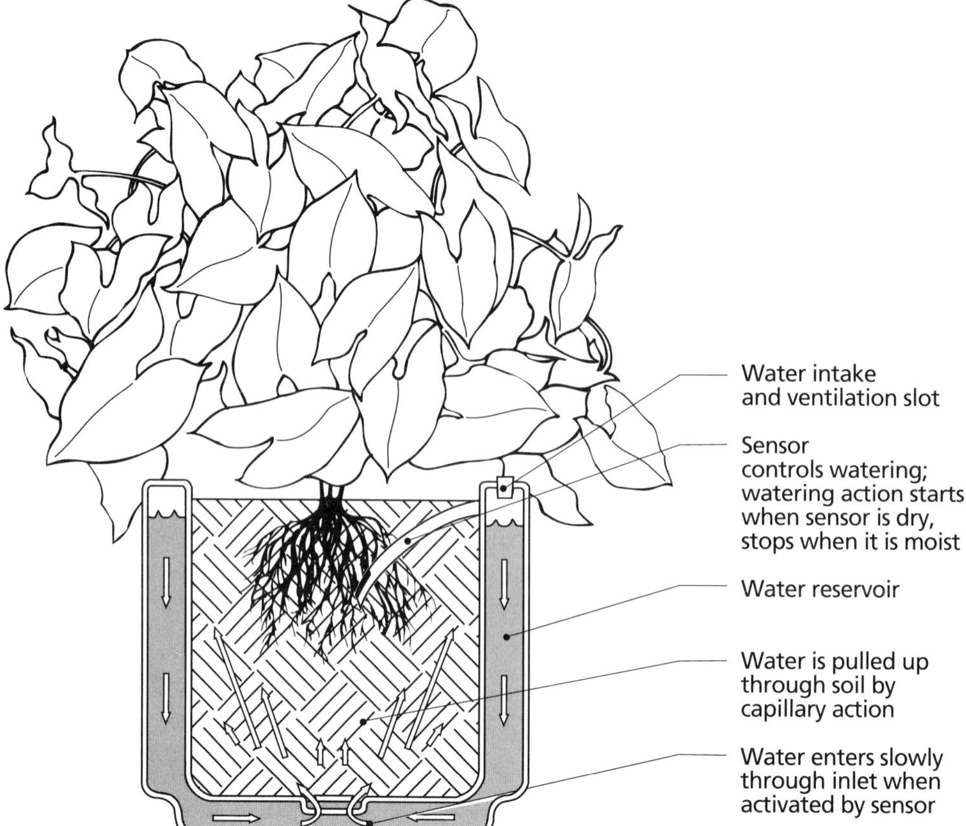
Water intake
and ventilation slot
Sensor
controls watering;
watering action starts
when sensor is dry,
stops when it is moist
Water reservoir
Water is pulled up
through soil by
capillary action
Water enters slowly
through inlet when
activated by sensor

Fig. 6-9.
A vacuum sensor system as designed for the Natural Springs. (Courtesy of Planter Technology, Inc.)

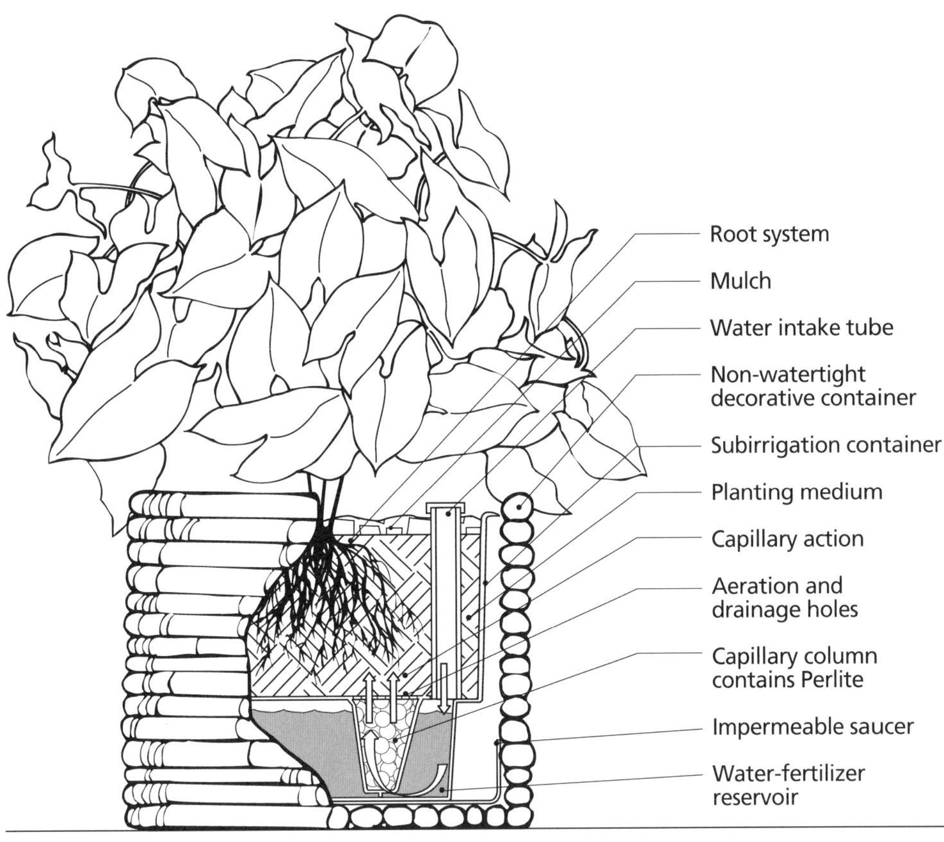

Fig. 6-10. Subirrigation in a non-watertight container. This section shows a subirrigation system (Jardinier) that can be placed in a non-watertight container if it has an impermeable saucer beneath it.

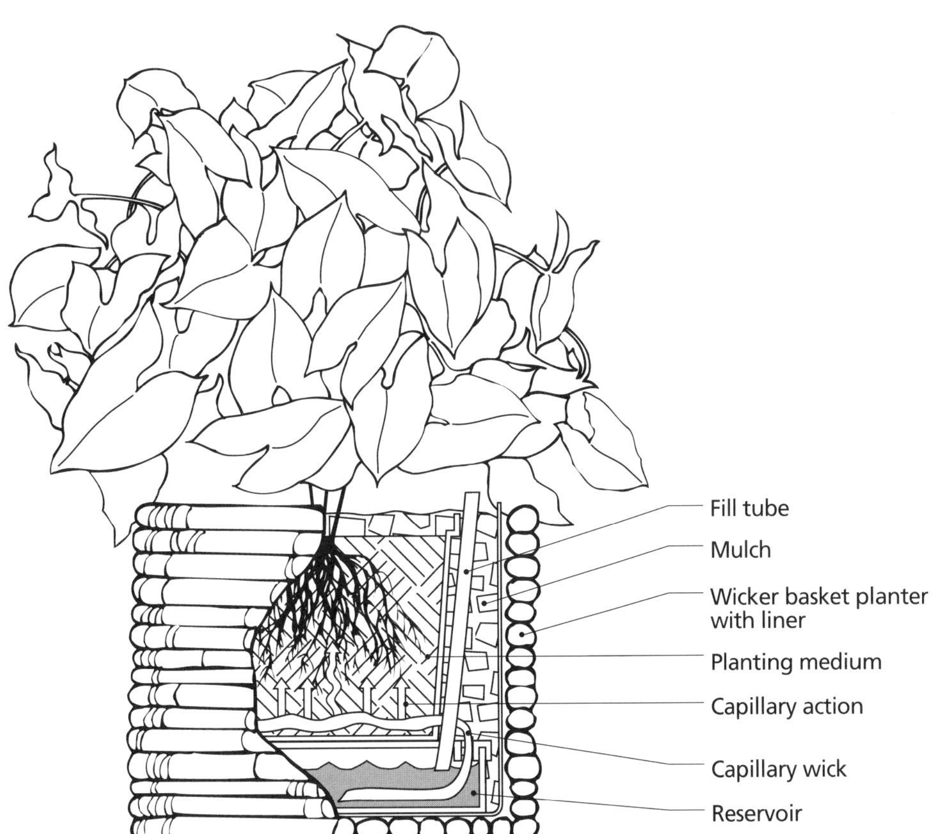

Fig. 6-11. Subirrigation in a non-water-tight container. To prevent water damage to a non-water-tight decorative container, water-tight liners must be installed. Some subirrigation systems would only require a water-tight saucer rather than an entire liner.

Subirrigation in planter beds

The subirrigation of garden-type settings is possible, but the system does not adapt as readily as it does toward individual containers. The Mona-Link by MPS-Scandinavia-USA is specifically designed for garden applications with connecting units capable of covering large areas requiring only one refill location (Fig. 6-12). Various configurations of the Mona Link components allow for changes in topography (Fig. 6-13) or for watering of plants with differing root depths (Fig. 6-14).

The next logical steps in the evolution of a garden-type subirrigation system would be the development of a means to provide one fill point for plantings at several different levels, and to enable the fill point to be connected to the building's plumbing network (Fig. 6-14).

Regardless of the means they use to regulate water flow, many brands of subirrigation systems have flourished in the interior landscape contracting business for a number of reasons:

• The planting medium of subirrigated plants draws water from the reservoir by capillary action, similar to the way outdoor plants draw water from the subsoil. The water is drawn from the reservoir at a more measured rate, allowing the root zone to avoid the extreme dry/wet/dry cycles prevalent with manual watering. With a more even rate of watering, plants are not under as much stress. They resist disease and insect infestations better, tolerate environmental extremes better, live longer, and are generally healthier.

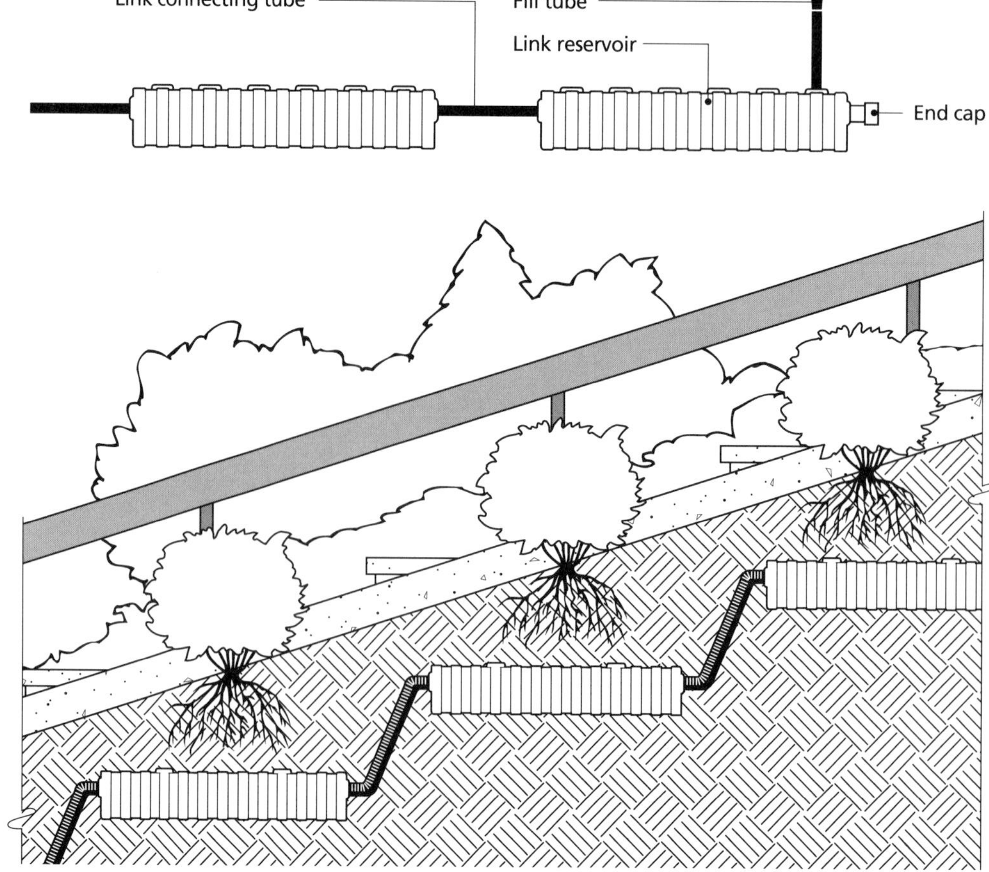

Fig. 6-12. The Mona-Link is used to subirrigate garden-style plant beds by interconnecting units in whatever configurations are necessary to provide even moisture applications. (Courtesy of MPS-Scandinavia-USA)

Fig. 6-13. The Mona-Link can adapt subirrigation technology to planter beds with changing topography, or to plants with varying root depths by adjusting the depth of the reservoir unit. (Courtesy of MPS-Scandinavia-USA)

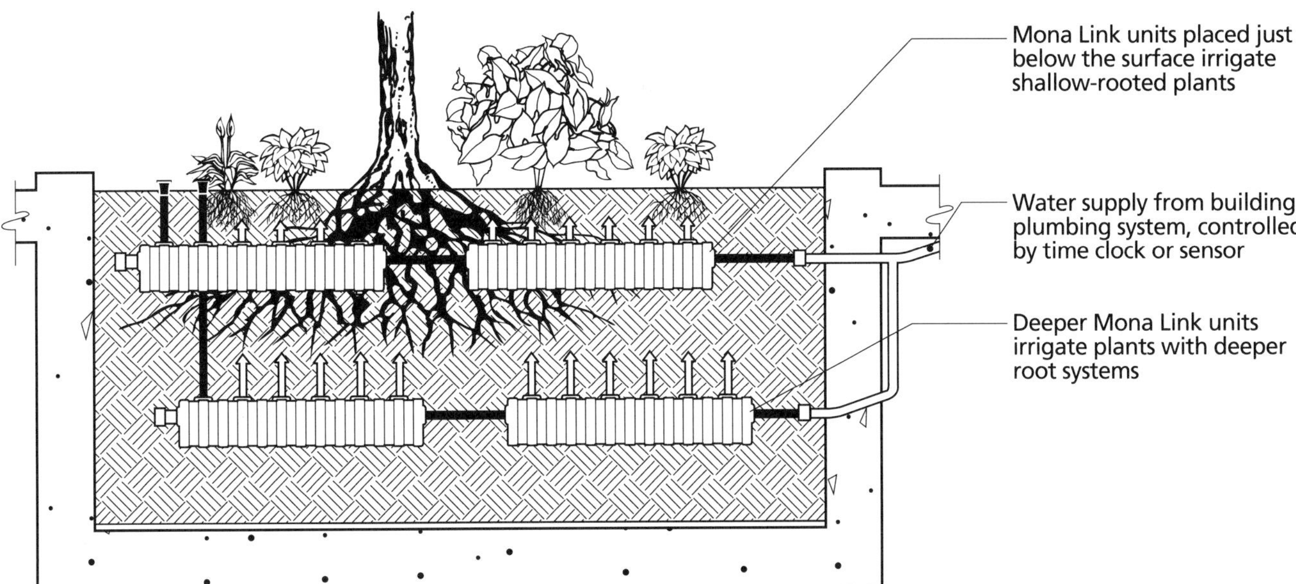
Mona Link units placed just below the surface irrigate shallow-rooted plants
Water supply from building plumbing system, controlled by time clock or sensor
Deeper Mona Link units irrigate plants with deeper root systems

Fig. 6-14.
Complete automation of a garden-style subirrigation system can be achieved when a system like Mona-Link can be filled by a sensor—or valve-controlled water line directly from a building plumbing system.
(Courtesy of MPS-Scandinavia-USA)

• It is possible to increase the interval between waterings for many species of plants beyond 7 days, which had traditionally been the typical watering cycle for office landscapes.

• It enables water-loving species like *Spathiphyllum* and many flowering plants to thrive on weekly waterings, when they typically might have demanded water more often if planted in standard fashion.

• Less frequent service visits are less of a disruption to staff in a commercial account.

• With water being drawn up from below at a continual rate, the roots of a plant spend less time searching for water. The roots will grow more slowly and result in a less frequent need to repot. This can be a great help to contractors, particularly on large specimens.

• Since it is not a top-watering system, the planting medium will not compact from constant settling. Pore space in the planting medium is maintained.

Subirrigation is not without some attendant problems (Many of which can be overcome with careful monitoring):

• Increased container size: The installation of subirrigation systems within decorative containers requires that the container be somewhat deeper (or wider, depending on brand) to accommodate the normal grow pot plus the volume of the water reservoir.

• Watering time: Subirrigation is not automatic. Filling is still required, and with a larger amount of water needed to fill a reservoir, watering cycles may decrease but the time spent actually supplying water may increase.

• Full reservoir: A reservoir that is constantly kept full can lead to continual soil saturation and the formation of molds and mildew if it is not properly monitored. This problem can be managed by specifying a planting medium that is not especially water retentive. Using less peat or vermiculite and more perlite or sand will reduce the potential for saturation in the root zone. Allowing the reservoir to dry out between fillings will help, and is actually recommended by many subirrigation container manufacturers.

• Capillarity: The soil used in a subirrigation system can lose its capillarity when it becomes totally dry and may have to be primed by top watering to re-establish capillary action. It can also be treated with a wetting agent as necessary.

• Planting medium pH: Most subirrigation containers are used in conjunction with a planting medium having a high content of peat or sphagnum moss to increase water retention capacity. Both have a natural pH of 3.5 to 5.4. Most interior foliage plants, however, prefer a medium with a pH of 6.5 to 7.0 and will suffer when out of balance. The maintenance of proper pH is necessary for the uptake of essential nutrients, as well as the prevention of fluoride and boron damage. To balance pH, the application of lime to the planting medium may be necessary from time to time. This cannot be accomplished through subirrigation because lime is not readily soluble, and if added to the water being placed in a subirrigation reservoir, it will settle to the bottom of the reservoir rather than be absorbed into the planting medium. Application of dry lime or even a lime/water slurry to the top of the plant will not suffice either, because the lime must be continually watered into the medium to dissolve completely and be totally absorbed. Only repetitive top down watering can make the application of lime effective.

• Pesticide and fungicide application: Similarly, the application of systemic insecticides and fungicides must be by top watering.

• Root damage to reservoir: Even when used in conjunction with soil separators, subirrigation reservoirs can be infiltrated by invasive root systems. In extreme cases, roots can become rotted, or can fill reservoirs to a point where they reduce capacity.

• Leaching: Plants well established in a medium for long periods of time can suffer from a build-up of soluble salts. This is normally resolved by leaching the medium; inundating the medium to wash to the salts out of the root zone. This can only be done with top watering, or by siphoning leachate from the reservoir.

• Leaks in the system: If root invasion or other physical damage occurs to a subirrigation system, repairs to the system may be labor intensive in a garden-type installation, and costly because of the location of the reservoir beneath the root zone.

Despite these concerns, the advantages to the interior landscape contractor of subirrigating their clients' plants are such that many major interior landscape maintenance firms throughout the country are retrofitting their clients' plants with subirrigation units, some even at their own expense. With the health of plants guaranteed by the contractor, there can be no better testament to the success of subirrigation.

DRIP IRRIGATION

Drip irrigation is the process of delivering extremely accurate quantities of water at slow, even rates directly to the root zone of a targeted plant. It is a commonplace water delivery system out of doors, having become especially popular in arid climates where water conservation is necessary because of the shortage or expense of water. Using a building's plumbing supply as a water source, drip irrigation can be a totally automated system of delivering water to interior plants in a garden setting. Although its automation may eliminate the time necessary to deliver water, it does not eliminate the

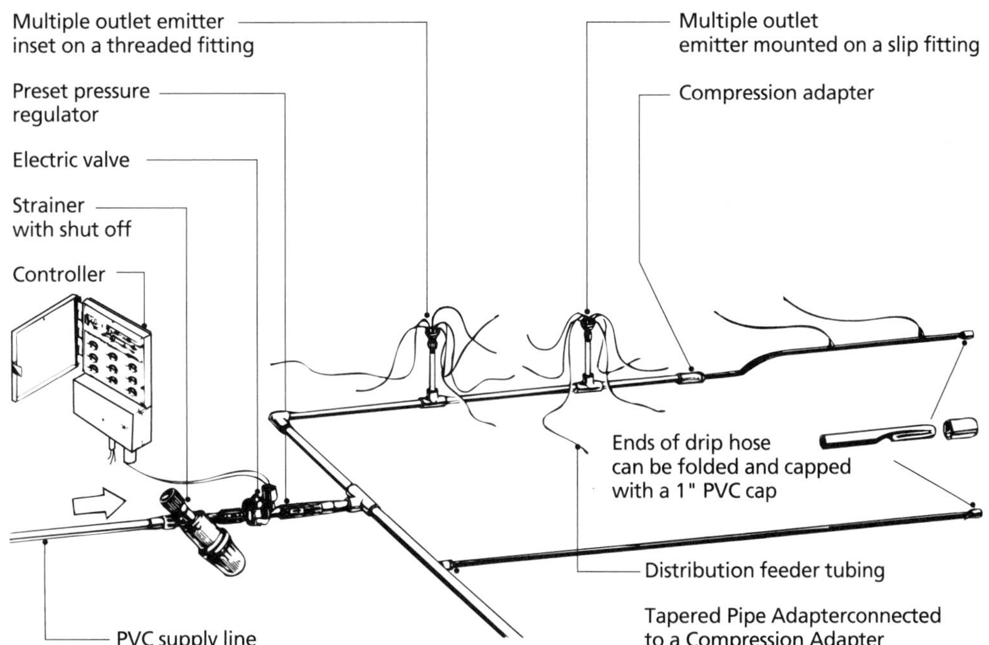

Fig. 6-15.
The components of a typical drip irrigation system. (Courtesy of The Toro Company)

need to assess irrigation efficacy. A drip system must be constantly monitored to ensure the system's integrity and to determine if adjustments to water flow are needed because of factors such as plant growth, plant health, or changes in environment.

The basic components of a drip irrigation system are (Fig. 6-15):

1. **Water source:** For interior landscape applications, this will be the building's plumbing supply.
2. **Supply line:** Will typically be 1/2" (1.27 cm) polyethylene tubing.
3. **Backflow preventer:** Is used to prevent water from flowing back into the supply line.
4. **Filter/Strainer:** Because drip irrigation is designed for precise, low-flow distribution of water, filters are required to avoid clogging the fine apertures in many drip irrigation components.
5. **Controller:** Is an electrically operated device used to establish the time and duration of water flow.
6. **Electric Valve:** The device which opens and closes to allow flow of water through the system.
7. **Pressure regulator:** Used to maintain constant water pressure despite fluctuations in incoming pressure.
7. **Emitter:** The outlet point for a drip irrigation system. It either discharges water directly to a plant, or discharges water from the supply line to the distribution feeder tubing.
9. **Distribution feeder tubing:** Small diameter (1/8" [3.2mm] inside diameter) polyethylene tubing used to provide precise locations for water distribution from emitter to plant.

The theory behind drip is completely different from subirrigation, and many of the drawbacks of subirrigation can be resolved by drip. Some of the advantages of drip irrigation are:

- It will not create a constantly saturated planting medium. Proper moisture levels and moisture/oxygen balance can be maintained at all times.
- No moisture stress or root rot from severe dry-wet-dry cycles will result.
- Although it is a top-watering method, the application impinges on a very small surface area, tending not to compact the planting medium as much as manual or sprinklered watering.
- It will not be a concern regarding loss of planting medium capillarity, since the water application is by gravity from above.
- It allows for the adjustment of soil pH.
- It allows for the application of systemic insecticide and fungicide.
- It is not as prone to damage by root invasion, since it is placed atop the planting medium, above the root zone.
- It allows for leaching of the medium, either manually or by increasing flow through the system. (However, leachate must still be removed via plumbing, siphoning from the drainage stratum, or percolation into substrate.)
- It can often be readily repaired when malfunctioning, because it will be visible either above the medium or hidden just below decorative mulch.
- It can deliver precise quantities of water to individual plants, and can be fine-tuned once installed by either adding and subtracting emitters or increasing or decreasing the flow of water through the emitters.

Like subirrigation, it is not fool-proof, and has downside issues of its own:

- With irrigation system components plainly visible or just below the surface, they can be prone to vandalism or accidental damage by service technicians.
- Visible portions of a drip system can be unsightly.
- When installed, a drip irrigation system must be balanced to ensure that emitters are in optimal locations and are releasing correct quantities of water for proper time periods. The process of balancing a drip system can be extremely time consuming, and in some cases can take as much time as actual hand watering for several months.
- Once balanced, they must be carefully monitored on a regular basis. Changes in microclimate, plant health, planting medium compaction or temperature, can alter irrigation needs enough to warrant adjustments in the system. This monitoring process must continue indefinitely.
- There will be an inherent concern for any automatic irrigation system whose components are hidden. Leaks or malfunctions in the system do not become apparent until symptomatic damage is noted. Leaks are a particular concern in high pressure drip systems, which operate under pressures of 55 to 70 psi. Evidence of leaks can manifest itself in declining plant health or damage to or outside the planter configuration. The tracing and correction of leaks or malfunctions and the repairs to damaged interior finishings can be costly. These

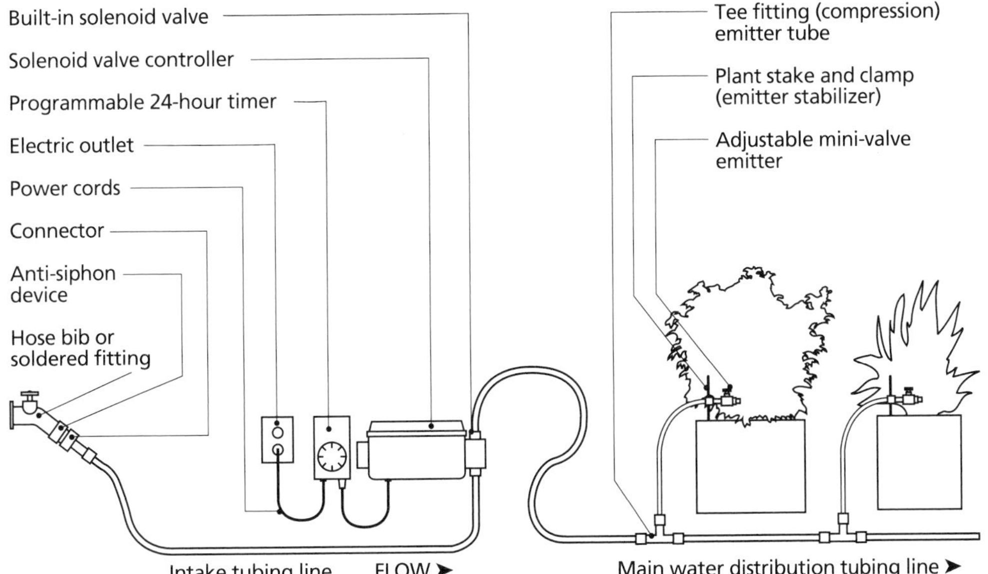

Fig. 6-16.
A schematic diagram of Aqua/Trends' typical high pressure Precision Micro-Irrigation System (Courtesy of Aqua/Trends, Inc.)

concerns, however, can be minimized by using well-designed components and by regular monitoring of the system while in operation.

- The initial installation cost can be considerable, and the cost and time to design such a system can be a factor as well.

Precision Micro-Irrigation

A new class of automated irrigation products has been specifically engineered for the interior landscape market by Aqua/Trends, Inc. The Mirage Series Precision Micro-Irrigation system is predicated on the use of extremely short yet frequent irrigation cycles, low operating pressures, and finely adjustable emitters at each plant. These factors provide a high degree of flexibility, control and safety, and have the ability, once they have been properly adjusted, to be, like conventional drip irrigation, fully automatic.

High-pressure versions of this system connect to the cold water plumbing and rely on structure water pressure (typically 55 to 70 psi) to motivate flow (Fig. 6-16). Short pulses of water flow are used—only 10 to 20 seconds in duration—just enough to furnish the limited moisture requirements. Unlike most drip systems, a user-adjustable emitter at each plant permits the delicate fine-tuning of water flow during the very short watering cycle– to permit only a few drops to issue during the 10 seconds of system operation to service dry-loving plants, or opened to permit application of greater volumes.

Another unique feature of the Aqua/Trends system which distinguishes it from conventional drip irrigation is that special irrigation receptacles were developed to be mounted on wall surfaces at convenient locations around the perimeters of furnished rooms, in much the same way as power or video cable receptacles are used. They access the irrigation water carried by tubing networks within the wall or partition cavity. Small diameter, clear plastic emitter tubes are simply plugged into these receptacles to service containerized planters anywhere in a room (Fig. 6-17).

Fig. 6-17.
An integrated Precision Micro-Irrigation System installed in a residence, showing an irrigation receptacle servicing a planter. (Courtesy of Aqua/Trends, Inc.)

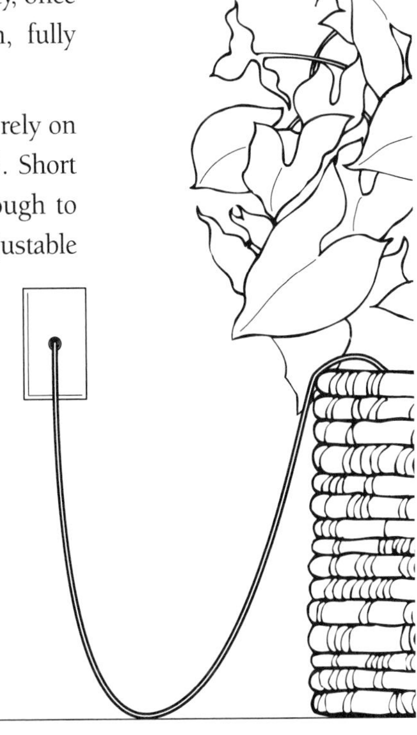

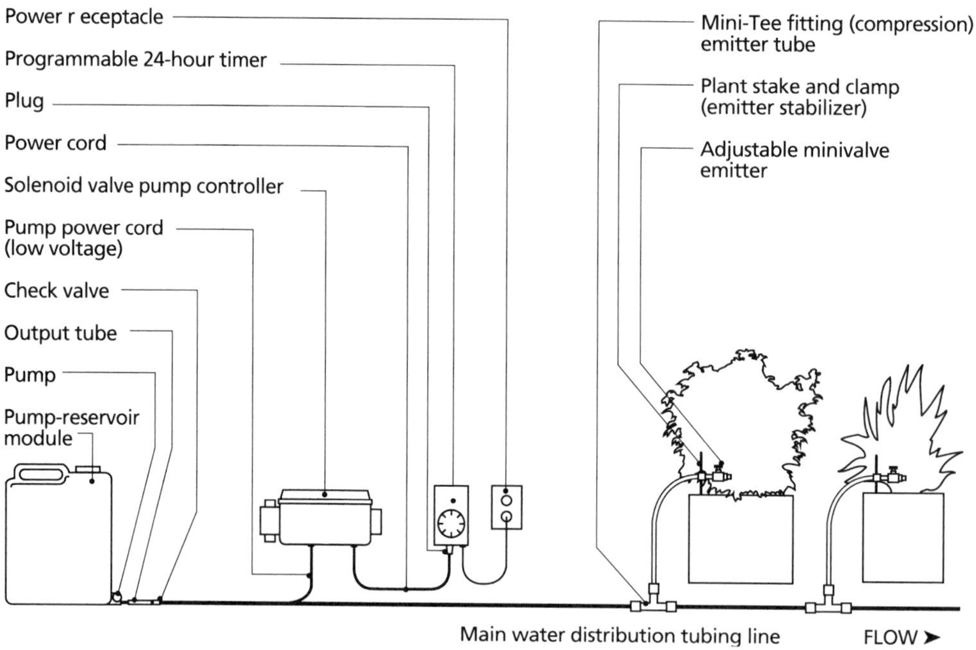

Fig. 6-18.
A schematic diagram of Aqua/Trends' typical low pressure Precision Micro-Irrigation System (Courtesy of Aqua/Trends, Inc.)

Low-pressure systems are also available for use where plumbing system connections are not convenient. Small water reservoirs with integral pumps replace solenoid valves as the flow motivator. Operating pressures are lower (3 to 15 psi), but most other aspects of the system are similar to the high pressure versions (Fig. 6-18). Low-pressure Precision Micro-Irrigation Systems are particularly useful for limited-area service in homes and offices. Because reservoirs must be periodically refilled, they cannot accurately be considered fully automatic.

In his book, *Building Interiors, Plants, and Automation,* (Prentice Hall, 1990), Stuart Snyder, President of Aqua/Trends, explains how state-of-the-art technology has been adapted to serve the needs of the interior landscape industry. Typical of the variety of uses, Fig. 6-19 shows how a multiple workstation in a commercial office can be outfitted with a Precision Micro-Irrigation system.

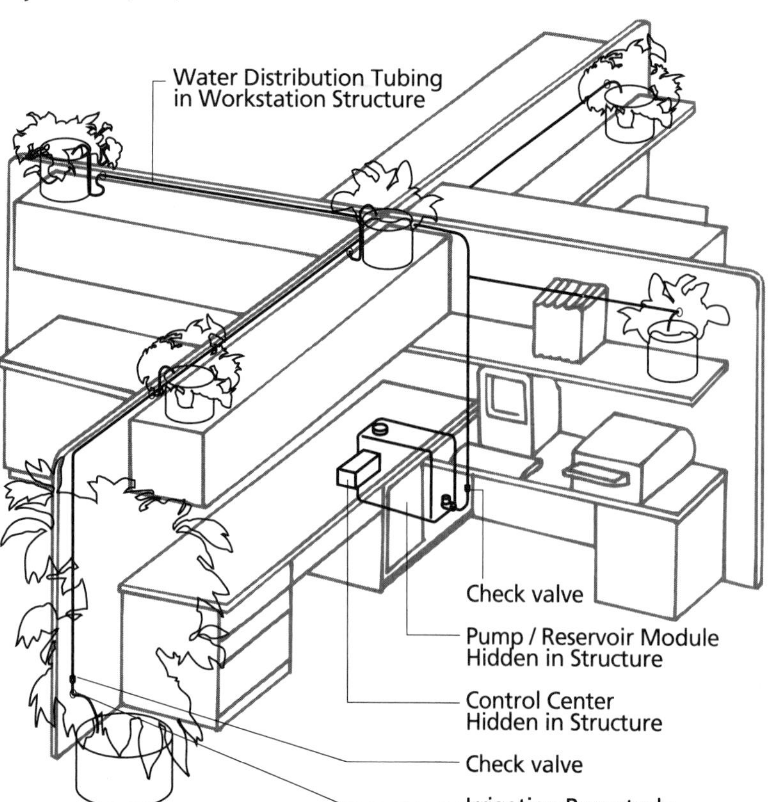

Fig. 6-19.
Aqua/Trends' Precision Micro-Irrigation System adapts drip irrigation technology to the commercial office or residential container plantings. (Courtesy of Aqua/Trends, Inc.)

OTHER AUTOMATED IRRIGATION SYSTEMS

Spray and bubbler irrigation

The most common method of automatically irrigating lawn grass is by spraying water, using a number of different mechanical devices: the impact rotor, the pop-up spray head, the oscillating sprinkler, etc. All can be successful, as mentioned at the beginning of this chapter, because water is removed from the root zone quickly enough to prevent the formation of mold, mildew, and root rot. The typical interior landscape utilizes water too slowly to be able to avail itself of this type of irrigation technology. With deeper root systems than lawn grass, no wind, slower growth, more water retentive planting media, and closely planted species of disparate watering needs, the interior environment will have too much water applied too inaccurately by a spray system to be used successfully indoors.

Although a bubbler irrigation system can provide more accuracy than a spray system, it, too, generally applies too much water to be considered for general use. Bubbler irrigation units do, however, have limited applications indoors. Whether manual or drip systems are used for the majority of the plantings in a landscape, there may be individual specimens such as large palms or trees whose root systems require deep watering, and more water in general, than the surrounding plants. Addition of bubbler units as integral components to a drip irrigation system to service these particular specimens can be very helpful.

HYDROPONICS

Strictly speaking, hydroponics is not a method of irrigating plants; it is a method of growing them. It is the growth of plants in a solution of water and nutrients using an inert medium (most frequently expanded clay aggregate) strictly as a support for the root structure (Fig. 6-20). Because no organic medium used, many of the problems attendant with soil as a growing medium (or what we typically call a "soilless" medium consisting of peat, bark, sand, etc.) disappear when using hydroponics: Soil-borne molds, mildew, insects, bacteria are all can be kept under better control in a hydroponic system than in traditional growing media. Plants grown in hydroponics are often healthier than plants grown in soil. The system has been used successfully in Europe for many years for both interior plants and potted plants out-of-doors.

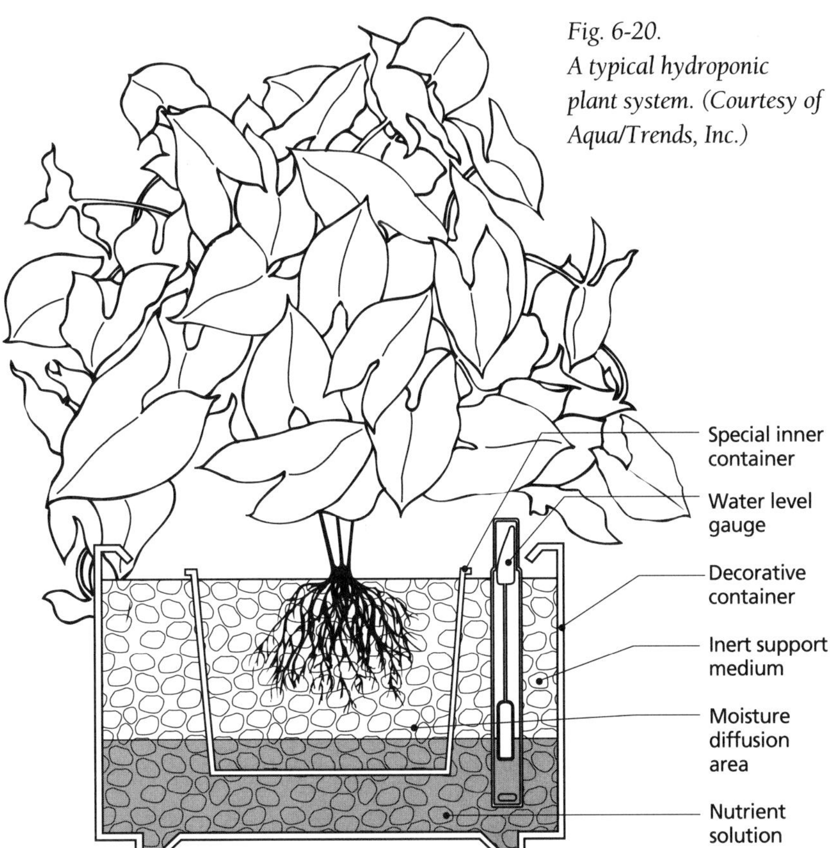

Fig. 6-20. A typical hydroponic plant system. (Courtesy of Aqua/Trends, Inc.)

Although hydroponics was introduced into the United States in the 1970s, its appeal has been limited, perhaps because of several inherent liabilities:

- There are a more limited number of plant species that can be grown hydroponically than the number which can be grown traditionally.
- A cost-effective method has not yet been developed to transfer plants grown in traditional media to hydroponics after the development of their root system has begun. The alternative is to grow from their inception in hydroponics. There are fewer sources of hydroponically grown plants from which to choose, so quantities of available species are limited.
- The number of contractors who maintain plants in hydroponics is relatively small, though interior landscape contractors should not have much trouble adapting to this method of culture.
- Large specimens have not been adequately tested to determine if their crowns can be properly supported by the inert media typically used. The system is much better geared to small and medium sized plants.

While perhaps not ideally suited to the contract commercial market, hydroponics can offer excellent benefits to the residential plant market:

- The care of plants grown in water rather than soil makes care—or transplantation—a much less messy proposition (i.e., fingers don't have to be stuck into soil to check moisture levels, since most hydroponic systems have water level indicators).
- The daily maintenance of plants is more straightforward. Unlike subirrigation, hydroponically grown plants cannot be over-watered. When the water level is down, more can be added safely. Guesswork is eliminated.
- The chances of plants developing significant fungal or mold problems is virtually eliminated, and pest infestations can be greatly reduced.

Because it is a growing system and not an irrigation system, hydroponics should not be compared to the other types of water delivery identified herein as a means of irrigating plants.

With the advent of subirrigation for individual containerized species and the increasing use of low pressure drip irrigation in garden settings, the means of applying water to interior plants through some automated means is finally catching up to the technology used in outdoor irrigation. The disparate water usage of many different types of indoor plants might be dealt with through soil sensing devices which supply water to specific plants or planting areas on an as-needed basis. The next few years will see even more advances in technology used to change the way interior plants are irrigated.

CHAPTER SEVEN

CONCEPTUAL COST ESTIMATION

At some point early in the design process of many projects, there may come a time when a designer might present two or more options to a client for consideration. The designer hopes that the client will select an option based primarily on aesthetic appeal, but it more often is a balance of quality versus affordability. The talented interior landscape designer must therefore be able not only to design a project and present the concept in an easy to understand fashion but to predict the cost of the project accurately enough to balance the design intent with economic reality.

The landscape architect who prepares an exterior landscape design can usually prepare a reasonable estimate of proposed installed cost by marking up the prices of a local nursery catalog 100 to 300 percent depending on whether the catalog prices are wholesale or retail and certain other predictable factors. There are also several nationally available publications on construction estimation devoted to, or which include sections on, exterior landscape costs. Some of these even have regional cost indices to allow for geographic fluctuations.

No such help exists in the interior landscape industry. There is no similar published documentation, and the marking up of Florida nursery catalog prices by an "x" factor is simply not as relevant because of the wide discrepancies in shipping costs, plant qualities, and contractor mark-ups.

There are two types of cost estimates attendant to any construction project. The *bid* is, of course, the estimate prepared by contractors who are ultimately willing to hang their hats on the bottom line and sign to build a project based on that estimate. This number is calculated by contractors by determining how much they will pay for

1. Plant materials at the nurseries
2. Shipping the plants to the job site or a holding area nearby
3. Related accessories, such as planters, planting medium, mulch, drainage fill, filter fabric, and observation tubing
4. Labor to prepare plants for installation
5. Labor to install the plants
6. How much they will set aside as a profit margin

Estimating the cost of a project as it goes out to bid requires the contractor to have a list of specific quantities of all the items to be incorporated into the project, plus a firm knowledge, based on historical data from recent actual costs, of the prices for all the above items. Although the cost data prepared from this information will be highly accurate, the interior landscape designer rarely will have the opportunity to prepare so detailed an estimate; the designer has neither the quantities of materials available—this information is determined only at the *end* of the design process—nor the historic cost information which contractors spend a great deal of time and effort to prepare, and wisely covet, since it is their key to staying in business.

Estimating the cost of a project after it has "gone out to bid" is critical to contractors, but by that time the design professionals' work is over. Interior landscape cost estimation at earlier stages in the design process might have a substantial effect on the extensiveness, or even the *existence*, of the interior landscape on the overall context of the project. What about the case where the architect hired by the large corporation asks the client "Do you want interior plants in your facility?" There can be only one out of three answers to this question:

a. "No."
b. "I don't know. I hadn't thought about it."
c. "Yes."

If the answer is (a), the case is closed. If the answer is (b) or (c), the very next question the architect will be asked, especially after (b), is "But what will it cost?" Some means must be created to conceptually estimate the cost of installing *and* maintaining an interior landscape *before* it is designed and while it is *being* designed.

Conceptual estimates of construction cost for buildings not yet designed are most popularly conceived in dollars per square foot. A 600 pupil public elementary school in Massachusetts, for example, may be predicted with reasonable accuracy to have an anticipated construction cost, in 1991 dollars, between $68 and $85 per square foot (at 10.76 SF per SM, this equals approximately $730 to $915 per square meter). Without going into detail, that number will include certain factors (foundations, structural steel, mechanical systems, etc.) and omit others (design fees, site costs, furnishings, etc.). The relevance of this number is that a client will be told precisely what a school will cost and precisely what the scope of work includes. Another example: A tenant fit-up for a first class law firm in a new high rise in Boston might run (again, in 1991 dollars) between $60 and $75/SF ($645 to $807/SM). Likewise, the client is told that for this amount they will get a certain level of quality for furnishings, finishes (wall coverings, window treatments, etc.), and equipment. Other design disciplines use this $/SF metric as a matter of course. Applied to the interior landscape, the process of producing a conceptual estimate of costs yields the following:*

* *Note: All the cost figures illustrated in this chapter are actual 1990 contract prices from built projects. They are subject to geographic, seasonal, and market fluctuation, and as time passes, escalation. Although the theory behind the conceptual estimation is fixed, adjustment of actual dollar values may be necessary to increase the accuracy given the factors causing fluctuation. The prices shown are higher than what might be paid for plants and planters in a retail or discount store. To calculate costs per square meter, multiply square foot costs by 10.76.*

It is important that the client knows the costs include purchase and installation of the plant and planter, plus any ancillary materials and labor charges such as the addition of mulch as a topdressing or the cleaning of plants prior to delivery. The plants and planters will not simply be thrown into the client's offices. This cost per planting can also include maintenance—if the plantings are leased—or just provide for purchase and installation, and a separate maintenance cost will be estimated. For our purpose, this exercise will show a purchase/installation cost, with a separate maintenance fee allocated.

ESTIMATING THE OFFICE LANDSCAPE INSTALLATION

A large corporation is moving into eight floors of a high-rise and wants to "landscape their offices". The floor plate (area of each floor) is 20,000 SF, yielding a total of 160,000 SF. No design work has been done yet. The client wants to establish a working budget for interior landscaping.

Because this is a commercial office landscape, the solution will involve plants placed in decorative containers, which we shall call "plantings". The key is to determine how many, and what quality, plantings will be placed in the 160,000 SF of space.

ESTABLISHING LEVEL OF QUALITY

A useful starting point might be to ask, "What level of quality does the client seek?" An all too common response is, "We don't know what we can afford". To address this response, three quality level options—inexpensive, moderate, and expensive—will give the client an idea of what to expect for each option. The level of quality will be determined by the size and cost of each plant, the size and material of each decorative container, and the density of the plantings within the interior space.

Inexpensive option

FLOOR PLANT ONLY		
Typical plant—4-ft (1.2 m) *Schefflera* or Areca Palm	Average cost:	$35.00
Typical decorative container— 14 in (35.6 cm) diam. wicker basket—	Average cost:	$68.00
Total cost for planting:	**Average cost:**	**$103.00**

Moderate option

FLOOR PLANT		
Typical plant—5-ft (1.5 m) Corn Plant or Dragon Tree	Average cost:	$110.00
Typical decorative container— 16 in (40.6 cm) diam. fiberglass with standard color	Average cost:	$88.00
Total cost for planting:	**Average cost:**	**$198.00**

TABLE OR CREDENZA PLANT		
Typical plant—8-in (20.3 cm) Chinese Evergreen	Average cost:	$24.00
Typical decorative container— 10 in (25.4 cm) diam. Fiberglass with standard color	Average cost:	$35.50
Total cost for planting:	**Average cost:**	**$59.50**

Expensive option

FLOOR PLANT		
Typical plant—6-ft (1.8 m) Kentia Palm or Ming Aralia	Average cost:	$275.00
Typical decorative container— 18 in (45.7 cm) diam. Aluminum with custom color	Average cost:	$218.00
Total cost for planting:	**Average cost:**	**$493.00**

TABLE OR CREDENZA PLANT		
Typical plant—10-in (25.4 cm) Peace Lily	Average cost:	$30.00
Typical decorative container— 12 in (30.5 cm) diam. aluminum with custom color	Average cost:	$129.00
Total cost for planting:	**Average cost:**	**$159.00**

HANGING PLANT		
Typical plant—10-in (25.4 cm) Pothos	Average Cost:	$18.00
Typical decorative container—		
12-in (30.5 cm) diam. aluminum with custom color	Average Cost:	$148.00
Total cost for planting:	**Average Cost:**	**$166.00**

Estimating Quantities

Now that a range of prices for individual plantings has been identified, the quantities of plantings used for each cost option must be calculated.

The easiest way to predict plant density is to look at previously prepared office landscape plans and do a takeoff of the number of plants per office, or plants per square foot. Having done so, we can presume the following planting densities:

A sparsely (i.e., inexpensively) planted office will contain an average of one floor plant for every 600 SF (55.7 SM). A moderately planted office will contain one floor plant for every 600 SF, plus a table plant every 600 SF, for an average of one plant per every 300 SF (27.9 SM). A densely planted office will contain one floor plant for every 300 SF, plus a table plant every 300 SF, plus a hanging plant every 300 SF, for an average of one plant per every 100 SF (9.3 SM), the density recommended by Dr. B. C. Wolverton in the NASA study.

An inexpensively planted office will have:		
267 floor plantings @ $103		
Total cost for an inexpensive solution:	**$27,501.00**	**or $0.17/SF**

A moderately planted office will have:		
267 floor plantings @ $198.00, sub-total:	$52,866.00; plus	
267 table plantings @ $59.50, sub-total:	$15,886.50	
Total cost for a moderate solution:	**$68,752.50**	**or $0.43/SF**

An expensively planted office will have:		
533 floor plantings @ $493, sub-total:	$262,769.00; plus	
533 table plantings @ $159, sub-total:	$84,747.00; plus	
533 hanging plantings @ $166, sub-total:	$88,478.00	
Total cost for an expensive solution:	**$435,994.00**	**or $2.72/SF**

For purchase contracts, these costs will cover only the installation of plants. A separate charge for maintenance must be established:
$8.50 per plant per month for floor plants
$4.25 per plant per month for table plants
$2.20 per plant per month for hanging plants

Monthly fees work out to:
$2,269.50 per month (or **$0.028/SF/month**) for the inexpensive option.
$6,795.75 per month (or **$0.042/SF/month**) for the moderate option.
$7,968.35 per month (or **$0.050/SF/month**) for the expensive option.

This concept pairs real costs with perceptible levels of quality and quantity, enabling the interior landscape designer to provide a client with an estimate of cost and a scope of work upon which the cost is based. Although the price range varies considerably, the client can assess how their particular quality level can be estimated by "mixing and matching" the various options. When the client knows what goes into an estimate, the statement "Your 100,000 SF office can be landscaped for a cost of $2.00/SF, plus $0.05/SF/month to maintain" has relevance.

Estimating the Garden-Type Interior Landscape

A client wishes to have an extensive interior garden in the lobby of a hotel. Specialized construction such as this makes the definition of the scope of work all that much more important, because specialized construction will have a cost premium attached to it for all design elements (not just the interior landscape). A very fine line must be drawn as to what the scope of interior landscaping is, because in the case of the garden-type planting, much of the "interior landscape" which should be included in the cost estimate will not be installed by the interior landscape contractor, such as a dropped structural slab, plumbing provisions for drainage and irrigation, plant growth lighting, and waterproofing. All these elements should be factored into an atrium interior landscape cost estimate.

Even before designing an interior garden, several assumptions can be made about its construction:

1. It will have to be either built up above the finish floor elevation, or dropped partially or totally below the finish floor elevation. If built up, the structural slab need not be lowered, but it must be reviewed for its ability to support large plants if desired.

2. The bottom of the planter should have a drain to the building's plumbing system, if possible.

3. The bottom and sides of the planter will be waterproofed.

4. The lowest portion of the planting medium "sandwich" will allow a provision for the lateral flow of water to the drain. This will be either a nominal depth of gravel or styrofoam pellets, or a specialty product like Enkadrain, Miradrain, or Drainage Board.

5. The surface treatment will be either bare soil or some type of decorative mulch.

To calculate costs per square foot, three levels of design quality (inexpensive, moderate, and expensive) are noted for a prototypical 1000 SF (92.9 SM) (about a 31.6 ft [9.6 m] square) interior garden. Each design will have both direct and indirect costs associated with it. Simply stated, direct costs would be for tasks to be provided by the interior landscape contractor: plants, planting medium, filter fabric, etc. Indirect costs would be for alterations to the building needed to support the growth of plants which the interior landscape contractor would *not* be providing: plant growth lighting (skylighting would be considered a primary architectural element, and not an added cost to support the growth of plants), plumbing work (drain lines to the building plumbing, water lines to the planting area for irrigation), structural work (additional reinforcing or reconfiguration of the structural slab), and waterproofing. As with the three office landscape options, the costs indicated are actual prices for projects completed in 1990.

INEXPENSIVE OPTION

Scope of work (indirect costs, installed)

a. STRUCTURAL:
Built directly atop the structural slab, and no plants are large enough to require special reinforcing of the slab (i.e., no extraordinary structural costs). $0.00/SF

b. DRAINAGE AND PLUMBING:
No drainage connection to plumbing system, and no automated irrigation or subirrigation system. $0.00/SF

c. WATERPROOFING:
Waterproofing consists of 20 mil polyethylene sheet material. $.50/SF

d. EXTRAORDINARY FEATURES:
No unusual site improvements often associated with interior plants are included, such as water features, rock work, or sculpture. $0.00/SF

e. PLANT GROWTH LIGHTING:
Existing (or previously proposed) natural and electric lighting will sustain plants. No provisions needed for plant growth lighting. $0.00/SF

f. CURBING:
around the planter will consist of precast concrete. With a square configuration, the perimeter curbing of a 31.5 ft square will need 126 LF, which at $10/LF would cost $1260, or $1.26/SF

Total of indirect costs for the "inexpensive" garden: $1,760.00 $1.76/SF

Scope of work (direct costs, installed)

Planting is sparse and modest. A fourth of the area is bark mulch. The other three-fourths is planted with mostly ground cover and some taller plants. The tallest plant is 6 ft. The cost of this portion of the work is estimated as follows, working from the bottom up:

a. DRAINAGE:
The drainage medium above the waterproofing will be 4 in of styrofoam pellets covered by filter fabric. $1.25/SF.

b. PLANTING MEDIUM:
The plants will be kept in their pots, but placed in a planting medium of pine bark nuggets. The tallest plant is 6 ft, supplied in a 17 in diameter pot; 14 in high. Maximum depth of planting medium will be 14 in. The average depth will be 12 in.
Cost: $14.10 per 3 CF bale, or $4.70/CF
12 in of planting medium $4.70/SF

c. OBSERVATION TUBING:
In lieu of a drain connected to the plumbing system, a series of observation tubes will be installed in four locations throughout the garden, which can be used to monitor water levels and, if necessary, remove standing water. Tubing will be corrugated, perforated polyethylene, 4 in diameter, with cap.
Cost: $12.50 per tube, or $0.05/SF

---

d. THE PLANTS:
One-fourth of the garden will be bark mulch; one fourth will be specimen plants, and the remaining half will be ground covers.

Specimen plants:
Assume an average plant size of 4 ft, with an average installed cost of $120. Assume approximately 40 specimen plants in the remaining area will be used. Cost: $4,800, or $4.80/SF

Ground-cover plants:
Sparsely planted, with 6-in Pothos spaced 18 in on center.
500 SF at 18 in oc.= 0.51 plants/ SF, or 255 plants.
Cost: 255 plants @ $12/plant = $3,060, or $3.06/SF

---

e. MULCH: pine bark nuggets.
Cost: $14.10 per 3 CF bale, $4.70/CF
At 2 in in depth, 167 CF are needed. $784.90, or $0.78/SF

Total of direct costs for the "inexpensive" garden: $14.64/SF

Add in indirect costs...
Total of all costs for the "inexpensive" garden: $16.40/SF

As with the office landscape, the atrium garden must also be maintained. Again, using actual 1990 contract costs, the inexpensive garden will be **maintained for $440 per month, or $0.44/SF/month.**

MODERATELY PRICED OPTION

Scope of work (indirect costs)

---

a. STRUCTURAL:
Built directly atop structural slab, but some plants are large enough to require special reinforcing of the slab to support the weight of the plants and planting medium.
Premium structural cost: $5,000, or $5.00/SF

---

b. DRAINAGE AND PLUMBING:
One drainage connection to the plumbing system, no automated irrigation system, but water source (flush-mounted box hydrant) is brought to garden area.
Premium plumbing costs: $2,000, or $2.00/SF

---

c. WATERPROOFING: Consists of Bituthene sheet membrane system.	$0.90/SF
d. EXTRAORDINARY FEATURES No unusual site improvements are included.	$0.00/SF
e. PLANT GROWTH LIGHTING: Some plant growth lighting is required to supplement existing natural and electric task and ambient lighting. Premium electrical costs $4,000, or	$4.00/SF.
f. PERIMETER EDGING is a seating height wall made of brick with a granite cap. Cost: $100/LF, $12,600 for 126 LF, or	$12.60/SF
Total of indirect costs for moderately priced garden:	**$24.50/SF**

Scope of Work (direct costs)

Planting is full and dense, but not outstanding in the choice of species or size of specimens. Tallest plant is 12 ft (22-in container). One quarter of the garden will be specimen plants, the remainder will be ground cover plants. No part of the garden will be bare of mulch.

a. DRAINAGE: The drainage medium above the waterproofing is Miradrain.	$1.50/SF.
b. PLANTING MEDIUM: is an inexpensive soilless mix. Cost: $20 per 4 CF bale, or $5.00/CF. Average depth of planting medium is 15 in.	$6.25/SF
c. THE PLANTS: Specimen plants, assume 30, average price $200, or $6,000.	$6.00/SF
Ground covers: Ground cover plants will be spaced densely: 6-in plants of various species at 12 in on center. 750 SF of ground cover @ 12 in oc. = 1.15 plants/SF, or 863 plants. @$12/plant, cost is $10,356, or	$10.36/SF.
d. MULCH: pine bark nuggets 2 in deep. @$14.10 per 3 CF bale, or $4.70/CF, the cost is $784.9 or	$0.78/SF.
Total direct costs for moderately priced garden:	**$24.88/SF**
Add in direct costs...	**$24.50/SF**
Total of all costs for moderately priced garden:	**$49.38/SF**
Maintenance for the moderately priced garden will cost $700 per month, or	**$0.70/SF/month.**

EXPENSIVE OPTION

Scope of Work (indirect costs)

a. STRUCTURAL:
The structural slab is depressed in order to allow planting to be built "at grade". Depressed slab is specially reinforced to accommodate a 20-ft Ficus.
Premium cost for structural work: $10,000, or $10/SF

b. DRAINAGE AND PLUMBING:
Structural configuration requires the creation of four separately depressed "cells", all of which need separate drains to plumbing system. Flush-mounted box hydrant is provided for water on an as-needed basis, but there is also a complete drip irrigation system for the garden.
Premium plumbing and irrigation costs: $8,500, or $8.50/SF

c. WATERPROOFING:
Consists of Bituthene sheet membrane system as per the moderately priced design, but the increased intricacy of the structural system kicks the unit price up to $1.50/SF

d. EXTRAORDINARY FEATURES
The garden has a stream running through it, with recirculating water and fiberglass reinforced concrete "rock" work.
Cost: $25,000, or $25.00/SF

e. PLANT GROWTH LIGHTING:
Substantial electric lighting is needed for plant growth.
Cost $12,000, or $12.00/SF

f. CURBING:
Perimeter edging is imported granite with honed finish.
Cost: $35/LF, $4,410 for 126 LF, or $4.41/SF.

Total indirect costs for expensive garden: **$61.41/SF**

Scope of Work (direct costs)

Planting is full and dense, with many outstanding specimens, including one 20-ft *Ficus benjamina*.

a. DRAINAGE: Drainage medium above the waterproofing is Miradrain, but with more handwork in a more intricate design, it more labor intensive to install.	$2.00/SF
b. PLANTING MEDIUM is Pro-Mix BX, $31.97 per 5.5 CF bale, or $5.81/CF. At an average depth of 18 in, the cost is	$8.72/SF
c. THE PLANTS:	
Specimen plants: The 20-ft Ficus costs $6,000 installed. Average cost of 30 other specimens is $300, or $9,000. Total cost of specimen plants is $17,000, or	$17.00/SF.
Ground cover plants: are dense, with many different species used. 6-in pots placed 12 in oc. for half the garden, or 500 SF. At 12 in oc., 1.15 plants per SF are needed, or 575 plants At $12 each, ground covers cost $6,900, or	$6.90/SF.
d. MULCH: pine bark nuggets, 2 in deep. At $14.10 per 3 CF bale, or $4.70/CF The cost is $784.90, or	$0.78/SF.
Total direct costs for expensive garden:	**$35.30/SF**
Add in indirect costs...	**$61.41/SF**
Total of all costs for the expensive garden:	**$96.71/SF**

Maintenance for the expensive garden will cost $2,100 per month, or **$2.10/SF/month.**

Two things are clear from the presentation of these three garden-type options. First, a wide disparity in conceptual costs can be projected for interior landscaping, depending on the level of quality selected. Second, the indirect costs for interior landscaping can be substantial, exceeding the direct costs in certain cases. It would be patently unfair to tell a client that a first quality interior garden can be provided for $30/SF complete, if it is only the direct costs to which you are referring. The identification of a precise scope of work for an interior landscape is as important a statement as is the cost itself. Simply stating that "Yes, you can have an interior garden in your atrium for $15 per square foot" may be accurate, but not relevant. When it is backed up with a scope of work containing special design elements, a client can visualize what they are getting for their money.

The foregoing creates a system for establishing predesign estimates based on costs per square foot. As a design concept evolves, and the number and quality of plants and related accessories becomes more specific, a predesign estimate can be "tightened" by applying itemized costs to the specific quantities of plants and other elements. The accurate projection of installation and maintenance costs at the conceptual and preconstruction levels will help the interior landscape industry achieve a higher degree of acceptance in the design community, for it will enable clients to better plan for the use of interior plants in the future.

CHAPTER 8
BUILDING TYPES

The use of indoor plants has become ubiquitous in recent years. With their use widespread, plants are found within the interior spaces of many different types of buildings. In some cases, very little adaptation is made to accommodate them. These spaces are designed for people, and clients are often not willing to spend any funds at all to alter environmental conditions to suit the horticultural needs of plants. In others, vast sums have been spent to design spaces to support the growth of plants and use them as architectural focal points.

While the individual design of each interior landscape may have unique characteristics, there will be similarities in the way plants can and should be used within certain building types, and knowledge of the similarities (or differences) of each type will enable the experienced designer to begin a concept with certain parameters in hand to make the task of creating a design that much easier. Just as architectural firms may specialize in specific construction types such as schools, high rise office buildings, or hospitals, it is possible to develop a specialty in the interior landscape design of certain building types through repetitious work in that one type. We will examine some of the generic building classifications and identify the "typical" conditions pertaining their interior landscapes.

COMMERCIAL OFFICE LANDSCAPING

In terms of dollar volume, the most common use of interior plants today is within commercial office buildings, where plants are often purchased as part of a capital expenditure (in new construction) and maintained professionally under an operating budget. It is these types of installations that keep professional interior landscape contractors in business with their "bread and butter" accounts. "Typical" office landscapes can be characterized by many similarities:

LIMITED CEILING HEIGHT Unlike atrium spaces with multi-story heights, the office landscape will have a one story ceiling, usually between 7 1/2 and 10 ft (2.3 and 3.0 m) in height, depending on the floor-to-floor height of the building and the use of hung ceilings or raised floors. Ceiling heights of this magnitude limit the size of usable plants to a maximum of perhaps 6 ft (1.8 m), or two-thirds the height of the space, the famous "two-thirds" rule mentioned in Chapter Two.

LIGHT AVAILABILITY Natural light is generally available only to plants lining windows at the perimeter of the spaces; skylights are seldom components of commercial office landscapes. Placed within several feet of unrestricted southern, southeastern, and southwestern exposures, enough light will reach plant locations to allow the specification of "high light" tolerant plants. Plants inboard of windows must rely on electric lighting, which in the case of commercial office space is often fluorescent. Unless electric lighting is specifically added for plant growth, the ambient lighting provided by typical office lighting is often no more than 50 footcandles at desk height.

(*Note*: Prior to the oil embargo of 1973, ambient light levels in buildings were often higher than 50 fc. Since then, attempts to reduce energy consumption and more detailed ergonomic studies have determined that task lighting of 50 fc is acceptable, but ambient room lighting is often reduced below that level.

Fig. 8-1.
A 4 x 2 ft (2.4 m x 1.2 m) fluorescent troffer will not be able to focus light on a plant, but it will generate enough light—perhaps 100 fc measured at 2 ft from the floor—to keep many types of interior plants viable within a fairly large floor area.

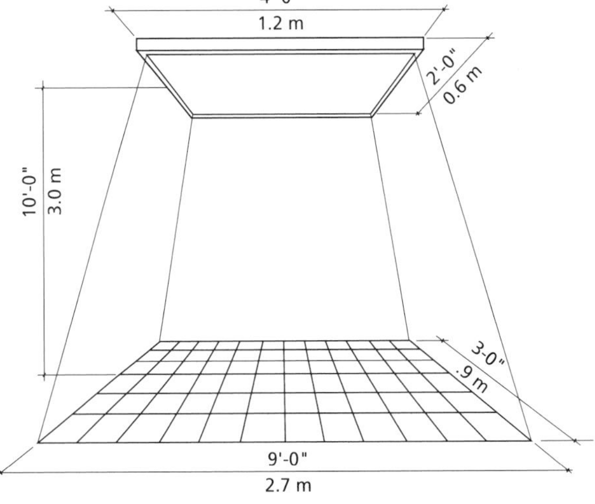

One of the idiosyncrasies of office landscaping is that lighting provided for general use, regardless of its electric light source type, is often not augmented to satisfy the specific needs of plants. Without "plant lights" per se, the plants must avail themselves of the ambient lighting of the space. Although the photometric quality of fluorescent (the most common office landscape electric light source) does not lend itself to providing bright or focused light, the configuration of fluorescent fixtures—2 x 2 ft (0.6 x 0.6 m) or 2 x 4 ft (0.6 x 1.2 m) troffers—provides a relatively large area of light output, allowing some flexibility in the location of plants beneath them (Fig. 8-1).

Incandescent or HID lamps used as ambient downlighting are more focused, increasing intensity directly beneath the source, but providing sharply reduced intensity as distance increases from its vertical axis (Fig. 8-2). The working drawing for a lighting design, or "reflected ceiling" plan, becomes an essential tool of the interior landscape designer, because it will dictate where plants can go inboard from the windows. The designer preparing a scheme for the landscaping of a commercial office space must superimpose the reflected ceiling plan over the furnishings plan to determine both the proposed location within the furniture layout and the light availability above.

The last piece of data the designer needs to assess the lighting of an office landscape is the potential presence of window treatments. A designer often assumes that plants adjacent to south-facing windows will get the benefit of a great deal of sunlight. But will the interior of the windows have drapes or blinds (Fig. 8-3) Will the curtain wall of the building have some type of architectural shade structure to mitigate direct sun or glare, a common occurrence in warmer climates? The designer must get whatever information is available from the architect and interior designer to answer these questions.

Fig. 8-2.
An incandescent or low wattage HID downlight can focus light of a much higher intensity on a target 10 ft (3.0 m) away, but the cone of light bright enough to keep plants viable becomes much smaller. Unlike the fluorescent troffer, different lamp types (flood vs. spot, incandescent vs. quartz, etc.) create widely differing light cone shapes.

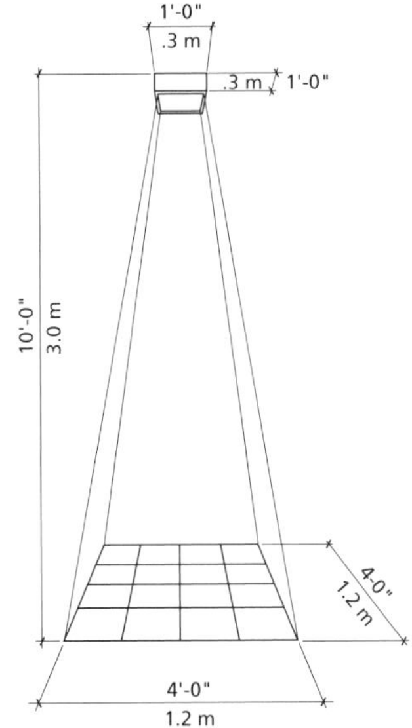

Fig. 8-3.
Awareness of window treatments near plants is essential to the interior landscape designer. Sun streaming through an unobstructed south-facing window can be completely blocked by drapes or blinds, leaving a plant placed nearby without light.

Fig. 8-4.
Straining to reach the light, these Ficus trees could have remained as symmetrical specimens had their planters been fitted with casters and rotated several times per year.

PLANTING CONDITIONS The office landscape typically consists of plants in decorative containers rather than built-in planters. There are three reasons for this. First, the use of plants in an office layout will be subservient to the human use of the space, and generally must be cost-effective. Plants in decorative containers will have a lower cost overall than built-in planters. Second, built-in planters usurp considerable floor space in a type of plan that is invariably space-poor. A decorative container can display a fairly large specimen using relatively little floor area. Third and most important, decorative containers are easily moved, providing flexibility to the layout in the event that furnishings must be relocated. Flexibility can be further increased by installing casters on containers too large to readily move from place to place. Casters also enable containers to be easily rotated for even growth if a plant receives all its light from window glazing (Fig. 8-4).

ATRIUM LANDSCAPING

The resurgence of the atrium as an key component of contemporary architecture has been a major contributor to the increased popularity of plants in the last two decades, and has created a market for the use of large scale plants which did not exist prior to its reintroduction in the 1960's. Elements which usually distinguish an atrium space are:

- A generally higher ceiling height than the surrounding floor area
- Natural lighting introduced into the space, via either skylight, sloped, or sidewall glazing
- A higher level of ambient light, even after dark, than the surrounding floor area
- An upgraded level of quality for all interior finishes—flooring, wallcoverings, and furniture—than the surrounding floor area.

- A sense of arrival; an ambience that states the atrium is a special place within the structure.

All these elements suggest that any interior landscaping occurring in an atrium space should be as special as the architectural elements of the space themselves. Rather than merely decorating a space or providing textural relief to the sharp angles and lines of an architectural interior, as plants do for the typical office, the atrium landscape becomes a focal point in the most highly visible portion of a building.

Specimen plants of the atrium will generally be taller and fuller. Since more light is generally available, the list of usable species will be more diverse. Flowers may be prevalent. The concept of plantings within decorative containers is often replaced with plantings in garden-style beds. The density of plantings increases, often massed for a more powerful effect. Other, unique elements may be introduced, such as water features, sculpture, seating, or real or fake rock formations. The cost per square foot increases, and special provisions for maintaining the interior landscape may be installed which might not be provided for the plants of the non-atrium space, e.g. plant growth lights, sophisticated irrigation systems and maintenance closets nearby for technicians to store supplies.

Fig. 8-5.
A responsible adult, relaxing on a bench in front of a planter, may casually, perhaps even unknowingly, cause damage to plantings. This situation is best remedied by eliminating the temptation caused by the close proximity of people and plants.

Many atrium spaces must cope with heavy pedestrian traffic, a factor affecting both the maintenance technician and the designer. An old adage of the interior landscape profession is that "Plants and people belong together", but time has taught us that this statement is only true to a point, after which people can become a plant's worst enemy. The seating height planter wall of an atrium landscape can turn a planted area into a large ash tray or trash receptacle (Fig. 8-5). Seating areas are best located outside arms' reach of plant beds or containers. A seated person is much more likely to dwell on plants than the standing or walking pedestrian.

Fig. 8-6.
A curbed plant bed keeps floor cleaning chemicals out, it helps prevent people from stepping off the pavement, and it helps prevent more direct interaction between people and plants.

The problem isn't limited to the public, either. Even employees can unwittingly cause damage. The need for curbing a plant bed discussed in Chapter Three is based on the penchant floor cleaning staff have to push floor cleaning solvents into the nearest receptacle: If a drain is not handy, a planter bed or tree grate will do nicely, thank you! (Fig. 8-6)

The designer of the heavily used public atrium landscape should clearly define zones for people and zones for plants. Any plants which extend into an area designated for pedestrians become possible targets for abuse. Walkways must be wide enough to prevent pedestrians from inadvertently stepping into plant beds or striking foliage with the swing of their arms (Fig. 8-7). For every person who will stop to admire the color, texture, or habit of growth of a beautiful specimen plant, there are unfortunately many more children and adults who will thoughtlessly or willfully pull on them, step on them, or tear them to pieces.

Fig. 8-7.
Wrong plant! A wide-spreading plant like Philodendron selloum should never be placed in a planting bed immediately adjacent to a walkway. Note, however, the lack of damage to the plant; the employees in this atrium bestow on this 15-year-old specimen a degree of respect bordering on reverence.

A case in point: The receptionist in the lobby of a firm for whom I used to work had a *Spathiphyllum* plant in an 8-in (20.3 cm) pot on her desk. Over a period of several weeks, she watched in wonder as a white spathe slowly unfurled. The very day it finally reached its full bloom, a salesman came in to meet with one of the staff. He identified himself and the employee he wished to see. As the receptionist turned her attention to the switchboard to call the employee, the salesman deftly pinched off the spathe and said to the receptionist, "You're pretty. Have a flower." The receptionist told me minutes after this incident occurred that her desire to keep her job was the only reason she did not spew out a stream of invective at the salesman.

The atrium landscape is a different design challenge than the commercial office. While the interior landscape plan of the office landscape is all too often the result of placing plants wherever there may be space left for them after the furnishings have been located, the placement of plants within a planting bed in an atrium will require a great deal of planning to look good and to be horticulturally acceptable.

Hotels

One idiosyncrasy of hotel lobbies is that they are open to the public 24 hours a day. The implications of this are more far reaching to the service technician responsible for maintaining the plants than to the designer, but there are design implications as well.

It is common for atrium spaces lighted predominantly or totally by electric lighting to have much of their ambient lighting provided by the same lamps that provide plant growth lighting. In hotel lobbies, this would mean keeping high intensity lights on 24 hours a day, leaving plants in the space with no darkness cycle during a 24-hour period. It would also mean leaving the ambient light level in the lobby at a much higher intensity than good taste would allow. Current thinking is that plants require at least several hours of darkness for a normal photoperiod. This can be accommodated by having plant growth lighting, if needed, be on during the day to either supplement daylight or simulate it, and providing non-plant growth ambient lighting for night-time use. A common alternative in lobbies where plants need copious amounts of electric lighting is to put plant growth lights on a time sequence starting when lobby activity begins to die down, perhaps at midnight, and have them shut off at five or six in the morning.

Fig. 8-8.
Large, above-grade planters can be both visually obtrusive and physically confining for pedestrians, while...

Shopping Malls

Shopping malls are generally the building type generating the most pedestrian traffic in which plants will be located. Extraordinary pedestrian traffic and often nonexistent security make interior landscaping an attractive target for the vandal, the careless adult, or the mischievous child. The designer can help mitigate potential problems caused by too close an interaction between plants and people:

- Plant beds designed at curb height will help keep hands away from plants better than plant beds at seating height or slightly higher or lower (Fig. 8-6).
- Trees in tree grates are preferable to trees in decorative containers, not only to help reduce vandalism but to improve pedestrian circulation (Figs. 8-8, 8-9).

Both these solutions help separate people from plants, but they require that the structural slab be depressed to accommodate the plantings. There are design, structural engineering and cost implications, and any intent to reconfigure the structural slab must occur relatively early in the design process to be successful (Chapter Three).

Fig. 8-9.
...trees in tree grates open up the ground plane to view and to circulation.

Fig. 8-10.
Limiting the interior landscape palette to taller trees, ground covers, and low shrubs can still provide for an interesting horticultural presentation...

Fig. 8-11.
...because of the diversity of textures and colors in these plant types.

Fig. 8-12.
Tilting the ground cover bed makes massed plantings seem more natural and increases the visibility of low specimens to longer fields of view.

Lush as some mall plantings may be, developers of malls do not lose sight of the project's intent: to bring in shoppers. Mall developers and tenants know that a key factor to the success of a mall store (heck, any store!) is visibility. Location of a store within a mall determines a great deal of its visibility, but open views unfettered by foliage provides visibility as well. The interior landscape designer of a mall will therefore often be directed to specify only plants which do not conflict with views down mall "streets", particularly with regard to the level of typical store signage about 7 to 9 ft (2.1 to 2.7 m) from the floor (Fig. 8-10). This relegates effective use of plants to those ground covers and small shrubs whose ultimate height extends no higher than waist level, about 4 ft (1.2 m) high, or those upper story plants whose foliage crowns begin at perhaps 10 ft (3.0 m) in height (Fig. 8-11).

Eliminating many of the more popular specimens of the mid-height range accentuates the importance of ground cover usage in the interior landscape, both in the garden installation and within decorative containers. Not only do they serve as a "design glue" (Chapter Two), but they can be focal elements themselves (Color Section C2-16, C9-8). The drawback to ground covers, especially when used en masse, is that they are best appreciated only when looking down at them from above. This can be remedied in the garden-type installation by injecting some natural topography into the finish grade. By "tilting" a plant bed, individual ground cover specimens can be made more visible from great distances down a mall street (Fig. 8-12). Ground covers used as underplantings in decorative containers help provide a textural transition from container to feature plant, and can help cover the sometimes awkward placement of grow pots within the decorative container (Fig. 8-13).

Escalators are the primary method of transporting people from floor to floor in a shopping mall because they can move a higher volume of people than elevators. But they usurp a much larger amount of floor space as well (including the area of limited ceiling height beneath them as they angle up), space that can be neither rented to produce income nor used for circulation. One method of introducing plants into a shopping mall without diminishing the rentable square footage is to use the area beneath escalators for plantings.

This use of space for planting is highly desirable. Transforming an unattractive portion of a mall into a visual focal point without using leasable space is obviously a positive marketing strategy. However, certain precautions must be taken to make sure that it can be made workable. Lighting for shopping malls is often provided by skylights, not only for plant growth, but for human comfort as well. Plantings under escalators will not get the benefit of either skylights or other general plant growth lighting which a mall may afford. To keep under-escalator plantings viable, plant growth lighting must be built into the soffit of the escalator. Plant growth lighting (metal halide is recommended) will generally be intense enough to bring unwarranted attention to the space if operated during shopping hours. Keeping plant growth lighting on between closing and opening (or for at least 6 hours per night if the mall has extended shopping hours) will solve the brightness problem, but result in another: with no lighting of any kind on under the escalator during shopping hours, the plantings will be "in the dark", losing much of their aesthetic appeal. This, in turn, can be resolved by incorporating into the escalator soffit ambient lighting for the plants (Fig. 8-14 and Color Section C9-14) during shopping hours.

Fig. 8-13.
Ground cover underplantings in decorative containers can cover up many minor installation flaws common to decorative container plantings.

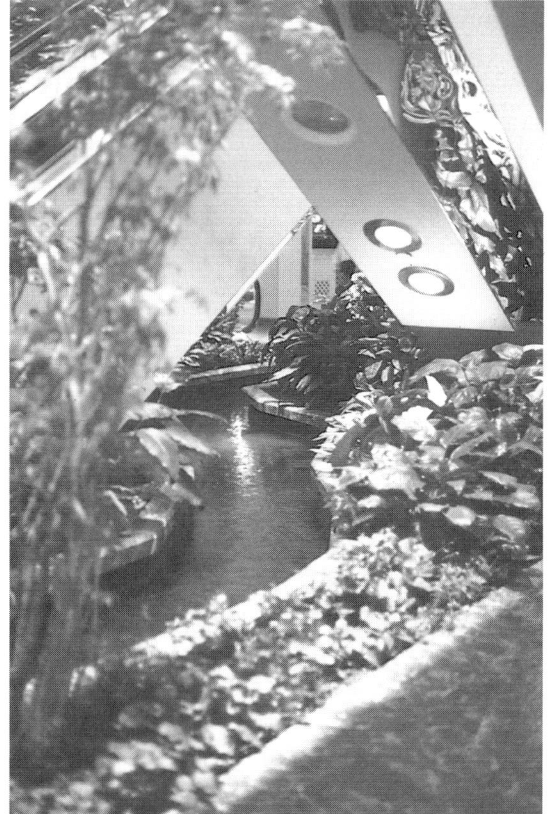

Fig. 8-14.
These plantings under an escalator have the benefit of incandescent ambient lighting (shown in operation) and high intensity discharge lighting for plant growth (visible, but not in operation).

Fig. 8-15.
Tree Ferns and Baby's Tears are two delicate species that can be considered in a secure atrium with proper environmental controls. Neither would last a month in a shopping mall.

Fig. 8-16.
Parkway North, Deerfield, Illinois.

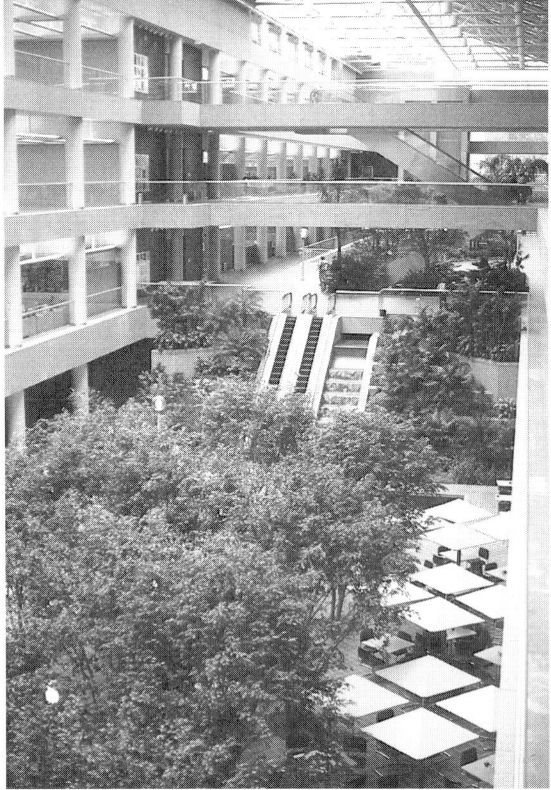

Fig. 8-17.
Cigna Corporation, Bloomfield, Connecticut.

The Corporate Atrium

Large plantings in corporate facilities have an advantage over mall and hotel interior landscapes in not having to deal with the down side of heavy pedestrian traffic. Fewer people and better security allow more flexibility to the designer, enabling the landscape to flow more fully to the edges of the planters. It also allows for the introduction of more delicate species than might be specified in the busier, less secure project (Fig. 8-15).

The signature of a company or its chief executives may be evident in the corporate interior landscape. Where a mall planting may be typical of literally hundreds of other projects nationwide, the corporate lobby may have as distinctive an interior landscape as its architecture. Depending on how committed the company hierarchy is to the use of plants, extraordinary design elements may be included in the corporate landscape: sculpture, water features, fish, birds, extensive rock formations, special humidity requirements, fog, etc. The statement made by the lobby—architecture, interior design, furnishings, fixtures, and plantings—establishes a first impression for guests and sets the tone of the company ethic for employees who sample it (Figs. 8-16, 8-17 and Color Section C8-6 through C8-9).

RESTAURANTS

The use of plants in restaurants can have a major impact on the ambience of the dining experience (Fig. 8-18). The key to the successful restaurant interior landscape lies in avoiding any direct interaction between seated diners and plants. Hanging plants placed directly over tables can drop dead leaves or drip excess water into a patron's lap (Fig. 8-19). While a patron might appreciate the feeling of a large palm arching up behind them, one's appetite can be lost if insects are visible while one sits down to a meal. When plainly visible, the webbing of spider mites or the white tufts of mealy bug on foliage close to a table can be disturbing.

The maintenance of plants in a restaurant calls for extraordinary measures. Insecticide use must be carefully monitored, and precautions must be taken to keep insecticides, fertilizers and other potent chemicals away from not only tables but all areas where food might be prepared, stored, or served. The designer must take these factors into account during the preparation of the interior landscape design for a restaurant.

Fig. 8-18.
Plants can dramatically improve the ambiance of a restaurant.

THE RESIDENTIAL MARKET

The private residence has long been a sales target of the retail flower shop or plant store. It has not been a focus of the interior landscape designer or contractor except at the high end, where well-to-do clients will demand expansive interior plant displays and the professional maintenance necessary to keep them healthy. Plants in the home are a highly personal touch that reflect the personality of the resident as much as it demonstrates their taste in decor.

The developers of speculative single-family residences have shied away from including built-in planters in their homes for precisely that reason: The belief that the appeal of plants is limited to only a portion of potential home buyers. They believe sales may be negatively influenced by the presence of built-in planters that people will not want to use because of the burden of caring for plants.

Fig. 8-19.
This "artificial ceiling" of plants is time-consuming to maintain. In addition, the use of a messy plant like Boston Fern, which drops leaves as a matter of course, is almost guaranteed to cause a patron to say, "Waiter, there's a leaf in my soup!" (Courtesy of ALCA)

Granted, the average single family resident is not in a position to have plants maintained professionally. But three factors have evolved in the recent past which may generate an increasing interest in the more widespread use of plants in the home. The first is the publication of the NASA study in September 1989 (see the Epilogue). With the knowledge that plants have the ability to cleanse indoor air of pollutants such as benzene, formaldehyde, and trichloroethylene (and undoubtedly many others), future residential customers may opt to include plants in their homes not only as items of decor but as low cost, low tech, attractive air filters as well. Environmental awareness has become a catch phrase of the 1990s, and it is no more personal than when one's home is the subject. As the interior foliage industry continues to promote the healthful attributes of plants to the public, more people will take advantage of the opportunity to use plants as a means of maintaining a healthier environment in their homes.

Fig. 8-20.
A residential sun room with both floor-to-ceiling glazing and skylights provides good light for a built-in planter along one window wall.

The NASA study alone will not change the status quo. The primary reason for only a limited use of plants in the contemporary home is the lack of available light to sustain their growth. The simple act of widening the window sills in new homes to accommodate a 6 or 8 in (15.2 to 20.3 cm) grow pot could dramatically increase residential plant sales.

But the interior landscape designer is not needed to place plants on windows sills. The use of plants as primary elements of interior design can best be achieved when they are fully integrated into a floor plan rather than relegating them to the periphery (Figs. 8-20, 8-21, and 8-22).

The second factor, the introduction of skylighting in residential design, allows this possibility, while also bringing enough natural light into the interior of a living space to reduce the dependence on electric lamps for ambient lighting during daylight hours.

With the price of fuel so volatile as a result of political instability in the Middle East (look no farther than the Gulf War of 1991), a future trend to reduce our reliance on fossil fuel consumption for heating and lighting our homes would make a great deal of sense. Skylights, particularly when integral to the design of a new home, are an attractive and cost-effective tool to provide this asset. The skylight can create horticulturally acceptable lighting conditions in any part of the home, enabling plants to provide their aesthetic and healthful benefits everywhere (Figs. 8-21, 8-22).

The third factor is the means to help overcome the reluctance of many people to take care of plants. Some people who don't feel comfortable with plants in their home are intimidated by the effort needed to keep them healthy. The introduction of subirrigation and Precision Micro-Irrigation as a means of watering can help, either with individual containers or in garden-style planters. Though these systems are used by professional maintenance companies because they are cost-effective, their ease of use can translate into increased sales of plants in the residential market, especially when combined with the potential for higher light levels throughout the home and the prospect of cleaner air in interior living spaces.

Figs. 8-21, 8-22. When used in conjunction with skylights, residential built-in planters can be located away from windows, where the plantings become integrated interior design elements in the space. (Top, courtesy of Landscape Images and ALCA)

Professional maintenance is a reasonable consideration for the atrium of a multifamily apartment or condominium building. The planting of a large public space in a residential project allows a developer to offer potential residents a haven which can serve as a place for relaxation or meeting fellow residents or guests. It can be especially beneficial in northern temperate climates when the weather is unsuitable for outdoor activities for 4 or 5 months per year (Color Section C8-12).

SPECIAL BUILDING TYPES

Most of this book has dealt with the placement of plants in interior spaces designed for people. Besides catering to the human inhabitants instead of the horticultural ones, these spaces must be operated as businesses—cost-effectively. Even humans are affected negatively by infringements on temperature regulation, low humidity, and light availability as a result of cost-cutting measures. Plants, of course, can be devastated. The commercial buildings housing the vast majority of the interior plants designed and maintained by the professional interior landscape community provide, in many cases, only for plant sustenance. Growth may actually have a negative effect, for it demands added maintenance considerations as plants shed old leaves and require pruning to keep their size or shape.

At the other end of the interior landscape spectrum are buildings whose very existence is a celebration of plants. They are either buildings designed for the expressed purpose of displaying plants indoors, or buildings ultimately adapted to that purpose by institutions who have committed themselves to the study, growth, or exhibition of plants. In between, many other building types take more than a passing interest in accommodating the environmental needs of plants in one form or another.

These special building types add tremendous diversity to the types of species which can be displayed, and allow this diversity to thrive in optimal or near optimal growing environments.

Conservatories and Botanical Gardens

The building designed at the outset for the display of plants will generally have clear or virtually clear glass walls and roof to allow not only for the maximum intensity of light, but for the longest duration and broadest spectrum of light as well. Unlike the orangery designers of the eighteenth century, contemporary conservatory designers will pay no heed to the prevailing architectural styles, nor will they be swayed by the trendiness of tinted or reflective glass. The only concession in the glazing design will be use of double or triple pane insulating glass to mitigate heat loss during the winter and heat gain during the summer.

The focus of attention on plants will also be noticed in the design of HVAC systems for these structures. The HVAC system for the commercial office building is designed to be quiet, invisible and relatively generalized in its supply of air to a space. The amount of air circulation is dependent on building codes with regard to the volume of air moved through the space within a given time period, and with regard to the percentage of fresh air makeup of the total volume. The code requirements are based on prevailing attitudes about how much air circulation, and how much fresh air, are necessary to maintain a healthful indoor environment.

Air movement will generally be the minimum necessary for human health, and actual movement of air is not readily seen or heard. Temperatures are kept within a range of several degrees Fahrenheit to satisfy human comfort, and would attempt to maintain similar temperatures throughout a building. Relative humidity can be controlled by the commercial air handling system, but often is not because of the added cost.

The HVAC system for a conservatory controls the indoor environment in a different manner. In order to satisfy the environmental idiosyncrasies of many different kinds of plants, temperatures in the conservatory will often fluctuate widely from one area to another, and from day to night. Species of like temperature requirements will be grouped together, and different groupings may vary by 15 or 20°F (8.3 to 11.1°C). Similarly, the humidity requirements of plants will range from arid to rain forest, and will be adjusted zone by zone to accommodate the plants' requirements.

The landscape design approach to a conservatory takes a completely different tack to that of a commercial office or atrium space. A bewildering variety of species of permanent plants and seasonal flowers will be at the designer's disposal, with the intention of displaying as many as possible, perhaps in a manner diametrically opposed to the way a commercial office or atrium design would be approached. The conservatory designer must work closely with production staff to determine which species will be in full flower or maximum visual effect at any given time, so that it can be worked into an overall concept.

Successful examples of conservatory design are described and displayed in two renowned examples of the genre:

LONGWOOD GARDENS, KENNETT SQUARE, PENNSYLVANIA: Longwood Gardens is perhaps the most outstanding example of an indoor facility established for the display, growth, and study of plant material in the United States and one of the premier horticultural attractions in the world. The gardens were created as the summer home of Pierre S. du Pont, grandson of the founder of the Du Pont Chemical Company. The indoor display houses at Longwood are maintained by a staff of 22 gardeners from the Production and Display Divisions, and an additional 13 specialists from Maintenance oversee miles of steam lines and the operation of three boilers capable of generating up to 24,000 pounds of steam per hour, and burning a total of 300,000 gallons of fuel per year.

As with other world-class conservatories, Longwood offers great environmental diversity in its twenty indoor gardens. Most houses are kept at least 10.0°F (4.7°C) lower at night, with night-time temperatures ranging between 35 and 65°F (1.6 and 18.3°C).

Fig. 8-23.
Fan Palms reach towards the Lamella arched roof of the East Conservatory at Longwood Gardens.

One of the many distinctions of the Longwood Gardens conservatories is its successful use of lawn grass indoors as a permanent exhibit. This has been achieved by having a near perfect environmental habitat and top quality maintenance. The sub-soil is native Kaolin Clay, with ballast-filled sumps scattered about for good drainage. Above the sub-soil is 6 to 8 in (15.2 to 20.3 cm) of soil, consisting of two parts field soil, one part peat, and one part aggregate. The seed mix used is 20 percent Georgetown, 20 percent Classic, 20 percent Glade, 20 percent 1757 and 20 percent Nassau. The available natural light intensity is about 6,000 fc. Watering is by manually placed sprinklers, as needed, which might be 2 to 3 in (5.1 to 7.6 cm) per week during the summer, while mowing is performed once a week during the winter, and twice per week during the summer, to a height of 1½ to 2 in (3.8 to 5.1 cm). Walking on the grass is strongly discouraged to avoid soil compaction and reduce the spread of pest and disease infestation.

The extensive use of lawn grass in the conservatory complex helps make the indoor landscapes of Longwood Gardens more attuned to the exterior environment of their native Pennsylvania. (Fig. 8-23 and Color Section C8-12 and C8-14)

(Text continued on Page 209)

COLOR SECTION

Color Plates C2-1 to C2-8. These specimens are displayed for their flowers and are usually discarded after the flowers have finished blooming.

Color Plates C2-9 to C2-14. Many permanent interior plants have foliage color so distinctive they can make almost as impressive a display as flowering plants.

C2-1. *Begonia*

C2-2. *Azalea*

C2-3. *Chrysanthemum*

CS-4. *Cineraria*

C2-5. *Cyclamen*

C2-6. *Impatiens*

C2-7. *Kalanchoe*

C2-8. *Primula*

C2-9. *Aglaonema 'Pseudobracteatum'*

C2-10. *'Calathea vittata'*

C2-11. *Calathea zebrina*

C2-12. *Cissus discolor*

C2-13. *Dieffenbachia 'Triumph'*

C2-14. *Gynura aurantiaca*

Color Plate for C2-!5. (far left) Mixing individual specimens of differing colors can create visual confusion, negating the benefits of flowering plants.

Color Plate C2-16. (left) Ground covers can serve as "design glue" to lead the eye through a design by virtue of their dramatic differences in color and texture, even if their heights are identical. (Courtesy of City Gardens, Inc.)

Building Types: Hotels

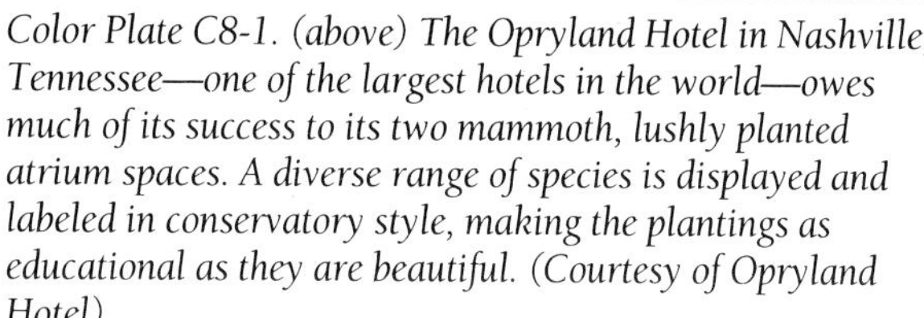

Color Plate C8-1. (above) The Opryland Hotel in Nashville, Tennessee—one of the largest hotels in the world—owes much of its success to its two mammoth, lushly planted atrium spaces. A diverse range of species is displayed and labeled in conservatory style, making the plantings as educational as they are beautiful. (Courtesy of Opryland Hotel)

Color Plates C8-2, C8-3. (top right, upper right) The Hyatt Regency Hotel in Greenwich, Connecticut, is a more traditional-style garden, but its use of lawn and shade trees in a temperate climate ambiance makes it quite distinctive as an enclosed atrium planting.

Color Plates C8-4, C8-5. (lower right, bottom right) The Embassy Suites Hotel in Deerfield, Illinois, is typical of the intensively planted atria found in most Embassy Suites' facilities. (Both courtesy of Rentokil Tropical Plants, Inc.)

Hotel chains like Hyatt and Embassy Suites are to be commended for their commitment to the extensive and innovative use of living plants in their hotels' public spaces.

Building Types: Corporate Atria

Color Plate C8-6. (above) Mine Safety Appliance Corporate Headquarters in Pittsburgh boasts this spectacular combination of water, plants and hardscape elements in a rigidly structured atrium design. (Courtesy of Plantscape, Inc. and ALCA)

Color Plate C8-7. (upper left) Parkway North in Deerfield, Illinois, is an excellent example of a large corporate atrium used as a public space for informal gatherings and for food service. (Courtesy of Rentokil Tropical Plants, Inc.)

Color Plate C8-8. (middle left) A more modestly sized yet no less impressively designed and built atrium landscape at the International Mineral and Chemical offices in Northbrook, Illinois, uses English Ivy as its focal point.

Color Plate C8-9. (bottom left) The atrium at John Deere West, an architecturally acclaimed addition to the John Deere Corporate Headquarters complex in Moline, Illinois, might be considered a reflection of the company's work ethic. (Courtesy of Rentokil Tropical Plants, Inc.)

Color Plate C8-10. (above) The Orangery of Longwood Gardens welcomes spring a few weeks early in February. (Courtesy of Larry Albee / Longwood Gardens)

Color Plate C8-11. (right) The East Conservatory at Longwood Gardens in Kennett Square, Pennsylvania, exemplifies the success which can be achieved from a blend of ideal environmental parameters, careful planning, and meticulous maintenance. (Courtesy of Larry Albee/ Longwood Gardens)

Color Plate C8-12. (above right) The residents of Tropics North, a condominium in Montreal, have the great benefit of this wonderful atrium space to enjoy when the outdoor weather turns colder. (Courtesy of Landscape Technologies, Inc. and ALCA)

Color Plate C8-13. (left) The Enid A. Haupt Conservatory of the New York Botanical Gardens in the Bronx, New York, as seen during the annual Chrysanthemum festival in November.

Color Plate C8-14. (above) The garden court of the Isabella Stewart Gardner Museum, Boston, combines classical architecture with a superbly maintained combination of rotated flowering plants and permanent ground covers and specimen plants.

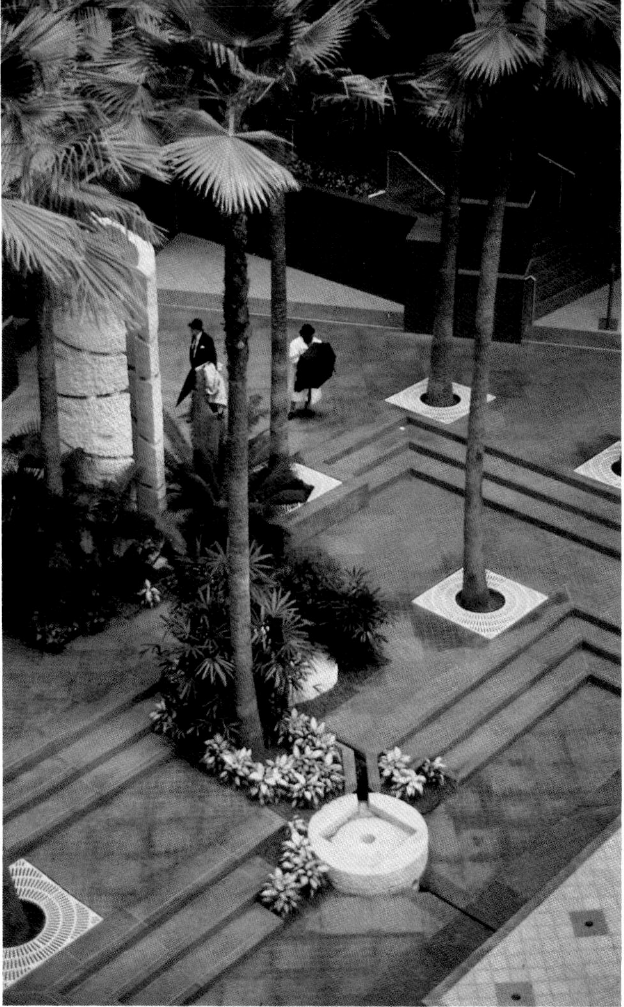

Color Plate C8-15. (above) The Fulton County Courthouse in Atlanta, Georgia, makes prominent use of large scale palms as focal elements. (Courtesy of M. Paul Friedberg & Partners)

Case Study 1: Ford Foundation, New York City

Color Plate C9-1. 1970: Two and a half years after installation, the garden contained much of the original temperate plantings.

Color Plate C9-2. The Magnolias were ultimately replaced by the tropical Norfolk Island Pine and Southern Yew (shown), but the garden design maintained its temperate climate ambiance. (Courtesy of John Mini Indoor Landscapes, Inc.)

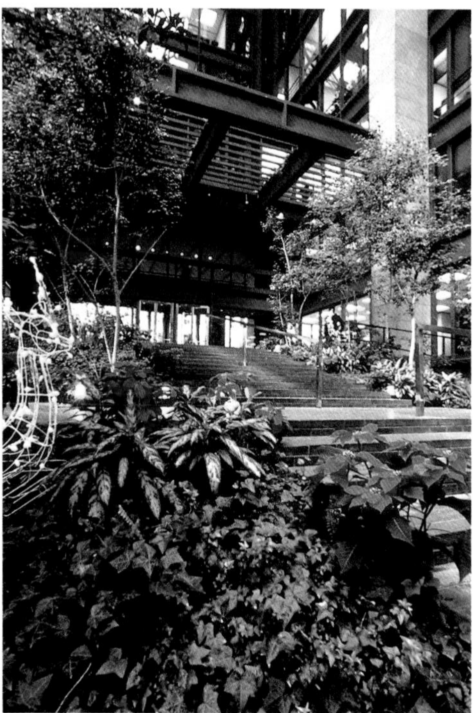

Color Plate C9-3. A typical holiday display adds a splash of red Pointsettia to the traditional green of the existing foliage.

Color Plate C9-4. Looking up the stairway from 42nd to 43rd Street, the full effect of the 13 foot (4.0m) grade change becomes apparent. (Courtesy of John Mini Indoor Landscapes, Inc.)

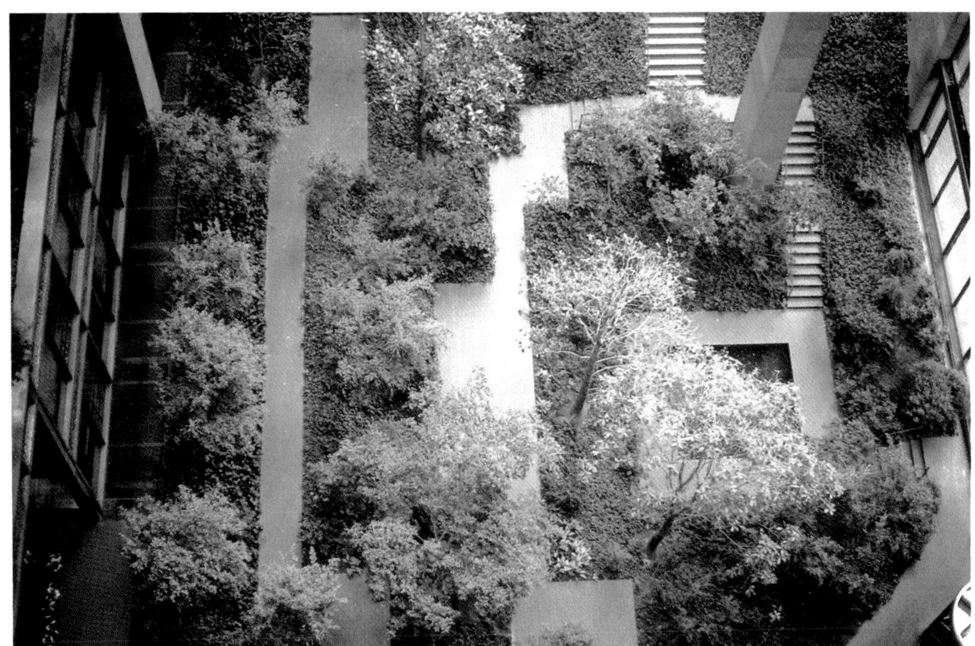

Color Plate C9-5. (left) By April of 1984, only three of the original Magnolias remained. The other five had been replaced by Ficus. *Although most of the 1967 plantings had been replaced with tropical species by 1984, the overall visual effect of the garden has remained faithful to the original design intent.*

Color Plate C9-6. (above) The central reflecting pool as it appeared in 1984.

Case Study 2: Copley Place, Boston

Color Plate C9-7. (above left) The large planter and "stream" are shown after installation of waterproof membrane, insulation, and protection board. A virtually identical view (C9-8, above right) shows the completed project the week it opened. The impact of ground covers and flowering accent plants is evident when seen from the second level of the shopping galleries. Note how even a single line of flowering plants makes a definitive statement in the landscape.

Color Plate C9-9. (Above left) Plants have been placed in their proposed locations (in this case, under the escalators) awaiting approval of the landscape architect prior to planting. Empty pots will be installed in the planting medium to accept slightly smaller grow pots of flowering plants. Note both the plant growth and ambient soffit lighting under the escalator are turned on. (C9-10, above right). Same view, opening week. Flowering plants are in place inside the larger grow pots. Only the ambient, decorative lighting is operating.

Color Plate C9-11 (above left) The planter adjacent to the waterfall seven months prior to opening. The 8 in (20.3 cm) pipe carries water from its source under the waterfall to the "stream" across the atrium floor. (C9-12, above right) similar view, opening week. Plantings are mounded up to provide cover for the piping.

Color Plate C9-13. (above) The successful integration of waterfall, "stream" bed, and landscaping requires close coordination of artist, architect, landscape architect, water feature consultant, mechanical engineer, and structural engineer.

Color Plate C9-14. (above) The floor area beneath and next to the escalators incorporates the same dense plantings and water feature as the Central Atrium. It turns an underutilized area into a visual amenity.

Case Study 3: Hyatt Regency Hotel, Orlando, Florida

Color Plate C9-15. (right) From the top of the atrium, the importance of the balcony plantings in tying the whole landscape concept of the space together becomes apparent. (Courtesy of Edward D. Stone Jr. and Associates, Inc.)

Color Plate C9-16. Looking down from above the lobby bar, one can appreciate the palms' textural qualities in "plan view". (Courtesy of Edward D. Stone Jr. and Associates, Inc.)

Color Plate C9-17. The magnificent specimen of Senegal Date Palm (Phoenix reclinata) *dominates the atrium at the ground level. (Courtesy of Edward D. Stone Jr. and Associates, Inc.)*

Case Study 4: Private Residence, Mexico City, Mexico

Color Plate C9-18.
The concrete foundation for the rock "hill" has been poured. Note plumbing lines extending above the top of the concrete. (Courtesy of Muray Arquitectos, S.A.)

Color Plate C9-19.
The completed plantings blend beautifully with an exterior court just outside the window wall. (Courtesy of Muray Arquitectos, S.A.)

Color Plate C9-20 (top) and C9-21 (below). The sights and sounds of a small tropical garden, properly designed and implemented, can transform even a relatively small residential room into a unique and pleasurable environment for its owner. (Courtesy of Muray Arquitectos, S.A.)

Case Study 5: John Hancock Child Care Center, Boston

Color Plate C9-22.
The children playing in the photograph are present to show the scale of the garden. Children's actual participation in activities in the garden will be carefully supervised by staff to maintain safety and avoid damage to plants. (Photograph by Nick Wheeler)

Color Plate C9-23.
The garden as seen from the stairway to the second floor.

Color Plate C9-24. (top)
The expansiveness of the view belies the small size of the garden, only a 16 foot (4.9m) square. (Photograph by Nick Wheeler)

Color Plate C9-25.
The 18 in (45.7 cm) wide bluestone walkway wends it way under the soffit of the stair landing.

Color Plates CE-1, CE-2. Above and right) This rooftop garden is the executive dining area of an office supply company in Mexico City, Mexico. (Courtesy of Muray Arquitectos, S.A.)

Color Plates CE-3, CE-4. (Above and right) The London Standard Chartered Bank, London, England; interior landscape design by the Office of Dan Kiley (Courtesy of the Office of Dan Kiley)

Color Plate CE-5 (Left) The Kuwait Fund for the Advancement of Science, Kuwait City, Kuwait; interior landscape design by The Architects Collaborative, Inc. (Photo by Mark Zarrillo, Courtesy of The Architects Collaborative, Inc.)

Fig. 8-24.
One of the display galleries of the Enid A. Haupt Conservatory, of the New York Botanical Garden.

(Continued from page 192)

NEW YORK BOTANICAL GARDENS, THE BRONX, NEW YORK: The Enid A. Haupt Conservatory of the New York Botanical Gardens is a Victorian glasshouse inspired by the Palm House at Kew Gardens. It was originally built in 1902, and underwent a major renovation that was completed in 1978. Eleven different galleries display varying themes, climates, and collections of plants under a total of one acre of glass.

The large central dome of the Conservatory is the Palm Court, 100 ft (30.5 m) in diameter and 90 ft (27.5 m) high. Other permanent environments include Economic Plants, the Old World Desert, the New World Desert, the Orangery, and the Fern Forest. In addition, other display galleries provide outstanding seasonal presentations to ensure that visitors will always have something different to see (Fig. 8-24 and Color Section C8-13).

Zoos and Aquaria

After hundreds of years of building zoos which looked like little more than prisons for animals, society has recently changed the concept by which zoos and zoological parks are conceived. A combination of emerging technologies and changing attitudes about the way in which animals are treated have resulted in the creation of habitats which are at once both more realistic and natural in their appearance, and more humane for their inhabitants.

For animals housed indoors, many of the changes have been technological. Indoor habitats of some of the newer facilities have benefited from the extensive use of translucent skylighting, which has permitted higher levels of light to penetrate these spaces. With more light, a greater variety of plant material can be specified.

The plant palette of zoo habitats must be carefully selected and placed in order to avoid conflict with the inhabitants. Many plants are poisonous *to* animals, and even ones that aren't are prone to damage *from* animals. The available foraging range of interior environments is quite limited, so animals in search of food could quickly defoliate any edible trees, shrubs, or ground covers within their reach.

The key to successful interior landscape planning for the zoo environment is to provide a diversity of plants which appear to recreate a particular animal's or group of animals' habitat. In the case of birds or other species for whom access to all parts of a habitat is possible, extensive research must be undertaken to ensure that the horticultural species in the exhibit will not be poisonous to the animals. Likewise, edible (but nontoxic) horticultural species should not be planted as permanent specimens, or they will quickly be damaged.

For larger animal species whose access can be limited to certain parts of an interior environment, the ideal interior landscape would place plants in locations inaccessible to the animal species. This is often done by creating "cliffs" out of fiberglass reinforced concrete, or using water features not only for the animals' enjoyment, but as barriers to other portions of a habitat (Figs. 8-25, 8-26, 8-27). Massed plantings placed atop "cliffs" or across moats will help create the illusion of a natural habitat while in actuality plants and animals are separated.

Besides the potential conflict between animals and plants from the standpoint of physical proximity, the long-term and daily care of interior plants must be taken into account as well. Large-scale use of plants will inevitably require some method of pest and disease control, and like the potential for plants themselves to cause toxic reactions to animals, treating pests and diseases must be accomplished with the health and safety of the animals in mind. Options include the use of nontoxic insecticidal soaps rather than toxic chemicals, or integrated pest management (IPM), and the use of insects or other biological species as predators to rid the plants of pests. Of course, the predators must not be dangerous to the animals, either. In either case, removal of the animals from the habitat may be required as an extra precaution.

Figs. 8-25, 8-26.
A wide variety of live plantings graces the Tropical Rain Forest Exhibit of the Franklin Park Zoo in Boston (above left) and the Gorilla House in the Topical Exhibit of the Buffalo Zoo, Buffalo, New York (above right, courtesy of Kalwall Corporation); both made possible by extensive use of translucent glazing.

Fig. 8-27.
With dense plantings adjacent to the visitor areas and atop the "cliffs" of the animal habitats, the casual visitor can experience a quite natural "wild" exhibit without realizing the extent to which plants must be segregated from animals in an indoor habitat like the Franklin Park Tropical Rain Forest. (Courtesy of Kalwall Corporation)

Fig. 8-28.
The Isabella Stewart Gardner Museum atrium—a peaceful haven.

Fig. 8-29.
The central spine of the Gardner Museum greenhouses leads to 6 offsets, each with the capability to maintain different temperature and humidity controls.

Other Specialized Building Types

Some building types have the advantages of both the conservatory and the commercial office. Displaying a wide variety of plant materials will involve ranges of both temperature and humidity that the human occupant may find uncomfortable. To enable people to appreciate the joys of these "exotic" plants, they must be grown in a horticulturally acceptable environment, but displayed in a comfortable one.

ISABELLA STEWART GARDNER MUSEUM, BOSTON, MASSACHUSETTS: Such is the case with the Isabella Stewart Gardner Museum in Boston. Built by the widow of John Lowell Gardner as a home and museum to house their art collection, "Fenway Court" was completed and opened to the public on February 23, 1903, although Mrs. Gardner lived there on the upper floors until her death in 1924. The building was fashioned after a Venetian palazzo and consists of a 4-story rectangle of rooms arrayed about an atrium filled with flowering plants supplied from adjacent greenhouses and maintained by a full time staff of 7 horticulturists.

At the time of the building's construction, the greenhouses supporting the atrium greenery had been built in Brookline, a suburb of Boston about 6 miles from the site. In order to better accommodate the needs of the horticulture staff, 6,000 SF (557.6 SM) of new greenhouse space was built on site in 1972, and the atrium glazing was replaced as well. The new greenhouses vary from 12 to 15 ft (3.7 to 4.6 m) in height and are arranged to maximize the potential diversity of plants that can be displayed in the atrium: A central spine has 6 distinct offsets, all of which maintain disparate temperature and humidity controls, enabling the staff to keep plants in flower all year long in the atrium garden (Figs. 8-28, 8-29 and Color Section C8-15).

The spectacular atrium greenery, coupled with the classical European architecture and art, give the garden court of the Isabella Stewart Gardner Museum a serene and contemplative character that is unique amid the bustle of contemporary Boston. The museum is undergoing a major renovation as of this writing.

Although different buildings will each warrant their own unique solutions to an interior landscape design problem, similarities of building use or type will often suggest similarities in interior landscape design approach. The experienced designer should be able to draw upon previous interior landscape experience when asked to plan a new space of the same type.

CHAPTER 9
CASE STUDIES

A reference text on the subject of interior landscape design must have as a goal the ability to teach the reader how to create an interior landscape design, from concept to reality. The material presented in earlier chapters provides general information needed to establish environmental parameters and document ideas. One proven method, however, of teaching virtually any subject is to present examples of how it has successfully been done previously by others. In this chapter, we will look at five built interior landscapes, and through their project descriptions, drawings, plant list, and photographs, we will see the design process at work. The five selected projects were chosen because they offer a diversity of project size, complexity, and use. They include a corporate atrium, a shopping mall, a hotel lobby, a private residence, and a child care center.

The plant lists accompanying each case study are those issued with the contract documents for construction, or were otherwise available for publication. Note that in many of the case studies, some of the plant materials displayed in the photography are not those indicated in the plant list. There may be several explanations for this: Originally specified plants might not have been available at the time of installation; they might have been planted but have since been replaced because of unanticipated environmental conditions; because they outgrew their space; because other species were found to be easier to care for; or because the client wished to have a different visual effect. Plant names, both botanical and common, are as presented in the original documents. No attempt has been made to conform nomenclature to currently accepted standards.

Case Study 1
GARDEN OF THE FORD FOUNDATION BUILDING, NEW YORK CITY, 1967
Designed by the Office of Dan Kiley, Charlotte, VT.

In addition to its many other attributes, the Ford Foundation Garden earned its place in this list by virtue of its historic importance to the discipline of interior landscape design. This project was the first large interior landscape built within a contemporary commercial building in the United States, and serves as a landmark in field.

Located on the east side of Manhattan's midtown area, the site fronts on both 42nd and 43rd Streets (and between First and Second Avenue), between which there is a 13 ft (4.0 m) grade change. Designed by Kevin Roche-John Dinkeloo and Associates of Hamden, CT, the building was built to house the 400 employee headquarters staff of the Ford Foundation, one of the largest philanthropic organizations in the world, in a square, 12-story structure. The 12 floors of offices occupy the northern and western faces of the structure, forming an "L" around the garden, whose atrium extends the entire twelve floors—156 ft (47.5 m)—to the skylit roof. The area enclosed by the offices and exterior glazing is a 120 ft (36.6 m) square, of which the garden represents about an 80 ft square (24.4 m) within it. To maximize the amount of light available to the garden, the eastern and southern faces of the building are glass as well. Design work on the Ford Foundation Building began in 1964, and it opened in December 1967.

The design concept and planting plan for the garden was, to a large extent, experimental in nature, since projects of similar scope did not exist on which to base conclusions or expectations, and the design team was not able to predict what kind of environmental conditions would be present in the garden on completion. The client was willing to accept this uncertainty. As result, the garden concept was revised many times over the course of design, construction, and post-construction, as previously untried ideas were put forth and later discarded.

The following three Planting Plans (Figs. 9-1, 9-2, 9-3) for the project (as illustrated in a Ford Foundation brochure) are presented in separate overlays: Trees, shrubs, and ground covers and aquatics (Courtesy of the Ford Foundation).

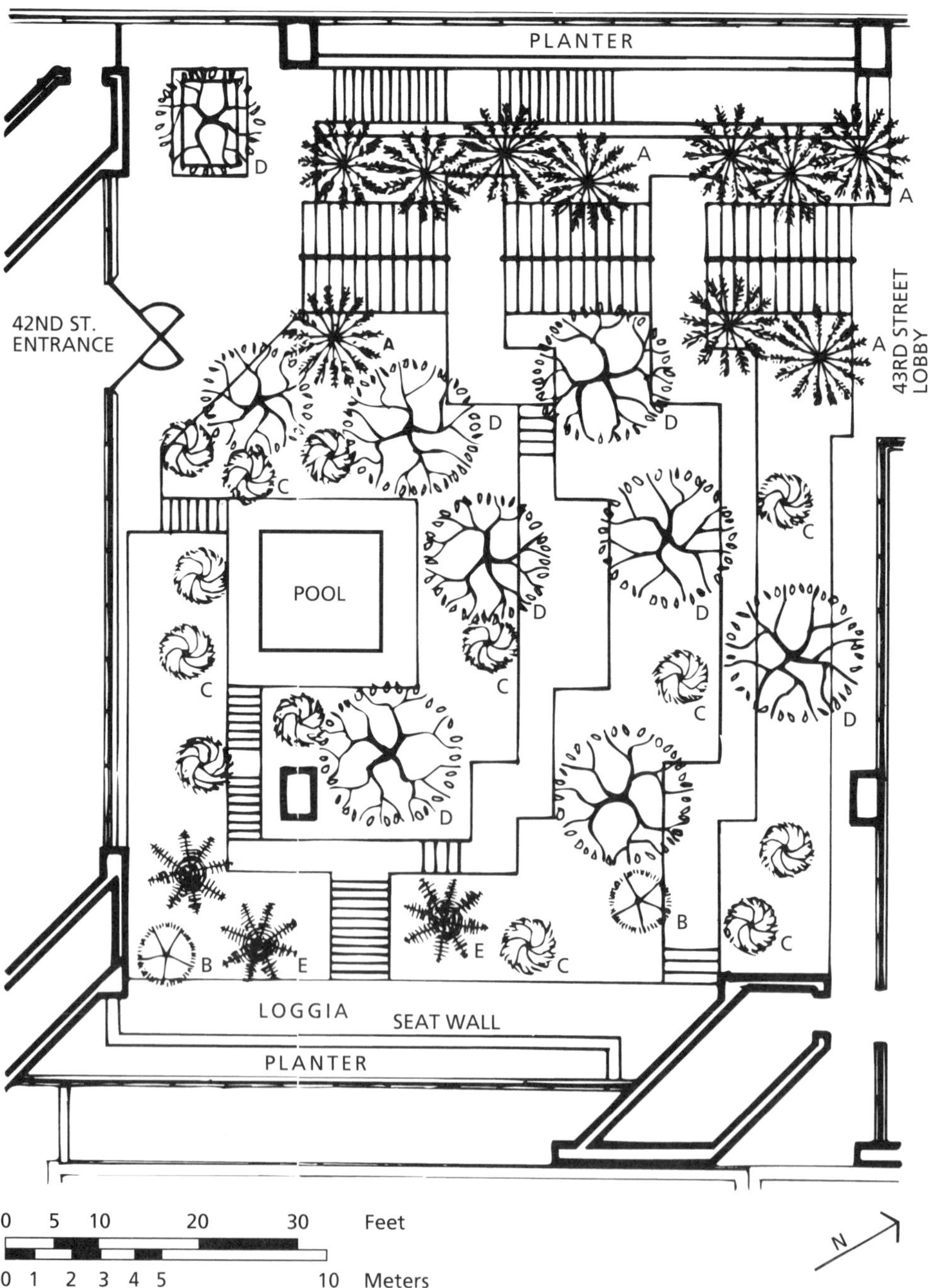

Fig 9-1. The Tree Planting Plan

Key:

- A *Sharpleaf Jacaranda (Jacaranda acutifolia)*
- B *Evergreen Pear (Pyrus kawakami)*
- C *Red Ironbark (Eucalyptus sideroxylon)*
- D *Southern Magnolia (Magnolia grandiflora)*
- E *Japanese Cryptomeria (Cryptomeria japonica lobbi)*

Various alternatives for glazing only portions of the roof and garden faces of the building were considered prior to the final decisions ultimately enacted. A suggestion for using tropical plants was made and later rejected when it was believed that the clear, single pane glazing of the skylight might prove to be a condensation problem for the humidity requirements believed necessary at the time for tropical species.

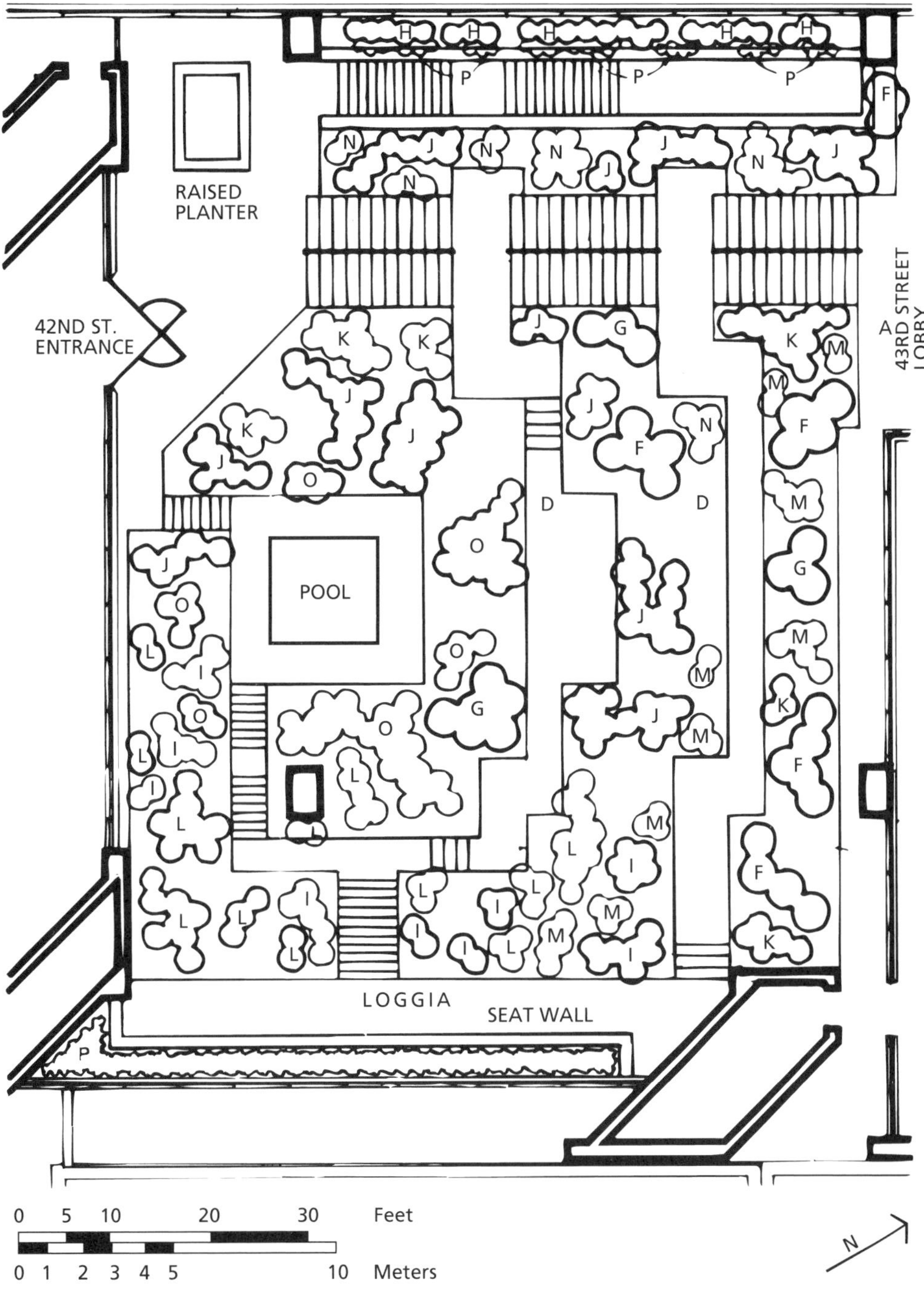

Fig 9-2. Shrub Planting plan

F *Red Japanese Camellia (Camellia japonica "No. 1 Red"*

G *Purity Japanese Camellia (Camellia japonica "Purity")*

H *Flame Fuchsia (Fuchsia fulgens)*

I *Japanese Andromeda (Pieris japonica)*

J *Azalea Glory of Sunnyhill (Rhododendron "Glory of Sunnyhill")*

K *Azalea Albion (Rhododendron Rutherfordiana "Albion")*

L *Azalea Pride of Dorking Rhododendron indica "Pride of Dorking"*

M *Azalea Formosa (Rhododendron indica "Formosa")*

N *Azalea Iceland (Rhododendron obtusum "Iceland")*

O *Azalea Pink Lace (Rhododendron pericat "Pink Lace")*

P *Star Jasmine (Trachelospermum jasminoides)*

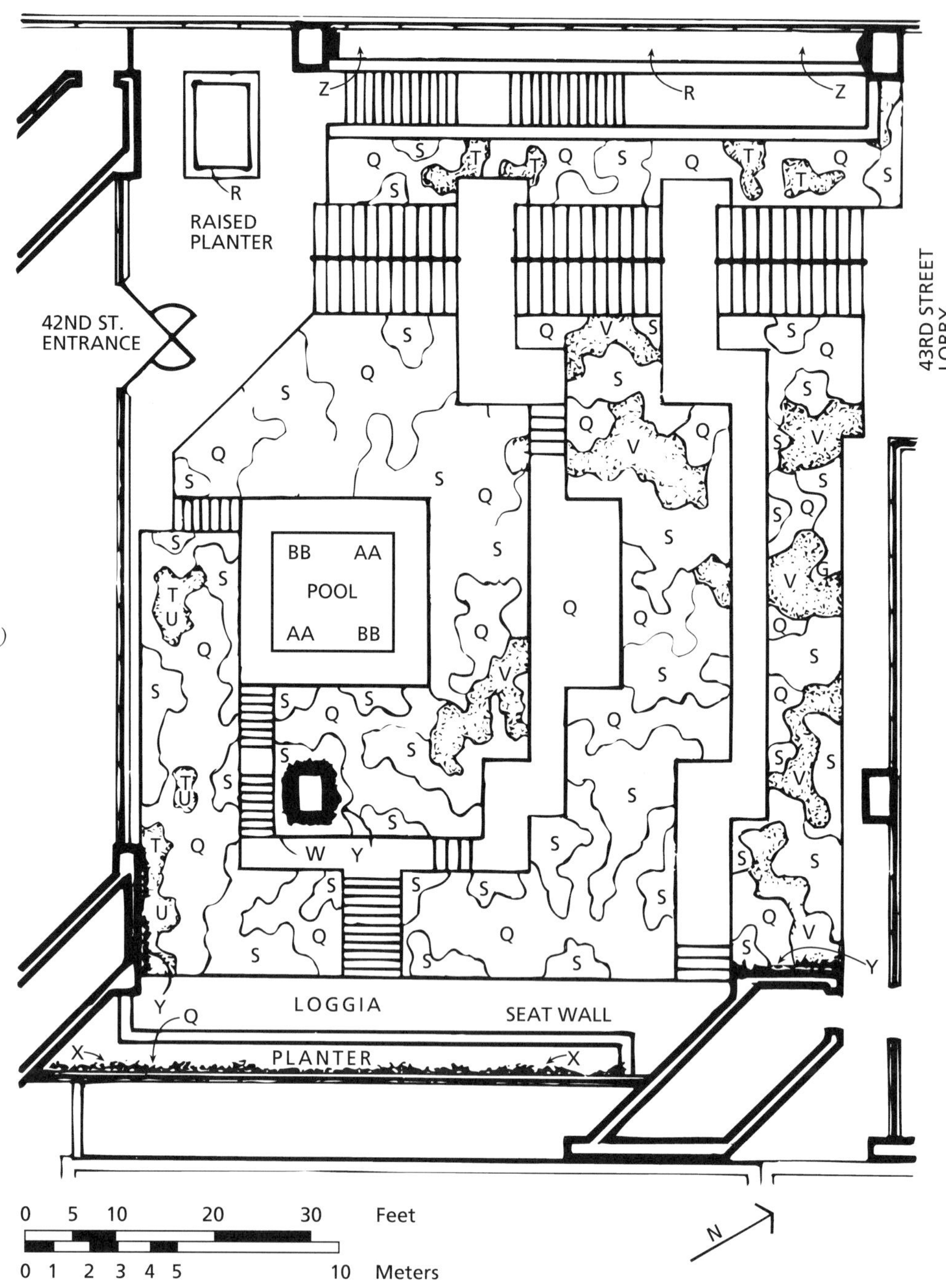

Fig. 9-3. Planting plan for Ground Covers, Vines, and Aquatics

- *Q Baby's Tears (Helxine soleirolii)*
- *R Mondo Grass (Ophiopogon japonicus)*
- *S Korean Grass (Zoysia tenuifolia)*
- *T Roundleaf Fern (Pellaea rotundifolia)*
- *U Tassel Fern (Polystichum setosum)*
- *V Mother Spleenwort (Asplenium bulbiform)*
- *W Herald Trumpet (Beaumontia grandiflora)*
- *X San Diego Red Bougainvillea (Bougainvillea "San Diego Red")*
- *Y Creeping Fig (Ficus pumila)*
- *Z Blood Trumpet Vine (Bignonia cherere)*
- *AA Tropical Waterlily (Nymphae "Mrs. George H. Pring")*
- *BB Double Arrowhead (Sagittaria sagittifolia floraplena)*

Rather than separately "zone" the HVAC requirements of the garden from the offices, it was decided to allow a free exchange of air between the two. In spite of this, it was believed by the design team that the temperatures of the atrium garden could not be maintained much above 50°F during the winter months, and so a palette of southern temperate climate plants were specified for the original installation. The original plant list of the garden proper was as follows:

Table 9-1

INTERIOR PLANT LIST: GARDEN OF THE FORD FOUNDATION BUILDING

Key	Botanical Name	Common Name
Trees		
A	Jacaranda acutifolia	Sharpleaf Jacaranda
B	Pyrus kawakami	Evergreen Pear
C	Eucalyptus sideroxylon	Red Ironbark
D	Magnolia grandiflora	Southern Magnolia
E	Cryptomeria japonica lobbi	Japanese Cryptomeria
Shrubs		
F	Camellia japonica 'No. 1 Red'	Red Japanese Camellia
G	Camellia japonica 'Purity'	Purity Japanese Camellia
H	Fuchsia fulgens	Flame Fuchsia
I	Pieris japonica	Japanese Andromeda
J	Rhododendron 'Glory of Sunnyhill'	Azalea Glory of Sunnyhill
K	Rhododendron Rutherfordiana 'Albion'	Azalea Albion
L	Rhododendron indica 'Pride of Dorking'	Azalea Pride of Dorking
M	Rhododendron indica 'Formosa'	Azalea Formosa
N	Rhododendron obtusum 'Iceland'	Azalea Iceland
O	Rhododendron pericat 'Pink Lace'	Azalea Pink Lace
P	Trachelospermum jasminoides	Star Jasmine
Ground Covers, Vines, and Aquatics		
Q	Helxine soleirolii	Baby's Tears
R	Ophiopogon japonicus	Mondo Grass
S	Zoysia tenuifolia	Korean Grass
T	Pellaea rotundifolia	Roundleaf Fern
U	Polystichum setosum	Tassel Fern
V	Asplenium bulbiform	Mother Spleenwort
W	Beaumontia grandiflora	Herald Trumpet
X	Bougainvillea 'San Diego Red'	San Diego Red Bougainvillea
Y	Ficus pumila	Creeping Fig
Z	Bignonia cherere	Blood Trumpet Vine
AA	Nymphae 'Mrs. George H. Pring'	Tropical Waterlily
BB	Sagittaria sagittifolia floraplena	Double Arrowhead

The original feature plants of the garden were 8 Southern Magnolia, 14 in (35.6 cm) in caliper and 35 ft (10.7 m) in height, with root balls weighing nine tons (8164 kg). The garden and other ancillary spaces also contained 29 other trees, 999 shrubs, 148 vines, 21,954 ground cover plants, and 18 aquatic plants in the central reflecting pool.

After completion, a recording thermometer in the garden indicated that the temperature never varied more than 4° Fahrenheit (2.2° C) from 70°F (21°C) at all times, day and night, winter and summer. Despite an environment without a winter dormancy, many of the originally specified plants normally requiring a dormant period were able to sustain themselves for some time. Although temperate ground covers were replaced by tropical ones very quickly, the *Cryptomeria* lasted about 20 months before deteriorating. Showing incredible adaptability, the Southern Magnolias were not completely replaced until 1984! In the years since the project was built, the entire planting plan has been replaced with tropical plants.

The plant palette may currently differ from its 1967 origins, but the basic design concept and overall effect of the dense plantings in this urban oasis is every bit as successful now as it was when it first opened.

The interior landscape was installed by The Everett Conklin Companies of Montvale, NJ, and has been maintained since 1983 by John Mini Indoor Landscapes, Inc., of City Island, NY.

Fig 9-4.
1970: 2 1/2 years after installation, the garden contained much of the original temperate plantings.

Fig. 9-5.
This view, taken in March of 1976, looking southeast from the 43rd Street side, illustrates what captured my attention back in 1970: A lush, green garden amid the snow of midtown New York in late winter.

Fig. 9-6.
All 8 Magnolias were still present in 1976, though 3 had begun to show signs of stress.

Fig. 9-7.
The garden in 1976 still gives the appearance of a temperate climate forest.

Fig. 9-8 (far left) and 9-9 (left).
The central reflecting pool over a span of years (1970, far left and 1976, left) indicates how two different solutions can solve the same design problem.

Case Study 2

THE COPLEY PLACE SHOPPING GALLERIES, BOSTON, MA

Designed by The Architects Collaborative, Inc. (TAC), Cambridge, MA

Conceived by Urban Investment and Development Company of Chicago, Copley Place is a mixed-use development in Boston's Back Bay, comprising a Westin Hotel, a Marriott Hotel, 100 units of housing, seven levels of offices, a 1432 care parking garage, and a two level-retail mall. The interior landscape displayed herein was executed in conjunction with the retail portion of the development, for which TAC was also the architect. Virtually all of Copley Place was constructed on air rights over the Massachusetts Turnpike, commuter rail lines, Amtrak lines, and the MBTA Rapid Transit Orange Line.

Interior landscaping was provided as one of two major visual amenities to the shopping public—the other being a 60 ft water sculpture by Dmitri Hadzi—in the focal point of the project, the Central Atrium. Although interior plants were specified liberally throughout the Copley Place complex, the use of plants in the Central Atrium is at its most dramatic, with three matched 25 ft (7.6 m) *Ficus benjamina* used as a focal counterpoint across the octagonal atrium floor from the granite, marble, and travertine waterfall. The three Ficus rest within a densely planted garden that was depressed into the space below in order to serve several of the client's wishes: First, it made the landscape look more integrated with the interior environment; second, lowering the finish grade of the planting made the Central Atrium look more spacious and open; and third, providing a 6 in (15.2 cm) curb rather than a seating height planter edge discouraged sitting, which the client recognized as a possible invitation to vandalism of the plants.

The space below into which the plantings were depressed was the upper of two levels of parking, so the amount of depression was quite restricted. To provide the necessary room for root depth of the large Ficus specimens, the more expansive garden areas were mounded up, creating a more natural appearance to the plantings.

The parking area below the plantings was unheated. As a precaution against winter cold damage to the root zone of the plantings above, 3 in (7.6 cm) of high density, rigid insulation lined the bottom and sides of all planter walls. The insulation also served as a protection board for the waterproof membrane which made the planter enclosure watertight. Another precaution was taken to mitigate the weight of the plantings above the insulation by eliminating a six inch (15.2 cm) layer of drainage gravel and placing in its stead Enkadrain, which took up about 1/2 in (1.3 cm) of depth and weighed virtually nothing.

Watering is performed manually. Box hydrants are found in four locations throughout the plantings to minimize hose length. The water is untempered, and during much of the winter the service technicians use other sources besides the box hydrants to provide water warm enough to avoid plant injury.

Lighting is supplied by both natural and artificial means. A 90 ft (27.4 m) wide octagonal skylight looms 110 ft (33.5 m) above the atrium floor, but provides direct sunlight for only a few minutes a day during the summer. During other times of the day, the indirect natural light dissipates dramatically as it descends to the atrium floor, leaving little for plant growth. Most light for sustenance is supplied by 200

500-watt quartz lights, specified at the request of the client to be more aesthetically harmonious with the incandescent lighting used elsewhere in the mall.

The visual effect of the interior landscape was to be reminiscent of the northern temperate plantings found outdoors in New England. The plant palette consisted of many low tropical shrubs (Hawaiian Schefflera, *Spathiphyllum, Aglaonema,* etc) representing typical temperate broadleaf evergreens:

Table 9-2
INTERIOR PLANT LIST: COPLEY PLACE SHOPPING GALLERIES

Quan	Botanical Name	Common Name	Height	Pot Size
Trees				
3	Ficus benjamina	Weeping Java Fig Tree	24'-26'	60" x 26"
5	Polyscias fruticosa	Ming Aralia	4.5'-5'	14"
5	Polyscias fruticosa	Ming Aralia	6'-7'	17"
3	Polyscias fruticosa	Ming Aralia	8'-10'	23"
Shrubs				
19	Aglaonema commutatum 'Pseudobracteatum'	White Rajah Chinese Evergreen	15"-18"	6"
36	Aglaonema commutatum 'Pseudobracteatum'	White Rajah Chinese Evergreen	18"-24"	8"
29	Aspidistra elatior	Cast Iron Plant	18"-24"	10"
18	Brassaia arboricola	Hawaiian Schefflera	2.5'-3'	8"
25	Brassaia arboricola	Hawaiian Schefflera	3.5'-4'	10"
3	Brassaia arboricola	Hawaiian Schefflera	4.5'-5'	12"
13	Brassaia arboricola	Hawaiian Schefflera	5'-5.5'	14"
9	Spathiphyllum 'Mauna Loa'	Peace Lily	15"-18"	6"
21	Spathiphyllum 'Mauna Loa'	Peace Lily	18"-24"	10"
29	Spathiphyllum 'Mauna Loa'	Peace Lily	2.5'-3'	14"
Ground Covers				
10	Cyrtomium falcatum	Holly Fern		8"
712	Davallia Mariesii	Squirrel's Foot Fern		6"
571	Pellaea rotundifolia	Button Fern		6"
393	Pteris ensiformis 'Victoriae'	Table Fern		6"
Accent Plants				
191	Chrysanthemum, Pointsettia, Cyclamen, Kalanchoe, Easter Lily, Begonia, Cineraria, Tulip, Azalea			6"

Note: For metric conversions: feet x .3048 = meters; inches x 2.54 = centimeters

Ground covers were to be several species of Fern, evocative of a New England forest floor. During construction, it was decided to use various cultivars of English Ivy in lieu of the ferns; both designer and contractor felt the ferns would not survive the anticipated conditions as well. Accent plants were an integral part of the permanent plantings, to be rotated every 2 weeks. They provided a low-level color focus to balance the focal height of the trees.

When the waterfall sculpture by Dmitri Hadzi makes the transition from a vertical element to a horizontal one, it becomes integral with the interior landscape, wending its way across the mall floor from the Central Atrium to the main bank of escalators. The floor area under escalators—that in most malls is underutilized—has been transformed into a visual highlight of the Copley Place Shopping Galleries. Both the interior landscape and the central water feature have been woven under and through the escalator areas, eliminating any potentially "dead" space.

Fig. 9-10.
The Planting Plan for the escalator plantings, originally drawn at a scale of 1/4" = 1'-0" (1:48), is reproduced here at a scale of 1/8" = 1'-0" (1:96).

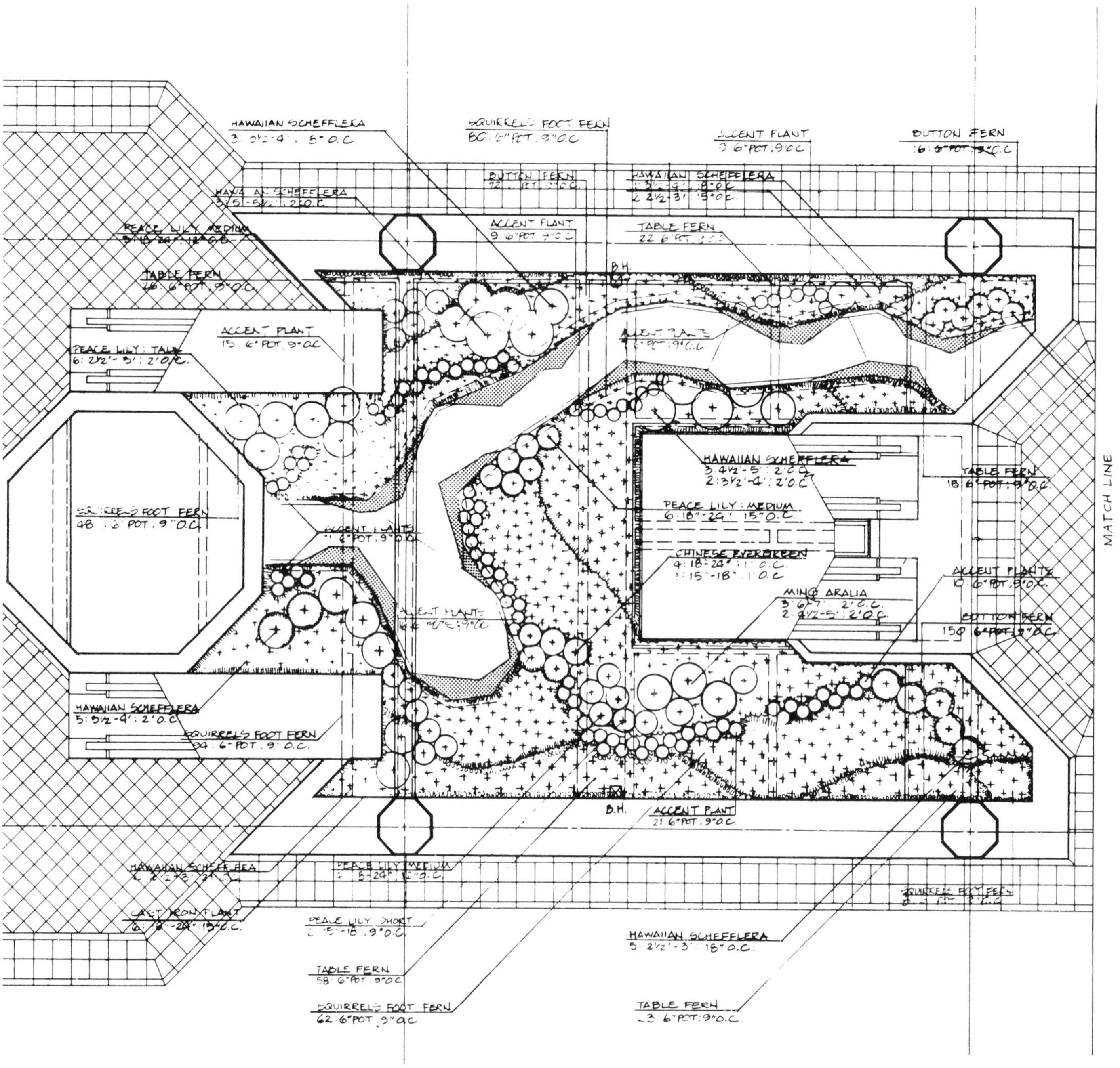

HAWAIIAN SCHEFFLERA
SQUIRREL'S FOOT FERN 80: 6" POT: 9" O.C
ACCENT PLANT
BUTTON FERN
BUTTON FERN
HAWAIIAN SCHEFFLERA
ACCENT PLANT
TABLE FERN
PEACE LILY: MEDIUM
TABLE FERN 26: 6" POT: 9" O.C.
ACCENT PLANT 15: 6" POT: 9" O.C
PEACE LILY: TALL 6: 2½'-3': 2' O.C.
B.H.
SQUIRREL'S FOOT FERN 48: 6" POT: 9" O.C
HAWAIIAN SCHEFFLERA 3: 4½'-5': 2' O.C. 2: 3½'-4': 2' O.C.
TABLE FERN
PEACE LILY: MEDIUM 6: 18"-24": 15" O.C.
CHINESE EVERGREEN 9: 18"-24": 1' O.C. 11: 15"-18": 1' O.C
ACCENT PLANTS 10: 6" POT: 9" O.C.
MING ARALIA
BUTTON FERN
ACCENT PLANTS
HAWAIIAN SCHEFFLERA 5: 5½'-4': 2' O.C
SQUIRREL'S FOOT FERN 24: 6" POT: 9" O.C.
B.H.
ACCENT PLANT 21: 6" POT: 9" O.C
HAWAIIAN SCHEFFLERA
PEACE LILY: MEDIUM
SQUIRREL'S FOOT FERN
CAST IRON PLANT
PEACE LILY: SHORT
HAWAIIAN SCHEFFLERA 5: 2½'-3': 18" O.C.
TABLE FERN 58: 6" POT: 9" O.C
SQUIRREL'S FOOT FERN 62: 6" POT: 9" O.C
TABLE FERN
MATCH LINE

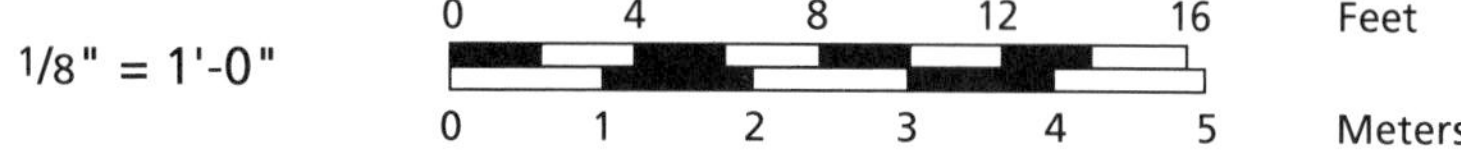

Fig. 9- 11.
The Planting Plan for the Central Atrium, also reproduced at one half actual size, 1/8" = 1'-0" (1:96).

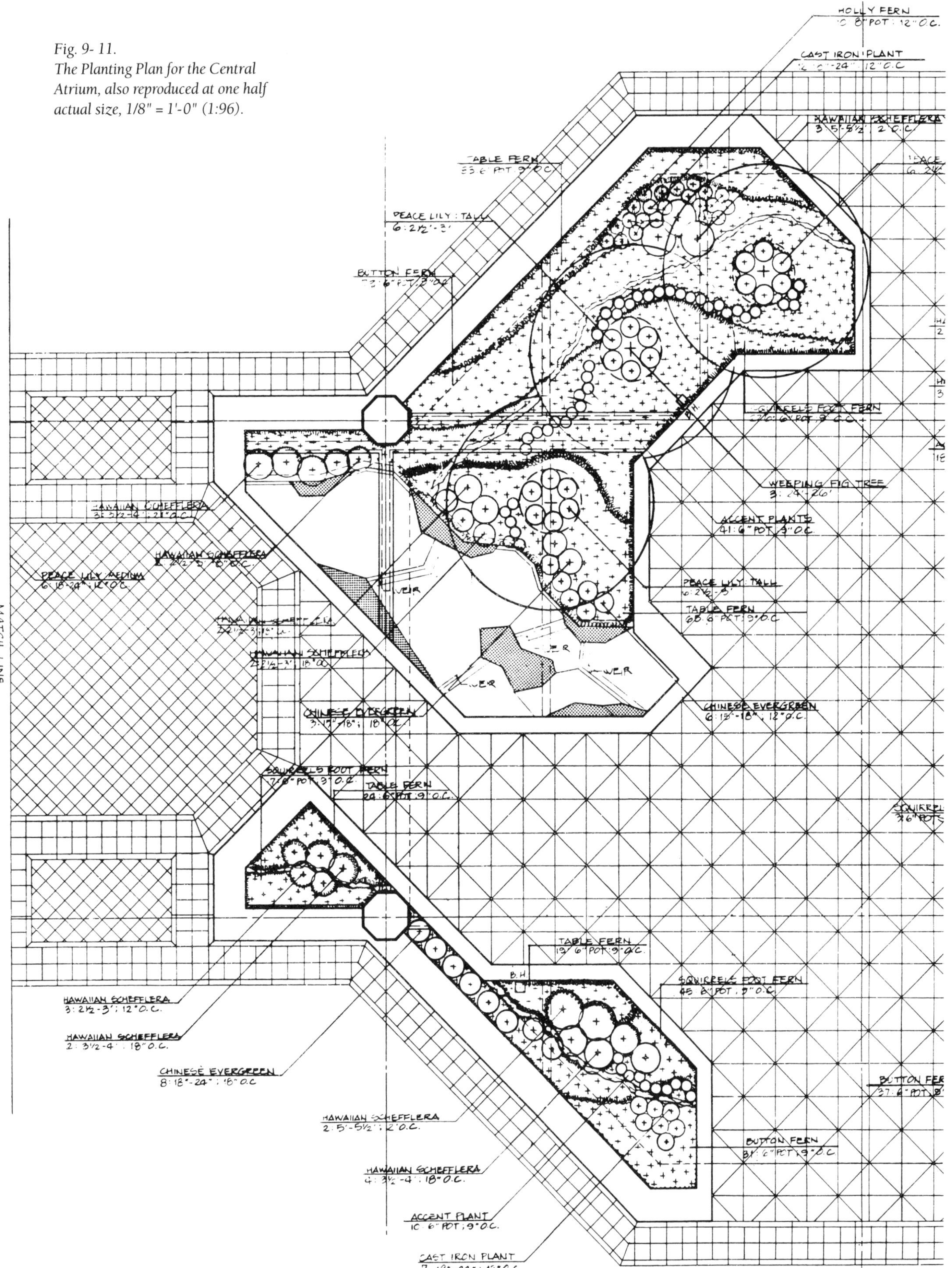

Fig. 9- 12.
Above: Several weeks prior to opening, the quartz plant lights have been installed and were operating, but were not yet aimed properly.

Fig. 9- 13.
After opening, the plant lights are shown in their correct positions, aimed under the direction of the landscape architect.

The interior landscape was installed by Rentokil Tropical Plants of Riverwoods, Illinois, and has been maintained since its opening in March 1984 by City Gardens, Inc., of Newton, MA.

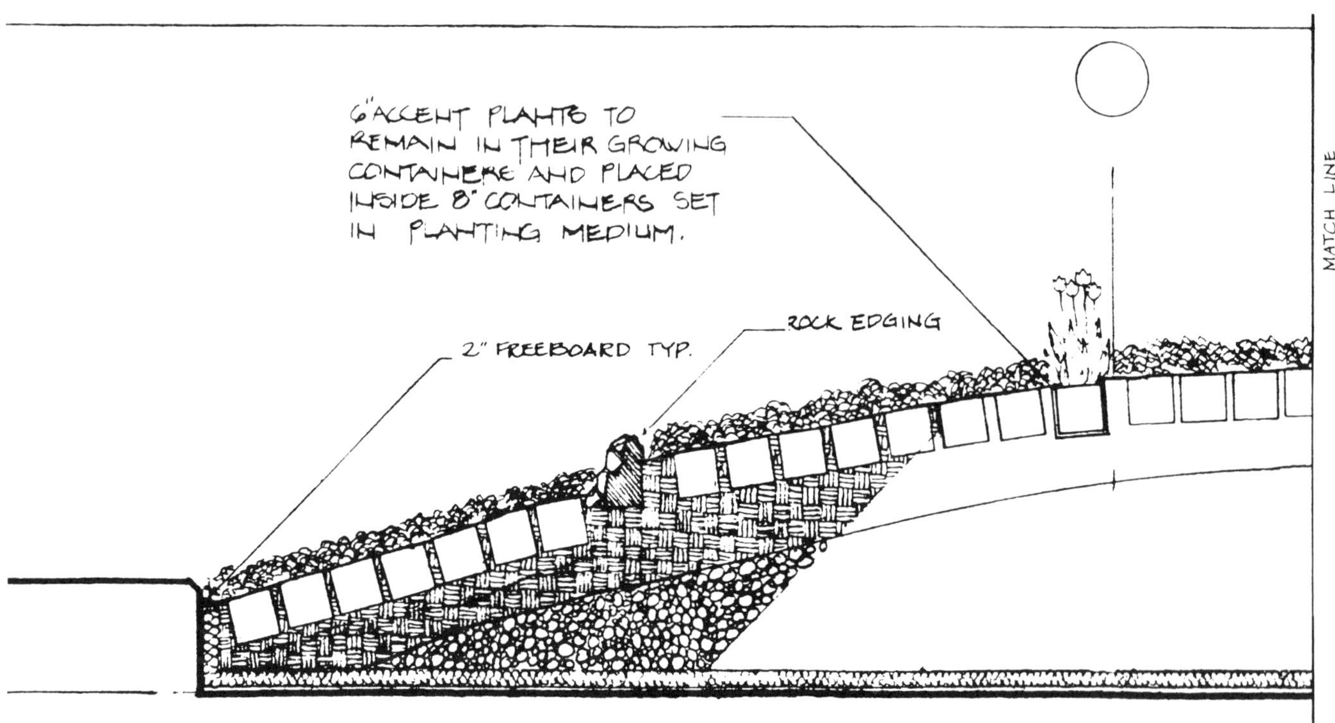

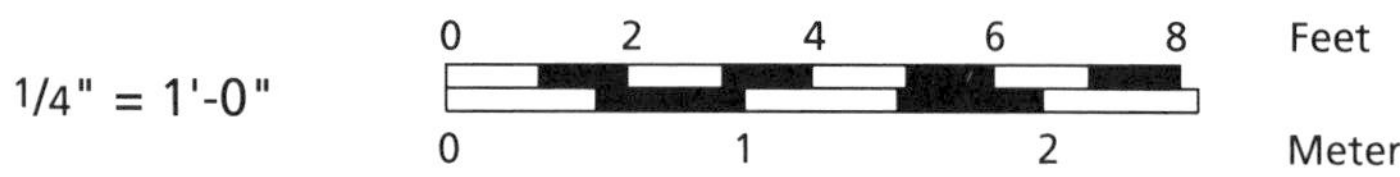

Fig. 9- 14. A section through a large plant bed illustrates how the bottom of the bed was depressed and the top of the bed was raised above the curb.

Fig. 9- 15.
Plantings follow the escalators to the second level of the Shopping Galleries. To accomplish this, steps were provided which pitched forward to allow excess runoff from the plants to drain to the stairs below. A drain was installed (Right) at the bottom of each set of steps to accept the runoff into the building's plumbing system.

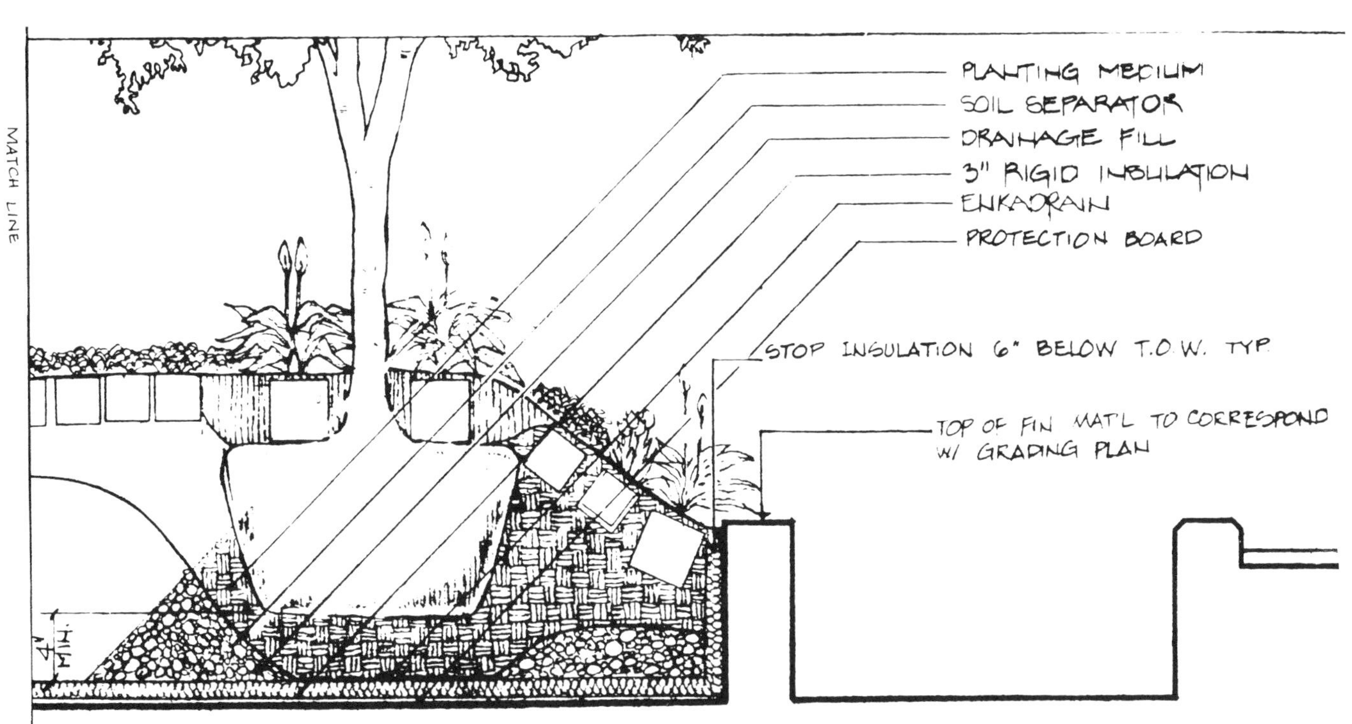

Case Study 3

HYATT REGENCY GRAND CYPRESS, ORLANDO, FL

Designed by Edward D. Stone, Jr. & Associates, P.A., Fort Lauderdale, FL

Continuing in the tradition of the Hyatt Hotel chain, begun with the Hyatt Regency in Atlanta in 1967, the Hyatt Regency Grand Cypress adds yet another distinctive example of large scale atrium interior landscaping to the "Hyatt touch". The Grand Cypress is a 750 room luxury resort hotel designed by HKS, Inc., of Dallas, Texas on 1,500 acres of land in Central Florida.

The plantings described are located in an 18-story atrium under clear glass skylights that provide between 300 and 350 fc of natural light on an average day. Supplemental lighting is provided by 36 1,000 watt metal halide fixtures mounted on upper floor balconies, with each fixture aimed at a specific specimen. Some major specimens have two or three spots allocated to them. The supplemental electric lighting is intended to be operated a minimum of 8 to 10 hours per day, during daylight hours.

The use of tropical plants in an interior setting for a Florida project allows a designer some flexibility in attempting to blend indoors with outdoors; many species of plants can be used in either location. In order to make a Florida atrium landscape distinctive, however, the design and construction team of the Hyatt Regency Grand Cypress opted to use individual specimens of spectacular size and quality, with similarly spectacular results.

3,150 sq ft (292.8 SM) of planted area occupies the lobby. In addition, a substantial water feature is closely integrated into the atrium landscape as well. The feature plant is a nine-stem Senegal Date Palm clump whose root ball was so massive that it had to be cut in half and installed in two pieces. The original plant list of the atrium proper is shown on the facing page.

The interior landscape was installed by Plantscape House, Inc. of Orlando, and has been maintained in-house since its completion in March of 1984 by the Hyatt Regency Grand Cypress.

Table 9-3

INTERIOR PLANT LIST: HYATT REGENCY GRAND CYPRESS

Key	Botanical Name	Common Name	Size	Remarks
Trees				
AW-3	Acoelorrhaphe wrightii	Paurotis Palm	10'-15' ht.	Multi-trunk
BA-1	Brassaia actinophylla	Schefflera	10'-12' ht	8 stem min./Full
CE	Chamaedorea elegans	Neanthe Bella Palm	6'-8' ht	9 stem min./Full
CH-2	Chamaerops humilis	European Fan Palm	3'-4' O.A.	5' O.C.
CL	Chrysalidocarpus lutescens	Areca Palm	8'-24'	12 can min.
FB	Ficus benjamina	Weeping Fig	8'-10' ht x 8' spd	Uniform Crown/Full
FB-1	Ficus benjamina	Weeping Fig	12'-16' ht x 12' spd	Uniform Crown/Full
FB-2	Ficus benjamina	Weeping Fig	18'-20' ht x 16' spd	Uniform Crown/Full
FN	Ficus nitida	Cuban Laurel	26' ht x 24' spd	Specimen (L.A. to select)
PB-3	Phoenix roebelenii	Pygmy Date Palm	6' ht/6' CT	Straight trunk
PR-3	Phoenix reclinata	Senegal Date Palm	15'-20' ht/CT 9 stem	Multi-trunk 5-7 stems min, Assortment
RE-1	Rhapis excelsa	Lady Palm	7'-9' ht/9 stem min	48" O.C. or as designated
RE-2	Rhapis excelsa	Lady Palm	4'-6' ht/7 stem min	48" O.C. or as designated
Shrubs				
BA-2	Brassaia actinophylla	Schefflera	6'-8' ht	6 stem min./Full
DA	Dieffenbachia amoena	Giant Dumb Cane	4 gal. plus	24" O.C./3 ppp
DD	Dracaena deremensis 'Janet Craig'	Dracaena Janet Craig	4'-5' ht	18" O.C./Full/5 ppp
DD-1	Dracaena deremensis 'Janet Craig'	Janet Craig Dracaena	6'-8' ht	3 head mira/Full
MD	Monstera deliciosa	Split-Leaf Philodendron	4 gal. 36" O.A.	24" O.C.
PJ	Philodendron selloum	Self-Heading Philodendron	4 gal. 36" O.A.	36" O.C.
SM	Spathiphyllum 'Mauna Loa'	Mauna Loa Peace Lily	4 gal. 36" O.A.	18" O.C./15-25 spp.
SW	Spathiphyllum 'Wallisii'	Peace Lily, White Flag	4 gal. 36" O.A.	18" O.C./15-25 spp.
YE	Yucca elephantipes	Spineless Yucca	10 gal./42" ht	Multi-stem/3 stem min.
Interior Vines and Basket Plants				
AG	Aglaonema modestum	Aglaonema	8" pots	Full
CCM	Chlorophytum comosum	Green Spider Plant	1 gal.	10"-12" O.C./Full
CCV	Chlorophytum comosum 'Vittatum'	Variegated Spider Plant	1 gal.	
CRA	Cissus Rhombifolia	Grape Ivy	1 gal.	Multi-stem 12" O.C.
CED	Cissus 'Ellen Danica'	Ellen Danica Ivy	1 gal./18" runners	Multi-stem 12" O.C.
CFR	Cyrtomium falcatum cv. 'Rockfordianum'	Holly Fern	1 gal.	12" O.C./Full
EA	Epipremnum aureum	Pothos	10" & 12" pots	Full 24" runners
NB	Nephrolepis biserrata cv. 'Furcans'	Fishtail Fern	1 gal./12" O.A.	12"-18" O.C./Full
NE-2	Nephrolepis exaltata	Boston Fern	1 gal./12" O.A.	12" O.C./Full
NEF	Nephrolepis exaltata cv. 'fluffy ruffles'	Fluffy ruffles Fern	1 gal./12" O.A.	12" O.C./Full
PRE	Philodendron 'Red Emerald'	Red Emerald Philodendron	1 gal./Multi-stem	10"-12" O.C./Full
PSO	Philodendron scandens 'Oxycardium'	Velvet Leaf Vine	1 gal./Multi-stem	10"-12" O.C./Full
PCM	Philodendron cordatum	Common Philodendron	1 gal./Multi-stem	10"-12" O.C./Full
PAE	Polystichum adiantiform	Leatherleaf Fern	1 gal.	12" O.C./Full

Note: For metric conversions: feet x .3048 = meters; inches x 2.54 = centimeters

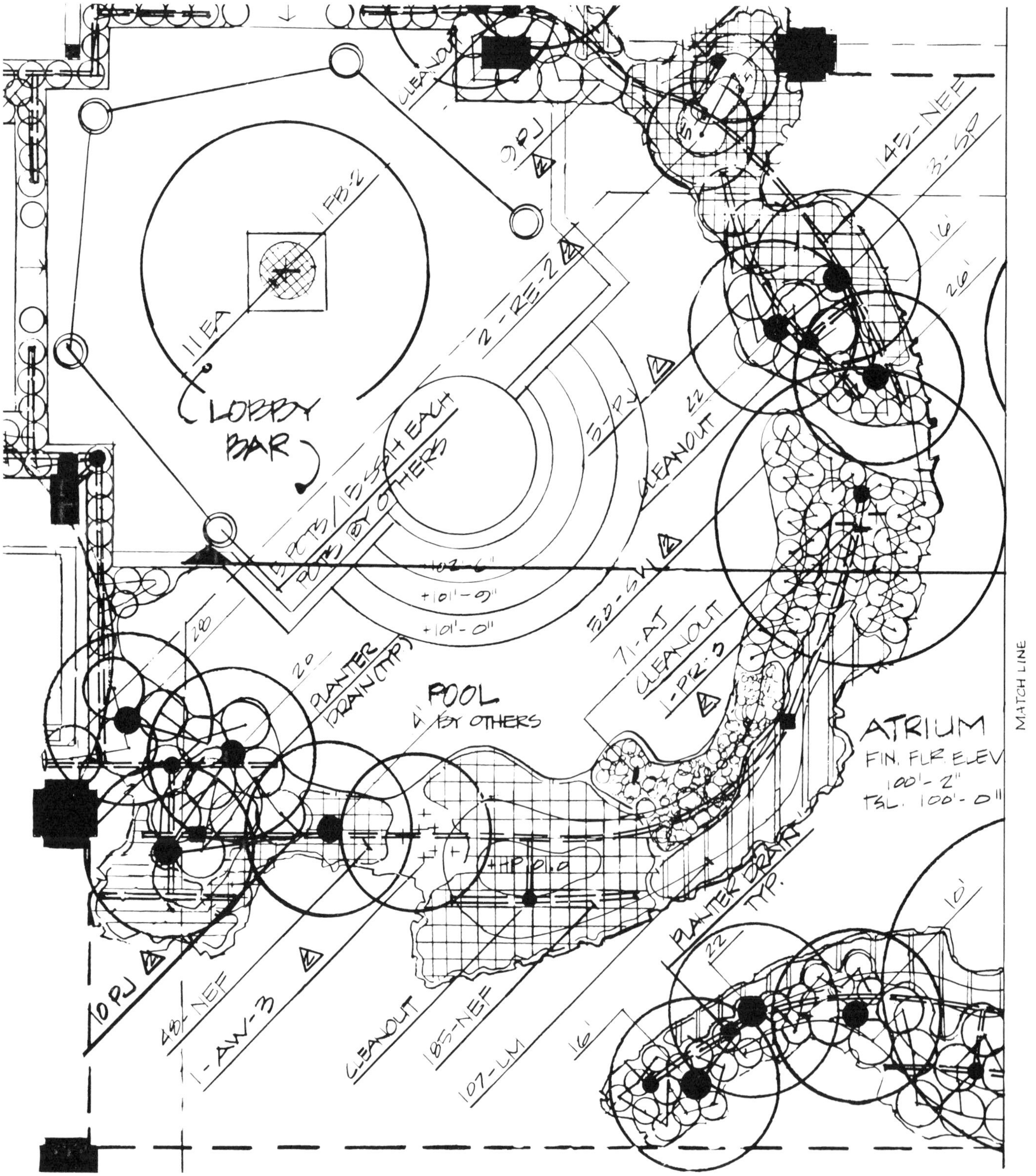

LOBBY BAR

POOL BY OTHERS

ATRIUM
FIN. FLR. ELEV 100'-2"
TSL. 100'-0"

MATCH LINE

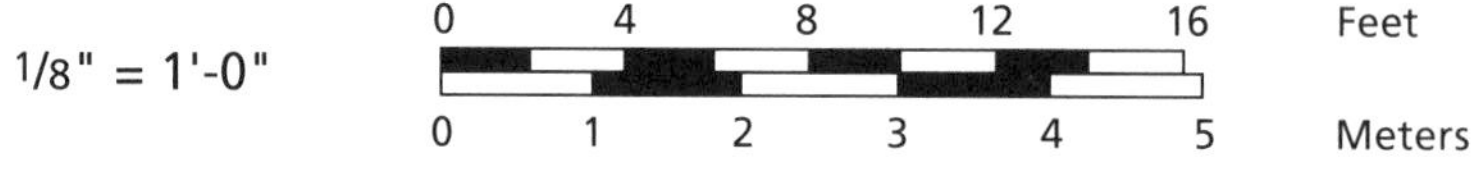

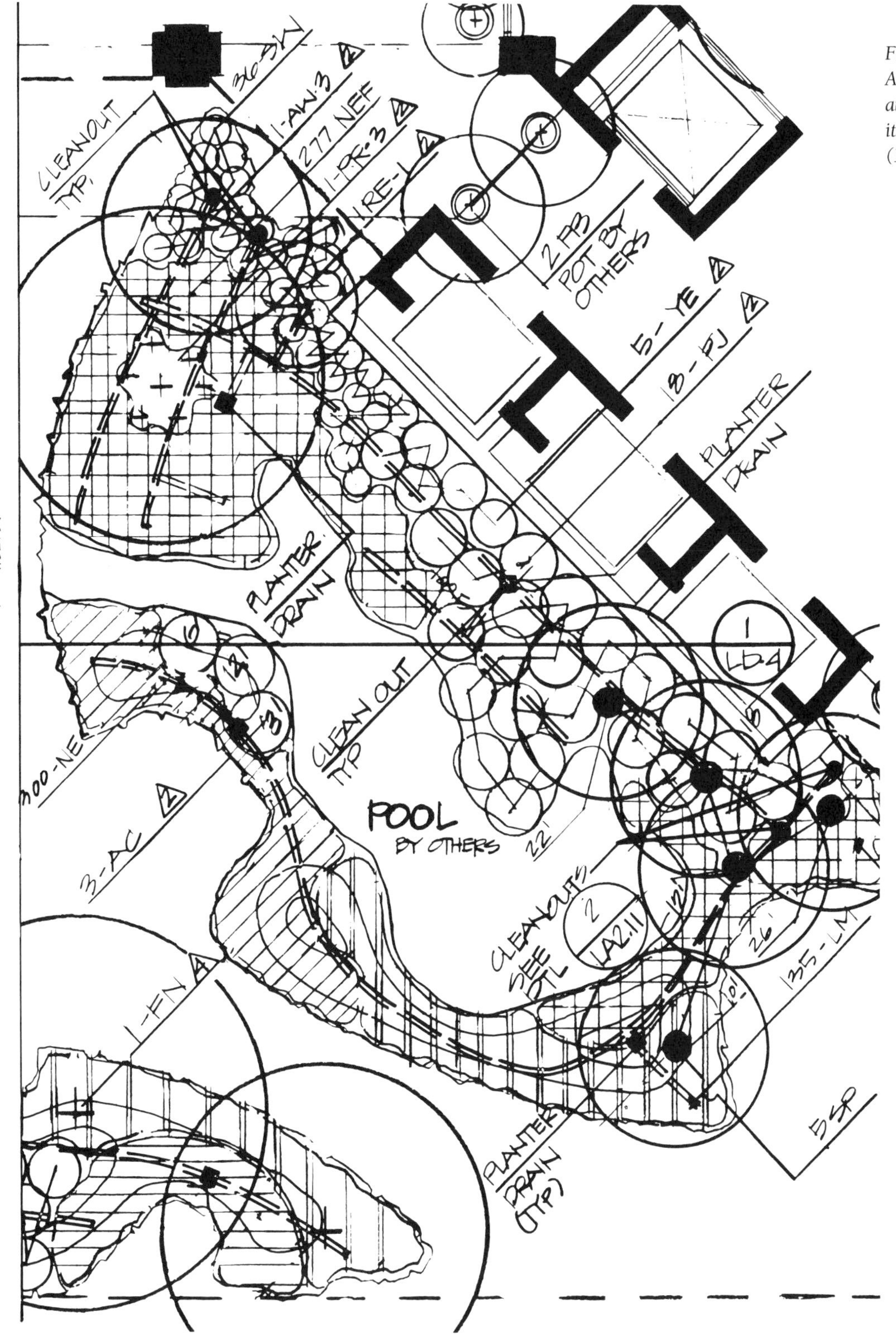

Fig. 9-16.
A partial Planting Plan for the atrium landscape, reproduced at its original scale of 1/8" = 1'-0" (1:96).

Fig. 9-17 and 18.
From the top of the atrium, the importance of the balcony plantings in tying the whole landscape concept of the space together becomes apparent.

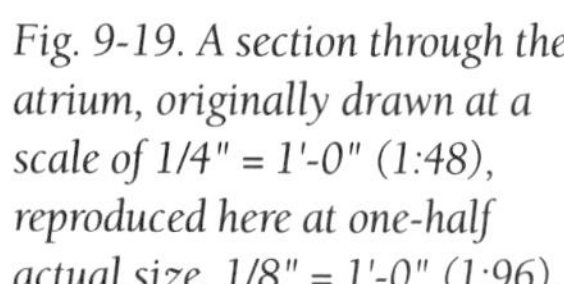

Fig. 9-19. A section through the atrium, originally drawn at a scale of 1/4" = 1'-0" (1:48), reproduced here at one-half actual size, 1/8" = 1'-0" (1:96).

1
LD-4
ATRIUM LEVEL CROSS SECTION
4

Fig. 9-20.
Looking down from above the lobby bar, one can appreciate the palms' textural qualities in "plan view".

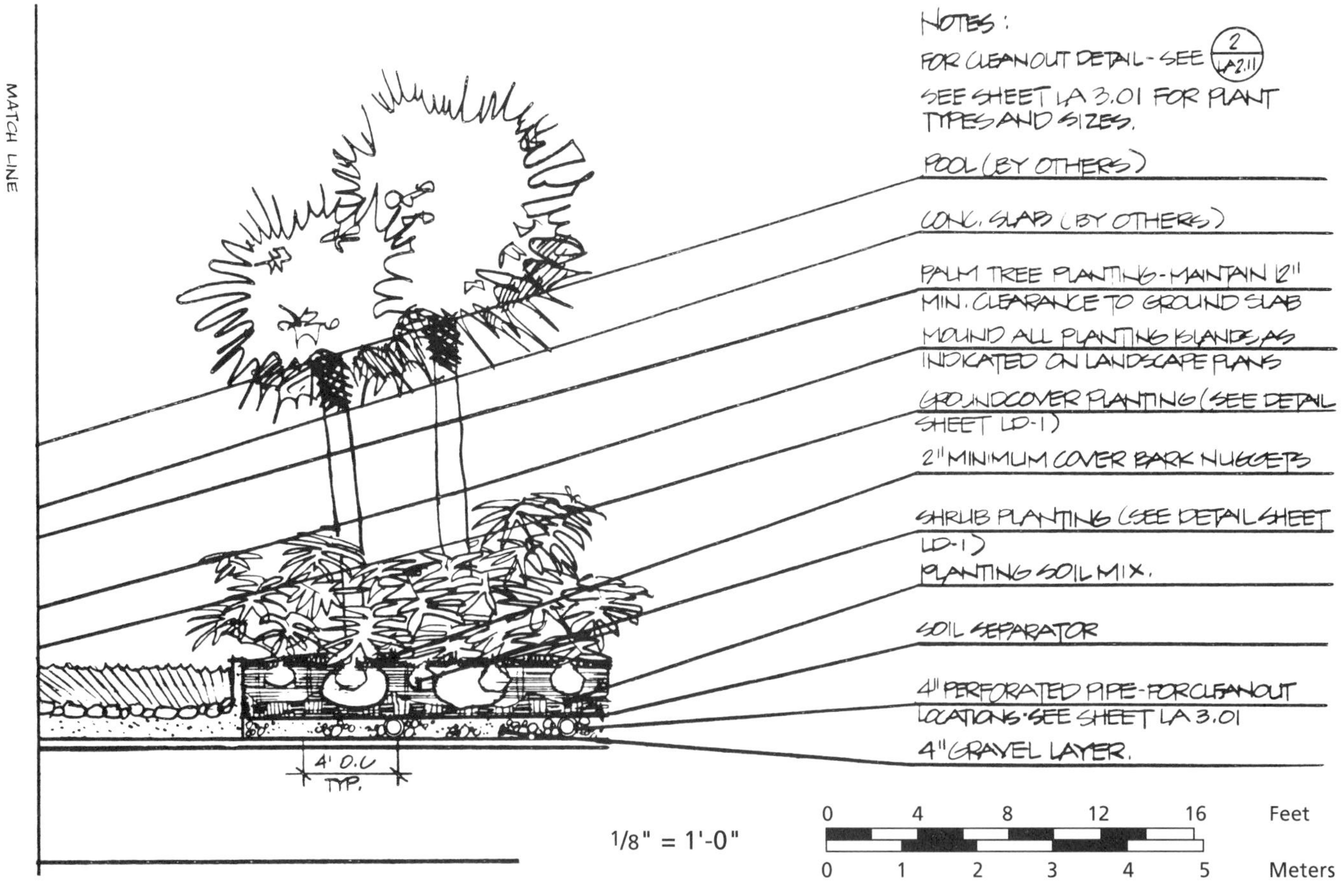

MATCH LINE

NOTES:

FOR CLEANOUT DETAIL - SEE 2/LA2.11

SEE SHEET LA 3.01 FOR PLANT TYPES AND SIZES.

POOL (BY OTHERS)

CONC. SLAB (BY OTHERS)

PALM TREE PLANTING - MAINTAIN 12" MIN. CLEARANCE TO GROUND SLAB

MOUND ALL PLANTING ISLANDS AS INDICATED ON LANDSCAPE PLANS

GROUNDCOVER PLANTING (SEE DETAIL SHEET LD-1)

2" MINIMUM COVER BARK NUGGETS

SHRUB PLANTING (SEE DETAIL SHEET LD-1)

PLANTING SOIL MIX.

SOIL SEPARATOR

4" PERFORATED PIPE - FOR CLEANOUT LOCATIONS - SEE SHEET LA 3.01

4" GRAVEL LAYER.

4' O.C. TYP.

1/8" = 1'-0"

0 4 8 12 16 Feet

0 1 2 3 4 5 Meters

Case Study 4

PRIVATE RESIDENCE, MEXICO CITY, MEXICO

Designed by Muray Arquitectos, S.A., Mexico City, Mexico

Mexico City was struck by a devastating earthquake on 19 September 1985. A small indoor pool in a private residence was badly damaged, flooding the immediate area. Rather than rebuild the pool, the owner decided to create another use for the space, and retained Muray Arquitectos, S.A., to design and build an interior garden and water feature in its place.

After making the original pool enclosure watertight again, the first steps in the evolution of the design were to set up the wood formwork for the cast-in-place concrete that served as the foundation structure for the water feature, and to install new plumbing for the water feature. With the plumbing lines and concrete in place, natural stones were used as a facing to the concrete, creating the effect of a natural rise in elevation. All stone work was done by hand due to the confined work space available to the contracting crew. Three separate waterfalls have been shaped, symbolizing God, Earth, and Mankind.

Prior to the commencement of planting operations, the completed stone work and water feature was tested for water-tightness and to ensure that the flow of water was as desired by owner and designer. The heart of the water feature is a 2 horsepower pump connected to the pool's original recirculating system. With the water effects tested and approved, the placement of planting medium and plant material was begun.

Lighting for the plantings is all natural, coming from skylights above and a window wall at one end of the space.

A relatively modest palette of plants (only 11 different species were installed) was used for the garden, with similar textures massed to visually define planted areas.

A background of Fig trees creates the illusion of forest, using four different size plants totalling only 8 specimens. The fine texture of the Dicksonia (Tree Fern) in the foreground contrasts with the coarseness of Schefflera, Hawaiian Schefflera, and Japanese Fatsia. The ability of the overall design to create the effect of a naturalized planting is remarkable considering the confined size of the volume in which it was created. In

Fig. 9-21.
The existing indoor pool, prior to the commencement of reconstruction.

Fig. 9-22.
Wood formwork is being put in place in preparation for pouring concrete.

Fig. 9-23.
Natural stone was used to create the elevation changes of the garden.

Fig. 9-24.
The water feature is tested for water-tightness and for proper flow of water prior to the installation of plants.

Fig. 9-25.
The installation of planting medium and plant materials is almost complete.

exchange for a small swimming pool, the owner has given himself a contemplative place where the sights, sounds, and smells of a miniature garden can be appreciated day after day.

Muray Arquitectos, S.A., of Mexico City designed all plantings, associated plumbing, and hardscape elements. They also installed the garden in 1986.

The complete plant list is shown here.

Table 9-4
INTERIOR PLANT LIST: PRIVATE RESIDENCE, MEXICO CITY

Quantity	Botanical Name	Common Name	Height
12	Asparagus densiflorus 'Meyersii'	Asparagus Fern	
6	Azalea indica	Azalea	2.0' (0.6 m)
1	Brassaia actinophylla	Schefflera	8.2' (2.5 m)
2	Brassaia actinophylla	Schefflera	5.6' (1.7 m)
2	Brassaia actinophylla	Schefflera	4.3' (1.3 m)
5	Dicksonia squarrosa	Tree Fern	
6	Dizygotheca elegantissima	False Aralia	3.3' (1.0 m)
15	Fatsia japonica	Japanese Fatsia	1.6' (0.5 m)
1	Ficus benjamina	Weeping Java Fig Tree	11.5' (3.5m)
2	Ficus benjamina	Weeping Java Fig Tree	9.8' (3.0 m)
1	Ficus benjamina	Weeping Java Fig Tree	8.2' (2.5 m)
4	Ficus benjamina	Weeping Java Fig Tree	6.6' (2.0 m)
3	Philodendron selloum	Self-Heading Philodendron	3.3' (1.0 m)
6	Pittosporum tobira	Japanese Pittosporum	3.3' (1.0 m)
3	Schefflera arboricola	Hawaiian Schefflera	3.3' (1.0 m)
5	Viburnum suspensum	Viburnum	

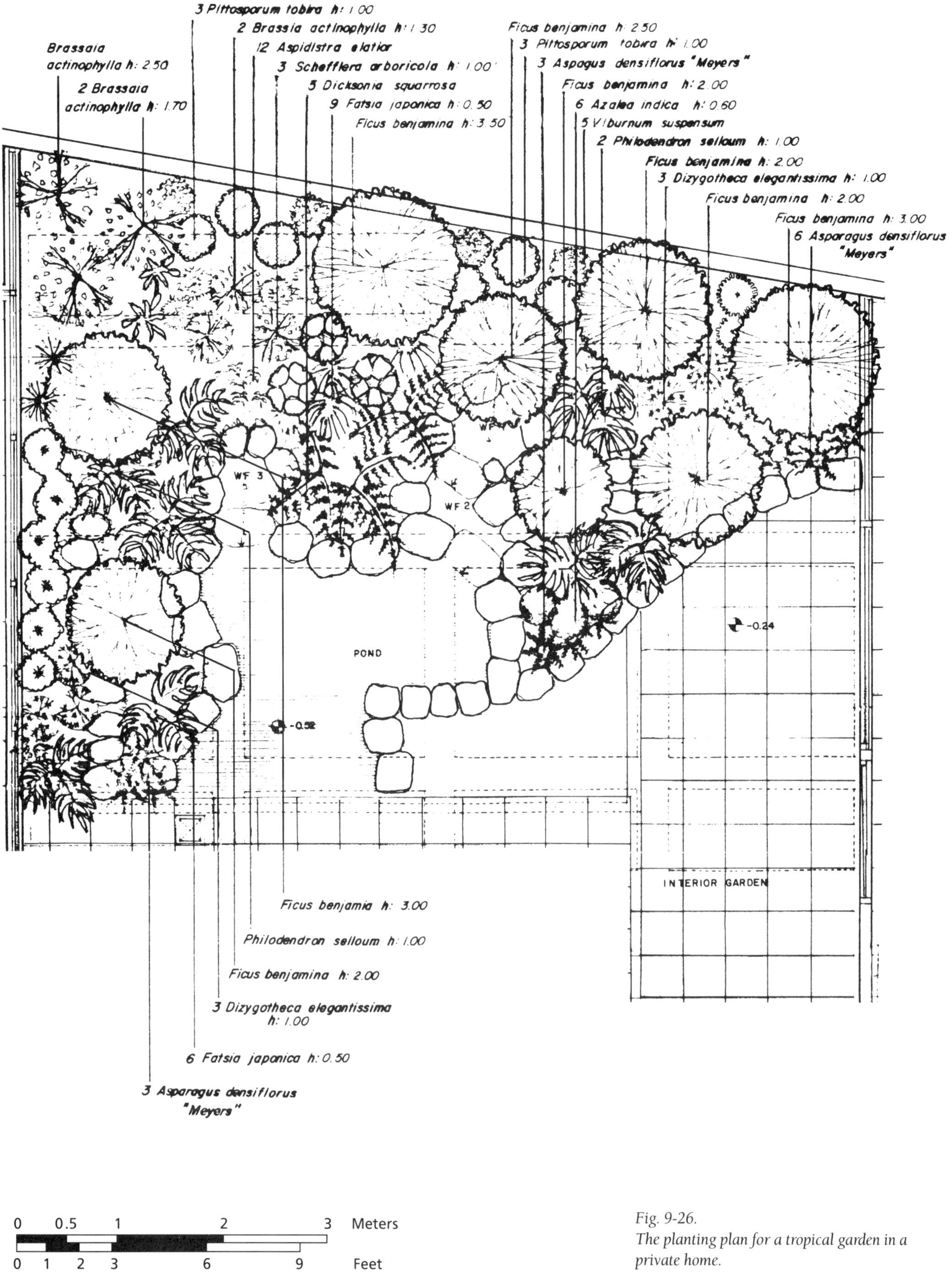

3 Pittosporum tobira h: 1.00
2 Brassia actinophylla h: 1.30
Brassaia actinophylla h: 2.50
12 Aspidistra elatior
3 Schefflera arboricola h: 1.00
2 Brassaia actinophylla h: 1.70
5 Dicksonia squarrosa
9 Fatsia japonica h: 0.50
Ficus benjamina h: 3.50
Ficus benjamina h: 2.50
3 Pittosporum tobira h: 1.00
3 Aspagus densiflorus "Meyers"
Ficus benjamina h: 2.00
6 Azalea indica h: 0.60
5 Viburnum suspensum
2 Philodendron selloum h: 1.00
Ficus benjamina h: 2.00
3 Dizygotheca elegantissima h: 1.00
Ficus benjamina h: 2.00
Ficus benjamina h: 3.00
6 Asparagus densiflorus "Meyers"
WF 3
WF 2
WF
POND
-0.52
-0.24
INTERIOR GARDEN
Ficus benjamia h: 3.00
Philodendron selloum h: 1.00
Ficus benjamina h: 2.00
3 Dizygotheca elegantissima h: 1.00
6 Fatsia japonica h: 0.50
3 Asparagus densiflorus "Meyers"
0 0.5 1 2 3 Meters
0 1 2 3 6 9 Feet

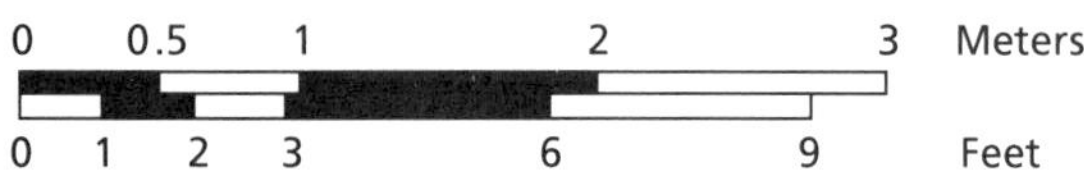

Fig. 9-26.
The planting plan for a tropical garden in a private home.

Case Study 5

JOHN HANCOCK CHILD CARE CENTER, BOSTON, MA

Designed by Earl R. Flansburgh + Associates, Inc., Boston, MA

When John Hancock Mutual Life Insurance Company decided to establish a child care center for its headquarters staff in Boston, an important element in the equation was the ability of the center's physical environment to challenge the children's imagination and provide a wide range of activities. In addition to being one of the few inner city child care centers in the United States to have ample, heavily landscaped outdoor play spaces on their grounds, the client and design team also decided to incorporate a densely planted interior garden to help enrich the children's daily experience.

The center was created by renovating the first and second floors of an existing 9-story office building less than a block away from the Hancock Tower, world headquarters for the company. A 16 ft (4.9 m) square area at the bottom of an existing stairwell to the second floor was selected to house the garden. A new stairwell was created in place of the old one, and a faux skylight of translucent glass with fluorescent tubes above it was installed to create the illusion of a light well over the plantings.

A key element of the concept was that the garden had to serve as an activity space and not just a visual attraction. Unless it become a "hands on" experience, its existence could not be justified. In spite of its small size—about 250 SF (23.8 sm)—a walkway through the garden became an integral design component.

Another element added to peak the curiosity of the "clientele" was water. The stairwell housing the garden had a drop in elevation of 20 in (50.8 cm) from one side to the other, just enough to produce a trickling sound from a waterfall built to accentuate the grade change. The water feature and surrounding topographic elements were built of fiberglass reinforced concrete (FRC) formed and painted to look like natural stone, all located adjacent to the walkway so children could use the water as a play element. Plumbing for the water feature was located directly beneath the garden in the basement of the building, where a 125 gallon (473.2 liter) reservoir fitted with a 3 hp submersible pump served as the heart of the recirculating system.

Although horizontal area was limited, the vertical space available reached to the faux skylight at the ceiling of the second floor. The client wished to have at least some of the landscape elements break the plane of the second floor in order to help tie the two levels together. With that in mind, a tall, narrow specimen was needed. A solitary palm would have been ideal, but lack of light steered the designer toward a preserved palm, which turned out to be the only non-living plant in the child care center.

Since the average "user" of the space was between 2 and 3 ft (0.6 to 0.9 m) tall, most of the live plants did not have to be large specimens to create a imposing appearance. Ground covers were used liberally to make the plantings look lush, and of those, *Ficus pumila* (Creeping Fig) was particularly successful, starting to climb the walls within a few weeks after they were installed. Being a Child Care Center, the client requested that only non-poisonous plants be specified for the project, indoors and out. The plant list included herein was specified after reviewing six published sources of poisonous plants and finding none of the specified plants on the lists. Some weeks after the installation, several of the species used were found to be poisonous in another source, and were replaced by other species. (See Appendix E: Poisonous Plants)

Natural light was supplied by a floor to ceiling window wall facing east, affording about one-third of the garden enough light for sustenance. The remainder was supplied by 8 250-watt metal halide lamps placed at the first and second floor balconies, and single tube four foot fluorescent fixtures located under the soffit of the stairway to the second floor.

Since the children who attend the center are from infant to pre-kindergarten age, staff accompany children on visits through the garden, carefully monitoring their activities while using the plantings as educational exhibits. The garden has become staple of the play experience and is a greatly appreciated addition to the child care center.

The fiberglass reinforced concrete work was fabricated by exhibit designer Jerry Johnson of Newton, Massachusetts. The garden was installed by City Gardens of Newton, MA, who have also maintained the project since it opened in November of 1990.

Table 9-5

INTERIOR PLANT LIST: JOHN HANCOCK CHILD CARE CENTER

Live Plants Quantity	Botanical Name	Common Name	Ht or Sprd	Size Pot	Remarks
3	Asplenium nidus	Bird's Nest Fern	15"-18" ht	8"	
6	Aglaonema 'Maria'	Maria Chinese Evergreen	15"-18" ht	8"	
2	Brassaia arboricola	Hawaiian Schefflera	3.5'-4' ht	14"	
3	Chamaedorea elegans	Neanthe Bella Palm	18"-24" ht	10"	
1	Dracaena fragrans	Corn Plant 'Massangeana'	5'-6' ht	14"	3 ppp min.
14	Epipremnum aureum	Golden Pothos	6"		
13	Epipremnum aureum 'Marble Queen'	Marble Queen Pothos	6"		
18	Epipremnum aureum 'Tropic Green'	Jade Pothos	6"		
125	Ficus pumila	Creeping Fig	6"	9" o.c.	
3	Howea forsterana	Kentia Palm	4.5'-5' ht	12"	
83	Pellaea rotundifolia	Button Fern	6"		
3	Polyscias fruticosa	Ming Aralia	2.5'-3' ht	12"	5 ppp min.
16	Pteris ensiformis	Brake Fern	6"		
1	Rhapis excelsa	Lady Palm	5'-6' ht	14"	
18	Sansieveria trifasciata 'Hahnii'	Hahn's Sansieveria	6"	6" oc.	
46	Soleirolia Soleirolii	Baby's Tears	6"	9" oc.	
6	Spathiphyllum 'Mauna Loa Supreme'	Mauna Loa Supreme Peace Lily	15"-18" ht	8"	
8	Spathiphyllum 'Petite'	Petite Peace Lily	15"-18" ht	8"	
21	Spathiphyllum wallisii	Wallis Peace Lily	15"-18" ht	6"	
Preserved Plants					
1	Phoenix sp.	Wild Date Palm	14'-16' ht	-	

Note: For metric conversions: feet x .3048 = meters; inches x 2.54 = centimeters

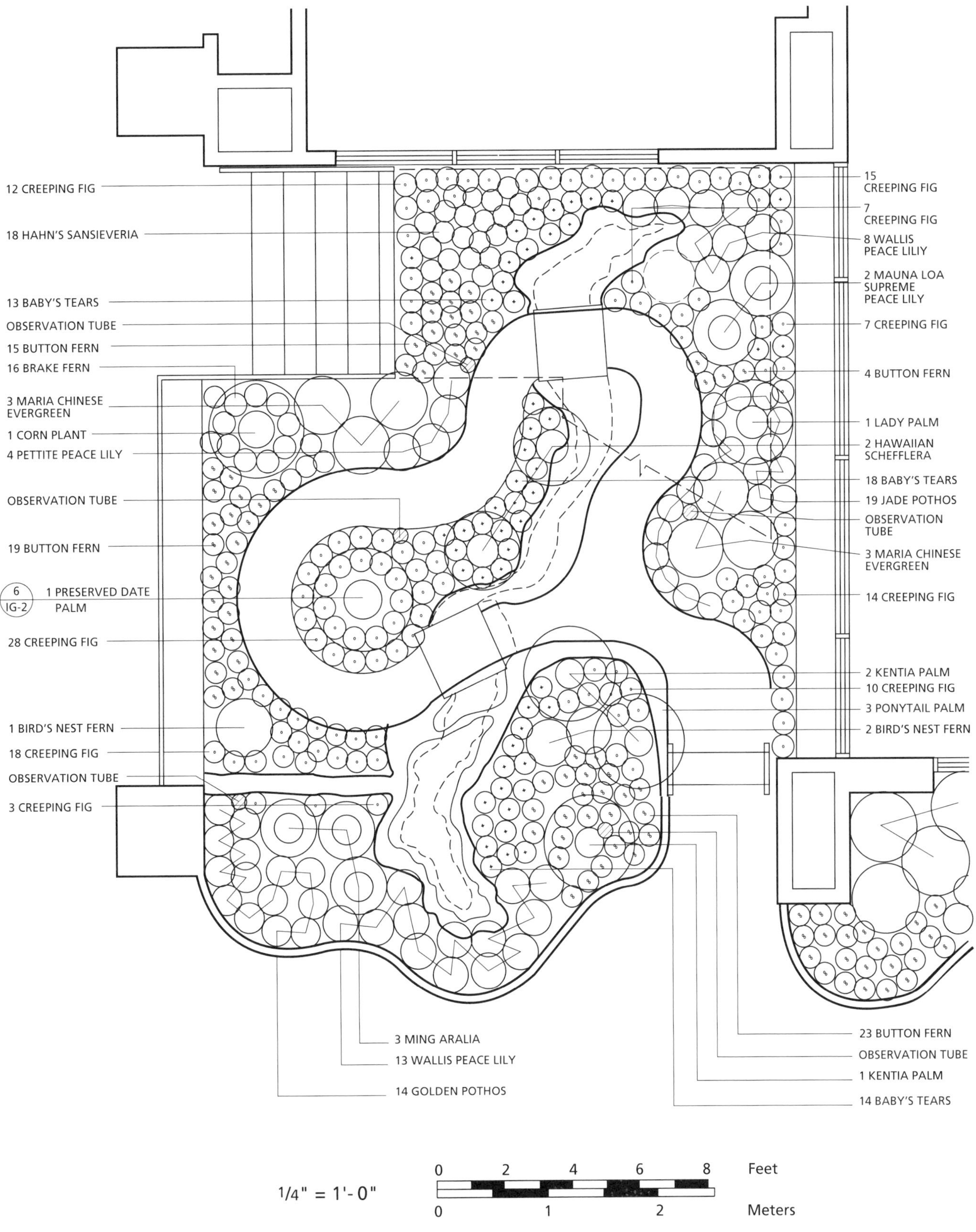

Fig. 9-27.
The Planting Plan for the Child Care Center illustrates the density of the plantings in the interior garden.

Fig. 9- 28. Jerry Johnson, an exhibit designer and contractor, fabricates some of the "rock" work using fiberglass reinforced concrete (FRC) panels cast off-site and tied together with wire mesh over an armature of "pencil rod"—thin, malleable metal rods that provide the foundation for the FRC work.

Fig. 9-29. The water feature and rock work are in place, and the areas to receive plants have been waterproofed.

Fig. 9-30. Sterilized planting medium is placed in the plant beds, while the preserved palm tree's base has been set in concrete.

Fig. 9-31. With planting completed, only the operation of the water feature remains to finish the garden.

Fig. 9-32.
The section through the water feature allows the fabricator of the fiberglass reinforced concrete (FRC) some flexibility in how to construct that portion of the work.

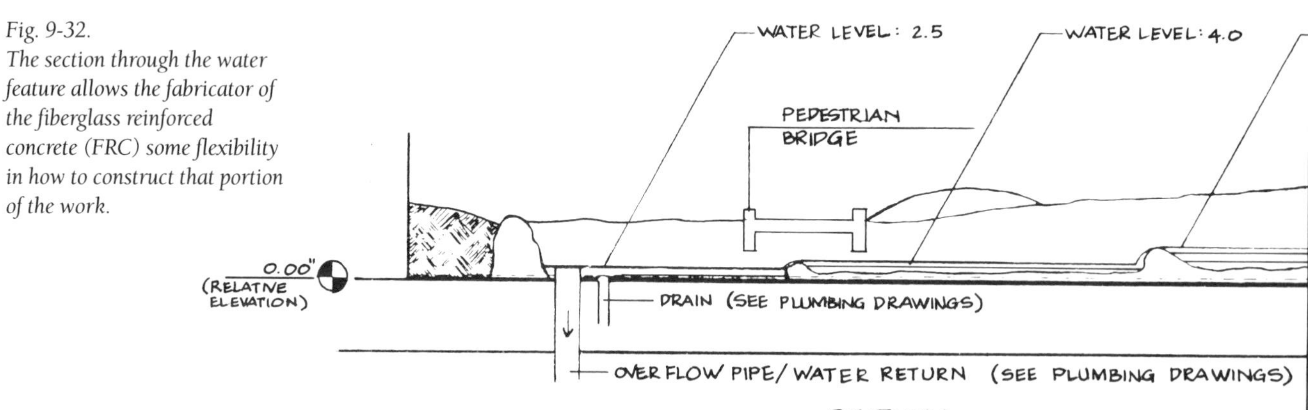

Fig. 9-33 (above).
A child's eye view of the FRC "ledge". Only 20 in (50.8 cm) high, it is quite imposing from the vantage point of a 3-year old!

Fig. 9-34 (left).
1 of the 2 bluestone bridges crosses the water feature just in front of the waterfall.

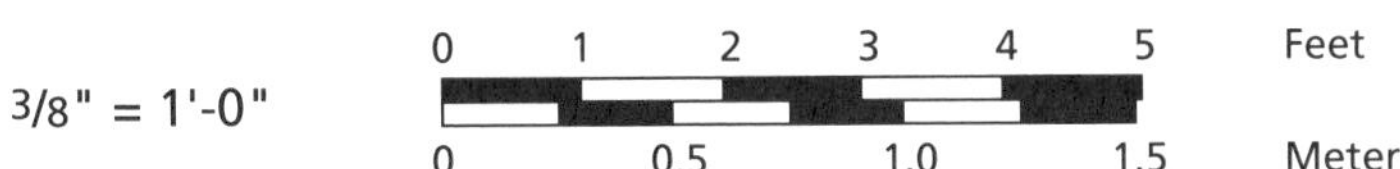

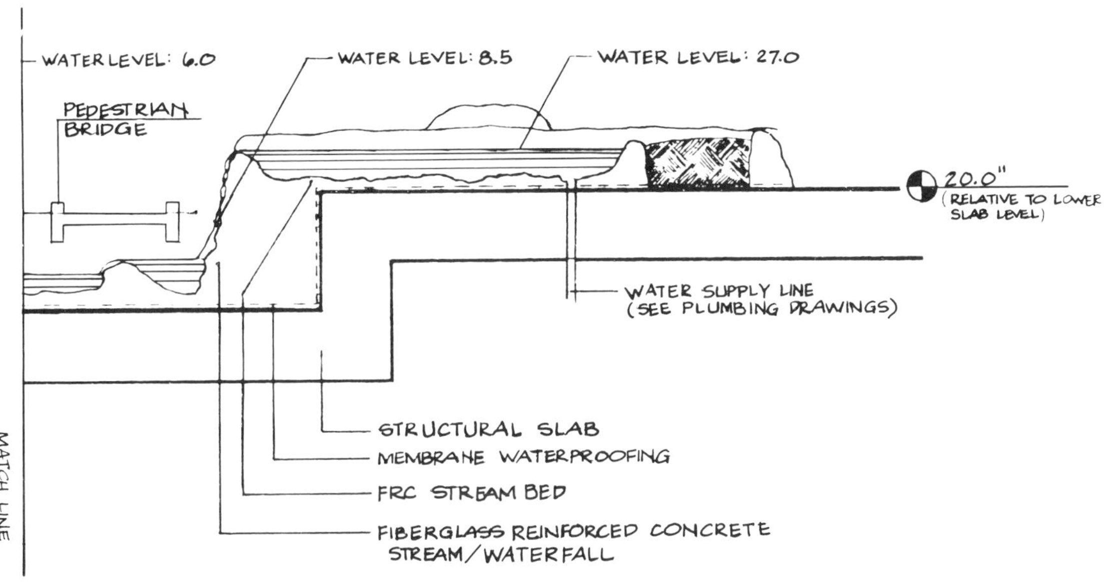

EPILOGUE

The use of plants indoors seems to be at a crossroads as this is being written in fall 1991. The United States and much of the rest of the world are mired in a depressed economy, and sales of interior plants are sluggish. Existing maintenance contracts are being canceled, with plants being eliminated or in-house staff taking on maintenance responsibilities. Other maintenance contracts are being put out to competitive bid each year at renewal time to give clients an opportunity to seek lower prices, and not necessarily the best maintenance. The Gulf War of 1991 pointed out once again the instability of fuel oil costs and its potential impact on building operating costs, which ultimately will, in turn, have a great impact on the use of plants indoors.

But factors are now at work that can spur a renewed interest in and—growth of—the interior landscape industry.

NEW MARKETS

Although the roots of interior landscape design as we know it were sown in Europe during the nineteenth century, much of the most important progress in the field in the last 25 years was either pioneered or perfected in the United States. The re-introduction of the atrium as a primary public space in buildings, the use of large scale trees and palms in these atria, the mass production of plants for interior use, the introduction of many new species of low-light- and low humidity-tolerant plants, and the introduction of many improved cultivars from tissue culture are but a few of the factors enabling the United States to take the lead in the field.

But it is presumptuous of Americans to think they have a monopoly on the products and expertise necessary to create successful interior landscapes. Indoor plants have been in vogue in Europe and other cultures for decades, and subirrigation technology was not only introduced in Europe; but many brands of subirrigation products are still manufactured in Europe or licensed to American companies.

With global communications and travel shrinking the planet, the sharing of knowledge, and hence, the ability to grow, ship, install and maintain plants has been spreading throughout the world.

Many American designers (and, of course, designers in foreign countries) are now getting the opportunity to participate in extensive or unusual projects involving interior landscapes throughout the world. Countries previously not able to avail themselves of the benefits of interior landscaping because of the lack of nursery stock or skilled labor to install and maintain indoor plants are finding that plants can be imported by ship from Florida or Hawaii, or by truck from The Netherlands, Italy, and other burgeoning sources of tropical foliage material. New sources of material are producing new species for interior use, and existing sources are producing better species. Multi-national companies are providing state-of-the-art crews and techniques to install major projects on all continents, and are training local personnel to maintain them. The result is that large and complex projects can now be found throughout the world. (See Color Plates CE-1 to CE-5)

THE NASA STUDY

Perhaps the most important reason for optimism about the future of interior landscaping is in the potential for plants to be used as a mitigating factor in a growing environmental concern. In September 1989, the National Aeronautics and Space Administration issued the Final Report of a 2-year study undertaken jointly with the Associated Landscape Contractors of America (ALCA) entitled "Interior Landscape Plants for Indoor Air Pollution Abatement". The study, whose principal investigator was Dr. B.C. Wolverton, is reproduced in its entirety as Appendix G.

Indoor air pollution, or "Sick Building Syndrome", is a problem that has plagued buildings for centuries (recall, as noted in Chapter One, the discussion of the Window Tax in eighteenth century England), and has become more noticeable, more prevalent, and more objectionable in the last 20 years with the advent of inoperable windows, reduced air exchanges to increase energy efficiency, and sensitive monitoring equipment able to identify minute concentrations of pollutant chemicals in indoor air.

The creation of airtight buildings has led to a complete reliance on mechanical ventilation systems to provide building occupants with fresh and recirculated air. One of the many steps taken in the last two decades to lower the cost of energy consumption has been to operate ventilation systems well below capacity, resulting in the reduced flow of air through interior spaces. With less fresh air, relative levels of carbon dioxide produced by human metabolism cannot be as readily controlled. In addition, recirculated air has been found to contain traceable amounts of chemicals emitted, or off-gassed, by the materials and substances typically found in indoor environments. Current technology allows for the accurate monitoring of literally thousands of chemical substances in indoor air at concentrations measured in parts per billion.

Products such as carpeting, paint, furniture polish and lacquer, wallcoverings, inks, carpeting and dyes, all emit substances into the air for months after fabrication or installation. Many of these substances (three of the most ubiquitous of which are benzene, formaldehyde, and trichloroethylene,—or [TCE]) have been found to cause health problems associated with Sick Building Syndrome (SBS), such as drowsiness, headaches, itchy eyes, and many other common maladies. Some are proven carcinogens. SBS has been identified as a source of absenteeism by personnel managers throughout the country, and attempts are now being made to mitigate this problem by increasing fresh air exchanges (which is costly), or retrofitting filtration devices on existing mechanical equipment to reduce the presence of harmful substances (also costly) in indoor air.

But the NASA study appears to provide what may be the most natural—and cost-effective—way to create a healthy and attractive environment in our buildings: by using plants as air filters, as they apparently been doing for millions of years *outside* buildings.

The data presented in the NASA study offered irrefutable evidence that under carefully controlled laboratory conditions, the placement of plants in sealed environments containing the three noted pollutants effectively removed a high percentage (as much as 89.8 percent) of the pollutants within a 24 hour period! The normal process of growth allows plants to draw pollutant chemicals into their systems through their roots or leaves and metabolize them as food. The data are all the more startling when one recognizes that only common house plants were used in the study (not exotic plants difficult to grow indoors), and that the tests were undertaken in the relatively normal light level range of 125 fc.

After determining the success of 12 different species of plants at removing the three test substances from the sealed chambers using just the standard plants in grow pots, Dr. Wolverton and his team then performed additional experiments using the same typical plants fitted with activated carbon filter systems which drew air through the soil mass and filter by small electric fans located under the grow pot. Using these devices, NASA found that Golden Pothos (perhaps the most easily grown house plant you can buy) was able to remove virtually all of the benzene and trichloroethylene in the sealed container, regardless of their concentration levels (see the NASA study in Appendix G, pages 267 and 268), within a 24 hour period.

Further studies now being undertaken will help determine whether plants fitted with carbon filters can remove cigarette smoke, pathenogenic mircroorganisms, and possibly even radon from indoor air. Other studies must determine the filtering capacity of many different types of interior foliage plants and the beneficial effects, if any, of plants on other harmful chemical substances besides benzene, TCE, and formaldehyde.

With plants now known to provide at least a certain degree of air filtration cability, their existence as merely aesthetic additions to the interior environment will be rethought by architects, landscape architects, and interior designers, whose designs must not only be attractive but must respond to their clients' increasing demands for healthful and productive work places and living spaces. Organizations like the Plants for Clean Air Council (PCAC) and ALCA have begun promoting the use of plants to clean indoor air. The efforts of these organizations and other allied groups such as the American Society of Landscape Architects, the American Institute of Architects, the Institute for Business Designers, and the American Society of Interior Designers in promoting the beneficial aspects of indoor plants can help launch a new chapter in the growth of the discipline of interior landscape design.

APPENDIX A

INTERIOR LANDSCAPE DESIGN CHECKLIST

I PRE-DESIGN

A. Meet with client or other consultants

B. Determine scope of work

1. Locate all areas within the building to receive plants
2. In garden-type situations, identify areas of planting vs. paving, seating, furnishings, etc.

C. Identify budget constraints, if any

D. Inventory and analysis of proposed site conditions

1. Determine building orientation and location of all sources of natural light
2. Locate provisions for plant-growth lighting, if any. Be aware of applicable energy codes governing the number of watts per square foot allowable for lighting
3. Familiarize yourself with the structural constraints of the spaces to receive plants, and be aware of applicable building code requirements for loading
4. Identify potential sources of irrigation
5. Identify potential location(s) for maintenance facility in-house, if any, or if possible
6. Identify access points in building for plant material installation

II SCHEMATIC DESIGN

A. Determine "scale" of the planting

1. In terms of the physical size of the plants
2. In terms of the numbers of plants
3. In terms of the cost of the project (installation)
4. In terms of the cost of maintenance (labor-intensive flowering plants vs. permanent live plants vs. artificial or preserved plants)

B. Prepare a "bubble diagram" indicating the relationship of plants to each other and to other elements within the space.

C. Coordination with other disciplines

1. Architectural: Relationship of plants to interior volume
2. Mechanical:
   a. HVAC requirements
   b. Irrigation (water source)
   c. Drainage provisions
3. Electrical
   a. Plant growth lighting
   b. Decorative lighting

4. Structural review planting medium depths and size (and density) of plant material to allow calculation of structural feasibility

D. Presentation to Client

1. Preliminary plan
2. Sections (as needed to convey scheme)
3. Preliminary cost estimate

III DESIGN DEVELOPMENT

A. Refine "bubble diagram" into scaled drawing to show more detailed indications of plantings. Show plants locations as they relate or contrast to each other and to the objects around them in size, texture, color, etc.

B. Develop plant list: genus, species, common name, height, quantity

C. Make adjustments to design based on input from client and architect

D. Coordinate with other consultants

E. "Tighten" cost estimate

F. Prepare outline specifications

G. Prepare sections and details as necessary to convey design intent to Client

H. Presentation to client

1. Planting plan
2. Plant list: name, size, quantity
3. Preliminary grading plan (if garden-type installation)
4. Sections
5. Details
6. Product samples
7. Cost estimate
8. Outline specifications

IV CONTRACT DOCUMENTS

A. Finalize planting plan(s) (1/8 in = 1 ft 0 in or larger)

B. Layout plan (if garden-type installation)

C. Grading plan (if garden-type installation)

D. Plant list: Genus, species, cultivar (if any), Common Name, quantity, height, spread, caliper, first-branch height, number of trunks or canes (ppp), growth habit (tip vs. cane, bush vs. standard, with "character", etc.)

E. Planter schedule (if office landscape-type installation)

F. Final specifications

G. Final pre-bid cost estimate

V BIDDING

A. Pre-qualification of bidders

B. Pre-bid meeting

C. Review of bids with Client

D. Award of Project

VI CONSTRUCTION ADMINISTRATION

A. Review of shop drawings

B. Approval of sample submissions

C. Selection and approval of plant materials

D. On-site inspection of planting operations

E. Acceptance of planting

APPENDIX B
GLOSSARY

Terms in italics are defined within this glossary.

Addendum — An adjustment to a design (either the working drawings or specifications) made after the contract documents have gone out to bid (or to a *Contractor* for establishing a contract price), but before a contract price has been finalized. In order to identify items of an addendum, separate drawings are prepared with special numbering, or the changes to an existing drawing are highlighted by "clouding" the change.

Artificial Lighting — Illumination by means of electric light sources, as opposed to *natural lighting*.

Artificial Plants — Manufactured representations of plants whose foliage is made from polyester, plastic or other materials, and sometimes used in conjunction with natural wood materials for the trunks and branches.

Automatic Irrigation System — A means of supplying water directly to a plant without the need for manually introducing water into the system, by having the system connected directly to a building's water supply line.

Blackline Print — A dry *Diazo* process producing a black image on a white- paper background.

Blueline Print — A dry *Diazo* process producing a blue image on a white paper background.

Blueprint — A blue-background print with white lines made on an iron-sensitized paper by printing through translucent positive copy. A wet process; outdated.

Change Order — An adjustment to a design after a construction contract has been signed. A change order usually involves an adjustment of contract price.

Contour Line — A line of equal elevation. Used in grading plans to graphically indicate proposed (usually solid) or existing (usually dashed) topography.

Contract Documents — The complete package of information required by a *Contractor* to construct a design.

Contractor — As used in this context, an interior landscape contractor, also known as an interiorscaper, interior landscaper, or interior plantscaper. A person or firm involved in the installation and maintenance of plants within interior spaces.

Diazo Print — A reprographic process using light-sensitive paper whose emulsion develops upon exposure to aqueous ammonia, heat, and light.

Footcandle or **fc** — A unit of illuminance on a surface that is everywhere one foot from a uniform point source of light of one candle, or equal to one lumen per square foot.

General Contractor — As used in this context, a person or firm engaged in the construction of new, or renovation of existing, buildings.

HVAC — Heating, Ventilating, and Air-Conditioning; the mechanical systems needed to properly circulate and condition air within a building.

Illustrative Plan — A plan drawn specifically to relay a design concept through the use of graphic techniques.

In situ — In the natural or original position.

Invert or **Invert Elevation** — The elevation of the inside bottom of a horizontal pipe. The invert of a drain pipe is the point at which the pipe becomes horizontal.

Lux — A unit of illuminance on a surface that is everywhere one meter from a uniform point source of light of one candle, or equal to one lumen per square meter.

Mylar — Trade name of Du Pont Company for a polyester-type film, of high strength and dimensional stability, used as a base stock for light-sensitive coatings or for direct use as a single- or double sided drawing and scribing media.

Natural Lighting — As used in this context, illumination useful for the growth of indoor plants consisting of either direct sunlight, daylight, or reflected outdoor light passing through transparent or translucent glazing into an interior space.

Office Landscape — As used in this context, the concept of using plant materials as an integral component of a commercial office's interior design. More typically used in the design community to mean the interior design of a commercial office space without floor-to-ceiling partitions for the creation of individual work spaces.

Photoperiod — The relative length of the alternating periods of light and darkness as they affect the growth of plants.

Preserved Plants — Natural foliage of plants—usually palms—which have been chemically treated to preserve their color and molecular structure which are then attached to a fabricated or natural trunk.

Rendering or **rendered plan** — A drawing prepared for presentation purposes which uses graphic techniques and/or color to represent a design concept.

Reproducible Drawing A translucent sheet of paper, polyester, or plastic film through which light can be directed to expose other specially treated media to create positive images.

Retrofit The process of installing a new device or system into an existing structure.

Revision A change to a design prior to the *Contract Documents*' being released for construction or for bid. They are normally identified so that the owner can assess eleventh-hour adjustments to the design.

Reverse-Reading Sepia A *Sepia* whose emulsion is developed on the reverse side to that which is displayed.

Right-Reading Sepia A *Sepia* whose emulsion is developed on the side which is to be displayed.

Semiautomatic Irrigation System A means of supplying water to a plant which requires the manual introduction of water to the system, but which gradually discharges water to the planting medium by its own means.

Sepia A 100 percent rag paper reprographic medium whose emulsion develops a brown image after exposure to light, heat, and aqueous ammonia.

Softened Water Water which has been treated to remove the minerals (calcium and magnesium) which make it "hard". Hard water does not dissolve soap readily and forms scaly deposits on pipes and other equipment. Water is softened either by an ion-exchange process, in which calcium and magnesium ions are replaced by sodium ions, or by a lime-soda process, in which soda ash and lime are added, combining with the calcium and magnesium to create insoluble compounds which settle out.

Specifications The written documentation (often in 8.5 x 11 in book form, but sometimes provided directly on drawings) portion of *Contract Documents* which a *Contractor* uses to construct a design, to be used in conjunction with *Working Drawings.*

Subirrigation System A *Semi-automatic Irrigation System* consisting of a reservoir to hold water located beneath or next to the planting medium which releases water to the planting medium either by vacuum pressure or capillary action, depending on system type.

Tempered Water Water which has had its temperature adjusted to include a mixture of both cold tap water and heated water.

Wash-off Mylar A polyester-type film with a light-sensitive coating that creates a positive image when developed, and whose image can be removed with a damp eraser.

Working Drawings The graphic documentation portion of Contract Documents which a Contractor uses to construct a design. It is often, but not always, accompanied by *Specifications.*

APPENDIX C

MASTER INTERIOR PLANT LIST

KEY

A	*Accent or seasonal plant*
GC	*Ground cover*
H	*Hanging plant*
P	*Palm*
S	*Shrub*
T	*Tree*
*	*Commonly used specimen*

Acoelorrhaphe wrightii
Paurotis Palm — P

Acorus gramineus
Acorus Grass, Japanese Sweet Flag — GC

**Aechmea fasciata*
Urn Plant — A

Aglaonema 'Abidjan'
Abidjan Chinese Evergreen — S

**Aglaonema* 'Cecilia'
Cecilia Chinese Evergreen — S

**Aglaonema commutatum*
Chinese Evergreen — S

Aglaonema 'Fransher'
Fransher Chinese Evergreen — S

**Aglaonema* 'Maria'
(*AKA* Emerald Beauty)
Maria Chinese Evergreen — S

Aglaonema 'Pseudobracteatum'
White Rajah Chinese Evergreen — S

Aglaonema 'Queen Juliana'
Queen Juliana Chinese Evergreen — S

Aglaonema roebelinii
Roebelinii Chinese Evergreen — S

Aglaonema 'Romano'
Romano Chinese Evergreen — S

Aglaonema 'San Remo'
San Remo Chinese Evergreen — S

**Aglaonema* 'Silver Queen'
Silver Queen Chinese Evergreen — S

Aiphanes caryotaefolia
Spine Palm — P

Alocasia cucullata
Chinese Taro — A, S

Alpinia zerumbet
Shell Ginger — S

Alsophila australis
Australian Tree Fern — S,T

Anthurium 'Bird's Nest'
Bird's Nest Anthurium — S

Anthurium 'Hookerii'
Hooker Anthurium — S

Anthurium 'Julia'
Julia Anthurium — S

Anthurium 'Lady Jane'
Lady Jane Anthurium — S

Araucaria bidwillii
Bunya-Bunya Pine,
Monkey Puzzle Tree — S,T

**Araucaria heterophylla*
Norfolk Island Pine — S,T

Ardisia crispa
Coralberry — A,S

**Arecastrum Romanzoffianum*
Queen Palm — P

**Asparagus sprengeri*
Asparagus Fern — H,GC

Asparagus plumosa
Asparagus Fern — H,GC

**Aspidistra elatior*
Cast Iron Plant — S

Asplenium nidus
Bird's Nest Fern — S

Aucuba japonica
Japanese Aucuba — S

**Bambusa vulgaris* 'Aureo-variegata'
Hawaiian Striped Bamboo — S,T

Bambusa vulgaris 'Vittata'
Feathery Bamboo — T

**Beaucarnea recurvata*
Ponytail Palm — S,T

Begonia spp.
Begonia — A

Bougainvillea spp.
Bougainvillea — A, H, GC

**Brassaia actinophylla*
Schefflera, Umbrella Tree — S,T

**Brassaia actinophylla* 'Amate'
Amate Schefflera — S

**Bucida buceras*
Black Olive — T

**Bucida buceras* 'Shady Lady'
Shady Lady Black Olive — T

Plant	Key
Bucida spinosa Dwarf Black Olive	S,T
Caladium hortulanum Elephant Ear Plant	A
Calathea Makoyana Peacock Plant	A,GC,S
Calathea ornata Peacock Plant	A,GC,S
Calathea roseapicta Peacock Plant	A,GC,S
Calathea vittata Peacock Plant	A,GC,S
Calathea Zebrina Peacock Plant	A,GC,S
Carpentaria acuminata Carpenter's Palm	P
*Caryota mitis Fishtail Palm	S,T
Cereus peruvianus Giant Club Cactus	S
Cereus peruvianus 'Monstrosum' Giant Club Cactus	S
Chamaedorea cataractarum Cataractarum Palm	S,P
*Chamaedorea elegans Neanthe Bella Palm	S,P
*Chamaedorea 'Florida Hybrid' Bamboo Palm	S,P
*Chamaedorea Seifrizii Reed Palm	S,P
*Chamaerops humilis European Fan Palm	S,P
Chlorophytum comosum Spider Plant	H,GC
*Chlorophytum comosum variegatum Variegated Spider Plant	H,GC
*Chrysalidocarpus lutescens Areca Palm	S,P
*Chrysanthemum spp. Chrysanthemum	A
Cibotium splendens Hawaiian Tree Fern	S,T
*Cissus antarctica Kangaroo Vine	H,GC
*Cissus 'Ellen Danica' Oakleaf Ivy	H,GC
*Cissus Rhombifolia Grape Ivy	H,GC
*Cissus Rhombifolia 'Mandaiana' Grape Ivy	H,GC
Citrofortunella mitis Calamondin Orange Tree	S,T
Clusia rosea Autograph Tree	T
Cocos nucifera Coconut Palm	P
*Codiaeum 'Norma' Norma Croton	S
*Codieaum 'Petra' Petra Croton	S
Coffea arabica Coffee Tree	S
Cordyline terminalis Hawaiian Ti Plant	S
*Crassula argentea Jade Plant	S
Cycas circinalis Queen Sago Palm	P
*Cycas revoluta King Sago Palm	P
Cyclamen spp. Cyclamen	P
Cyperus alternifolius Umbrella Plant	S
Cyperus papyrus Egyptian Paper Plant	S
Cyrtomium falcatum Holly Fern	GC,S
Davallia fejeensis Rabbit's Foot Fern	H,GC
Davallia trichomanioides Squirrel's Foot Fern	H,GC
Dicksonia antarctica Tasmanian Tree Fern	S,T
Dieffenbachia amoena Giant Dumb Cane	S
Dieffenbachia 'Bali Hai' Bali Hai Dumb Cane	S
*Dieffenbachia 'Camille' Camille Dumb Cane	S
Dieffenbachia 'Hilo' Hilo Dumb Cane	S

KEY

A	Accent or seasonal plant
GC	Ground cover
H	Hanging plant
P	Palm
S	Shrub
T	Tree
*	Commonly used specimen

KEY

A	*Accent or seasonal plant*
GC	*Ground cover*
H	*Hanging plant*
P	*Palm*
S	*Shrub*
T	*Tree*
*	*Commonly used specimen*

Dieffenbachia 'Paradise'
Paradise Dumb Cane S

Dieffenbachia 'Perfection Compacta'
Perfection Compacta Dumb Cane S

Dieffenbachia 'Picta'
Dumb Cane S

Dieffenbachia 'Triumph'
Triumph Dumb Cane S

Dieffenbachia 'Tropic Alix'
Tropic Alix Dumb Cane S

**Dieffenbachia* 'Tropic Snow'
Tropic Snow Dumb Cane S

Dieffenbachia 'Wilson's Delight'
Wilson's Delight Dumb Cane S

**Dizygotheca elegantissima*
False Aralia S,T

Dracaena augustifolia 'Honorii'
Malaysian Dracaena S

**Dracaena deremensis* 'Janet Craig'
Janet Craig Dracaena S

Dracaena deremensis
'Janet Craig Compacta'
Dwarf Janet Craig Dracaena S

**Dracaena deremensis* 'Warneckii'
Striped Dracaena S

Dracaena Draco
Dragon Tree S
(AKA D. arborea)

**Dracaena fragrans* 'Massangeana'
Corn Plant S,T

Dracaena godseffiana
Gold Dust Dracaena S

**Dracaena marginata*
Madagascar Dragon Tree S,T

**Dracaena reflexa*
Malaysian Dracaena S
(AKA *Pleomele reflexa)*

Dracaena sanderiana
Sander's Dracaena S

Dracaena thalioides
Lance Dracaena S

**Epipremnum aureum*
Golden Pothos, Devil's Ivy H,GC
(AKA *Scindapsus aureus)*

**Epipremnum aureum* 'Marble Queen'
Marble Queen Pothos H,GC
(AKA *Scindapsus aureus)*

Epipremnum aureum 'Tropic Green'
Jade Pothos H,GC
(AKA *Scindapsus aureus)*

Eucharis grandiflora
Amazon Lily S

Euphorbia acurensis S

Euphorbia grandicloris S

Euphorbia ingens
Candalabra Tree S

Euphorbia Milii
Crown-of-Thorns A,S

Euphorbia pulcherrima
Poinsettia A

Fatshedera lizei
Tree Ivy GC

Fatsia japonica
Japanese Fatsia S

**Ficus* 'Alii'
Alii Ficus S,T

Ficus australis *T*

**Ficus benjamina*
Weeping Java Fig Tree S,T

Ficus diversifolia
Mistletoe Fig S,T

Ficus elastica 'Asahi'
Asahi Rubber Tree S,T

Ficus elastica 'Burgundy'
Burgundy Rubber Tree S,T

**Ficus elastica* 'Decora'
Indian Rubber Tree S,T

Ficus elastica 'Honduras'
Honduras Rubber Tree S,T

Ficus elastica 'Robusta'
Robusta Rubber Tree S,T

Ficus elastica 'Variegata'
Variegated Rubber Tree S,T

**Ficus lyrata*
Fiddleleaf Fig Tree T

Ficus Nekbudu
Zulu Fig S,T
(AKA *F. utilis)*

**Ficus nitida*
Indian Laurel Fig Tree S,T
(AKA *F. retusa)*

**Ficus nitida 'Green Gem'*
Green Gem Fig Tree S,T

Ficus pumila
Creeping Fig GC
(AKA *F. repens*)

Ficus rubiginosa
Rusty Leaf Fig Tree T

Fittonia Verschaffeltii
Silver Nerved Fittonia H,GC

Garcinia Mangostana
Mangosteen T

Grevillea robusta
Silk Oak T

Gynura aurantiaca
Velvet Plant,
Purple Passion Vine H,GC

**Hedera canariensis*
Algerian Ivy H,GC

**Hedera Helix*
English Ivy H,GC

**Hedera Helix*
'California Self-Branching'
California Self-Branching Ivy H,GC

Hedera Helix 'Hahnii'
Hahn's Ivy H,GC

Hedera Helix 'Manda's Crested'
Manda's Crested Ivy H,GC

Hedera Helix 'Marengo'
Marengo Ivy H,GC

Heliconia 'Flame' *A,S*

Heliconia 'Andromeda' *A,S*

Hibiscus Rosa-sinensis
Chinese or Hawaiian Hibiscus A,S,T

Homalomena wallisii 'Emerald Gem'
Emerald Gem Homalomena S

Homalomena wallisii 'Camouflage'
Silver Shield Homalomena S

**Howea forsterana*
Kentia Palm S,P

**Hoya carnosa*
Wax Plant H,GC

Hypoestes phyllostachya
Polkadot Plant H,GC

Kalanchoe blossfeldiana
Kalanchoe A

Ligustrum lucidum T

Liriope spp.
Lily Turf GC

**Livistona chinensis*
Chinese Fan Palm P

Maranta leuconeura kerchoveana
Prayer Plant H,GC,S

Mascarena verschaffeltii
Bottle Palm, Spindle Palm P

**Monstera deliciosa*
Split-Leaf Philodendron S

Murraya paniculata
Orange Jasmine S

Neodypsis decaryi
Triangle Palm P

Nephrolepis exaltata 'Bostoniensis'
Boston Fern H,GC

Ophiopogon japonicus
Mondo Grass GC

**Pandanus utilis*
Screw Pine S

Pellaea rotundifolia
Button Fern H,GC

Peperomia 'Emerald Ripple'
Emerald Ripple Peperomia S

Peperomia obtusifolia
Baby Rubber Plant S

Philodendron 'Angel Wing'
Angel Wing Philodendron S

Philodendron bipennifolium S

**Philodendron cordatum*
Heart-leaved Philodendron H,GC
(AKA *P. scandens* and *P. oxycardium*)

Philodendron 'Emerald King' S

Philodendron 'Emerald Queen' S

Philodendron 'Imperial Green' S

Philodendron 'Imperial Red' S

Philodendron panduraeforme S

Philodendron pertussum S,GC

Philodendron 'Red Emerald' S

**Philodendron selloum*
Self-Heading or Saddle-leaved
Philodendron S

Philodendron 'Wendembii' S

KEY

A	*Accent or seasonal plant*
GC	*Ground cover*
H	*Hanging plant*
P	*Palm*
S	*Shrub*
T	*Tree*
*	*Commonly used specimen*

KEY

A *Accent or seasonal plant*
GC *Ground cover*
H *Hanging plant*
P *Palm*
S *Shrub*
T *Tree*
* *Commonly used specimen*

Phoenix canariensis
Canary Island Date Palm P

Phoenix dactylifera
Date Palm P

Phoenix reclinata
Senegal Date Palm P

**Phoenix Roebelenii*
Miniature Date Palm P

Pilea Cadierei
Aluminum Plant S

Pittosporum tobira
Japanese Pittosporum S

Pittosporum tobira 'Variegata'
Variegated Japanese Pittosporum S

Pittosporum tobira 'Wheeleri'
Wheeler's Dwarf Japanese Pittosporum S

Platycerium bifurcatum
Staghorn Fern S

Plectranthus australis
Swedish Ivy S

Podocarpus gracilior
Weeping Podocarpus S,T

**Podocarpus macrophyllus Makii*
Southern Yew S,T

**Polyscias balfouriana*
Balfour Aralia S,T

**Polyscias fruticosa*
Ming Aralia S,T

Pteris ensiformis 'Victoriae'
Table Fern, Brake Fern H,GC

Ptychosperma elegans
Alexander Palm P

Ravenala madagascariensis
Traveler's Tree T

**Rhapis excelsa*
Lady Palm P

Rhapis humilis
Slender Lady Palm P

Rhoeo spathacea
Moses-in-the-Cradle S,GC,H

Saintpaulia spp.
African Violet A

**Sansevieria trifasciata*
Mother-in-Law's Tongue, Snake Plant S

Sansevieria trifasciata 'Hahnii'
Hahn's Sansevieria S,GC

Sansevieria zeylanica
Bowstring Hemp S,GC

Saxifraga sarmentosa
Strawberry Geranium H,GC

**Schefflera arboricola*
Hawaiian Schefflera S

Schefflera 'Emerald Ripple'
Emerald Ripple Schefflera S

Schlumbergera Bridgesii
Christmas Cactus S,H

Sinningia speciosa
Gloxinia A

Solanum Pseudocapsicum
Jerusalem Cherry *A, S*

Soleirolia Soleirolii
Baby's Tears GC
(AKA Helxine soleirolii)

Spathiphyllum 'DeNeve'
DeNeve Peace Lily S

Spathiphyllum 'Kristina'
Kristina Peace Lily S,GC

Spathiphyllum 'Lillian'
Lillian Peace Lily S

**Spathiphyllum* 'Lynise'
Lynise Peace Lily S

**Spathiphyllum* 'Mauna Loa'
Mauna Loa Peace Lily S

**Spathiphyllum* 'Mauna Loa Supreme'
Mauna Loa Supreme Peace Lily S

**Spathiphyllum* 'Petite'
Petite Peace Lily S,GC

Spathiphyllum 'Phoenix'
Phoenix Peace Lily S

Spathiphyllum 'Sensation'
Sensation Peace Lily S

Spathiphyllum 'Starlite'
Starlite Peace Lily S

**Spathiphyllum* 'Tasson'
Tasson Peace Lily S

Spathiphyllum 'Viscount'
Viscount Peace Lily S

**Spathiphyllum wallisii*
Wallis Peace Lily S,GC

Sphaeropteris Cooperi
Australian Tree Fern S,T

**Strelitzia nicolai*
White Bird-of-Paradise A,S

Strelitzia reginae
Bird-of-Paradise A,S

Syngonium macrophyllum
Arrowhead Vine H,GC

Syngonium podophyllum xanthophyllum
Nephthytis, Arrowhead Vine H,GC

Tetrastigma Voinierianum
Chestnut Vine, Lizard Plant H,GC

Trachycarpus fortunei
Windmill Palm P

Tradescantia fluminensis
Wandering Jew H,GC

Tupidanthus calyptrus
Tupidanthus S
(AKA *Schefflera tupidanthus*)

**Veitchia Merrillii*
Manila Palm, Adonidia Palm P

Washingtonia robusta
Thread Palm, Washington Palm P

**Yucca elephantipes*
Spineless Yucca S,T

**Zamia pumila*
Florida Arrowroot, Sago Cycas
(AKA *Zamia furfuracea*) S

Zebrina pendula
Quadricolor Wandering Jew H,GC

KEY

A	*Accent or seasonal plant*
GC	*Ground cover*
H	*Hanging plant*
P	*Palm*
S	*Shrub*
T	*Tree*
*	*Commonly used specimen*

APPENDIX D
FAMILIES OF COMMONLY SPECIFIED INTERIOR PLANT GENERA

Identification of plants for landscape design use, indoors and out, is normally made by genus, species, and common name. More recently, with the introduction of tissue culture as a means of propagating new plants, cultivar names are often added to a species. Specification of family name is not relevant, for the design professional must be quite precise in identifying plants to be used, and the family name does not assist in this effort.

However, as species of plants fall within a certain genus, and genera of plants fall within a certain family, the designer acquainted with family names and the genera associated with them will be able to identify similarities of one genus to another because they belong to the same family. Genera of the same family will often (not always) exhibit similar characteristics regarding light tolerance, temperature tolerance, soil pH requirements, irrigation requirements, and other environmental factors, the awareness of which may be helpful to the specifier.

With that in mind, the following represents a list of plant families whose genera are commonly used as interior plants:

Acanthaceae	Aphelandra, Fittonia, Hemigraphis, Hypoestes
Agavaceae	Agave, Beaucarnea, Cordyline, Dracaena, Sansevieria, Yucca
Amaranthaceae	Iresine
Amaryllidaceae	Eucharis, Narcissus
Apocynaceae	Trachelospermum
Araceae	Acorus, Aglaonema, Alocasia, Anthurium, Caladium, Dieffenbachia, Epipremnum, Homalomena, Monstera, Philodendron, Spathiphyllum, Syngonium, Anthurium
Araliaceae	Brassaia, Dizygotheca, Fatshedera, Fatsia, Hedera, Polyscias, Schefflera, Tupidanthus
Araucariaceae	Araucaria
Asclepiadaceae	Hoya
Balsaminaceae	Impatiens
Begoniaceae	Begonia

Bromeliaceae	Aechmea, Ananas, Cryptanthus, Neoregelia, Vriesia
Cactaceae	Cereus, Schlumbergera, Opuntia
Combretaceae	Bucida
Commelinaceae	Dichorisandra, Rhoeo, Setcreasea, Tradescantia, Zebrina
Composite	Gynura, Senecio, Chrysanthemum
Cornaceae	Aucuba
Crassulaceae	Crassula, Echeveria, Kalanchoe
Cyatheaceae	Alsophila, Sphaeropteris
Cycadaceae	Cycas
Cyperaceae	Cyperus
Dicksoniaceae	Cibotium
Droseraceae	Dionaea
Euphorbiaceae	Codiaeum, Euphorbia
Gernaciaceae	Pelargonium
Gesneriaceae	Aeschynanthus, Columnea, Episcia, Nautilocalyx, Saintpaulia, Sinningia
Gramineae	Bambusa, Zoysia
Guttiferae	Clusia, Garcinia
Heliconiaceae	Heliconia
Iridaceae	Freesia, Crocus, Iris
Labiate	Plectranthus, Coleus
Leguminosae	Mimosa
Liliaceae	Aloe, Asparagus, Aspidistra, Chlorophytum, Liriope, Ophiopogon, Tulipa
Malvaceae	Hibiscus
Marantaceae	Calathea, Maranta
Moraceae	Ficus
Myrsinaceae	Ardisia
Nytaginaceae	Bougainvillea, Pisonia
Oleaceae	Ligustrum
Orchidaceae	Orchids of many genera
Palmae	Acoelorrhaphe, Aiphanes, Arecastrum, Carpentaria, Caryota, Chamaedorea, Chamaerops, Chrysalidocarpus, Cocos, Howea, Livistona, Mascarena, Neodypsis, Phoenix, Ptychosperma, Rhapis, Trachycarpus, Veitchia, Washingtonia
Pandanaceae	Pandanus
Piperaceae	Peperomia
Pittosporaceae	Pittosporum
Podocarpaceae	Podocarpus

Polypodiaceae	Adiantum, Aglaomorpha, Asplenium, Cyrtomium, Davallia, Dryopteris, Nephrolepis, Pellaea, Platycerium, Polypodium, Polystichum, Pteris
Primulaceae	Cyclamen, Primula
Proteaceae	Grevillea
Ranunculaceae	Anemone
Rubiaceae	Coffea, Gardenia, Serissa
Rutaceae	Citrus, Citrofortunella, Murraya
Saxifragaceae	Saxifraga
Scrophulariaceae	Calceolaria
Solanaceae	Solanum, Streptosolen
Strelitziaceae	Ravenala, Strelitzia
Theaceae	Camellia
Urticaceae	Pilea, Soleirolia
Vitaceae	Cissus, Tetrastigma
Zamiaceae	Dioon, Zamia
Zingiberaceae	Alpinia

APPENDIX E
POISONOUS PLANTS

The health benefits of using plants indoors have been clearly established, yet there are species of interior plants which can cause harmful reactions to people if ingested, or even touched. The following is a compilation of plants found to be poisonous to some extent which have been used indoors. The most comprehensive source for this list is the AMA Handbook of Poisonous and Injurious Plants, by Dr. Kenneth F. Lampe and Mary Ann McCann, Division of Drugs and Technology, American Medical Association, Chicago, Illinois, 1985. This source lists plants alphabetically by genus, and also gives the common name, a description of the plant, where it can be found in nature, the parts that are toxic, the type of the toxin present, the symptoms of toxicity, and recommendations for management of the toxicity.

Some of these plants are listed below only because of isolated incidents reported to various poison control centers throughout the United States. In many cases, the degree of toxicity has not been properly established.

For proposed projects in which ingestion of plants by young children or animals is a possibility (residences, child care centers, nursery schools, elementary schools, zoos, etc.), deletion of all plants on this list should be considered. However, since this list contains several of the more commonly specified interior plants, it is inevitable that some of these plants will continue to be specified. If used, the nature of a plant's toxin, their level of toxicity, and their health hazards should be investigated and made known to the client by the specifier on a plant by plant basis. Information regarding plant toxicity can be obtained from your state or local poison control center. This list is not intended to be comprehensive, and as the use of plants continues to proliferate, reporting of toxic reactions to interior plants to poison control centers will continue to add names to this list.

Botanical Name	Common Name
Allamanda cathartica	Allamanda
Alocasia species	Alocasia
Aloe spp.	Aloe, Medicine Plant
Amaryllis spp.	Amaryllis
Anthurium spp.	Anthurium, Flamingo Flower
Aucuba japonica	Japanese Aucuba
Caladium spp.	Elephant Ear
Clivia spp.	Kaffir Lily
Colocasia spp.	Elephant's Ear
Crocus spp.	Crocus
Cyclamen spp.	Cyclamen
Dieffenbachia spp.	Dumb Cane
Epipremnum aureum	Pothos, Devil's Ivy
Eriobotrya japonica	Loquat
Euphorbia spp.	Euphorbia
Hedera spp.	English Ivy
Hyacinth spp.	Hyacinth
Iris spp.	Iris
Lantana Camara	Lantana
Monstera deliciosa	Split-Leaf Philodendron
Narcissus spp.	Daffodil, Jonquil
Nerium oleander	Oleander
Philodendron spp.	Philodendron
Solanum Pseudocapsicum	Jerusalem Cherry
Spathiphyllum spp.	Peace Lily
Zamia pumila	Zamia, Coontie

APPENDIX F

BIBLIOGRAPHY

American Standard for Nursery Stock,
American Association of Nurserymen, Washington, D.C., 1990.

Austin, Richard L., ASLA, *Designing the Interior Landscape,*
Van Nostrand Reinhold, Inc., New York, 1985.

Bailey, L. H., Hortorium, *Hortus Third,*
Macmillan Publishing Company, Inc., New York, 1976.

Baker, Paul R., *Richard Morris Hunt,*
MIT Press, Cambridge, Mass. 1980.

Berrall, Julia S., *The Garden: An Illustrated History,*
The Viking Press, Inc., New York, 1966.

Bickford, Elwood D., and Dunn, Stuart, *Lighting for Plant Growth,*
The Kent State University Press, Kent, Ohio, 1972.

Crockett, James Underwood, *Foliage House Plants,*
Time-Life Books, New York, 1972.

Current, Richard N., "Garfield, James Abram", *The World Book Encyclopedia,*
Volume 8, World Book, Inc., Chicago, 1985.

Donovan, William P., *The World Book Encyclopedia,* Volume 17,
World Book, Inc., Chicago, 1985.

"Crystal Palace", *Encyclopaedia Britannica,*
Volume 3, 15th Edition, Chicago, 1985.

Fraser, Hugh Russell, "Thomas A. Edison", *The World Book Encyclopedia,*
Volume 6, World Book, Inc., Chicago, 1985.

Friedman, Robert, "The Air-Conditioned Century", *American Heritage* Magazine, American Heritage Publishing Company, New York, Volume 35, Number 5, August–September 1984.

Gaines, Richard L., AIA, *Interior Plantscaping: Building Design for Interior Foliage Plants,* Architectural Record Books, New York, 1977.

Gore, Rick, "The Dead Do Tell Tales at Vesuvius", *National Geographic,*
National Geographic Society, Washington, D.C., May 1984.

Guide to Interior Landscape Specifications, (ALCA Guide), Associated Landscape Contractors of America, Falls Church, Virginia, Fourth Edition, 1988.

Hamlin, Talbot, *Architecture Through the Ages,*
Putnam's Sons, New York, 1940, 1953.

Helms, Ronald N., "Electric Light", *The World Book Encyclopedia,*
Volume 6, World Book, Inc., Chicago, 1985.

Hitchcock, Henry-Russell, *Architecture 19th and 20th Centuries,*
Penguin Books, Baltimore, 1958.

Koppelkamm, Stefan, *Glasshouses and Wintergardens of the Nineteenth Century,* Rizzoli International Publications, Inc., New York, 1981.

Kuhn, Herbert, *On the Track of Prehistoric Man,*
Random House, Inc., New York, 1955.

Manaker, George H., *Interior Plantscapes: Installation, Maintenance, & Management,* Prentice-Hall, Inc., Englewood Cliffs, N.J., 1987.

Martin, Tovah, *Once Upon a Windowsill,* Timber Press, Portland Oregon, 1988.

Mpelkas, Christos C., "Interior Landscape Lighting", *Lighting Design & Application,* Illuminating Engineering Society of North America, New York, July, 1990.

Perl, Philip, *Ferns,* Time-Life Books, Inc., Alexandria, Va., 1977.

Pierceall, Gregory M., *Interiorscapes: Planning, Graphics, and Design,* Prentice-Hall, Inc., Englewood Cliffs, N.J., 1987.

Rogers, Frances, and Beard, Alice, *5,000 Years of Glass,* Frederick A. Stokes Company, New York, 1937.

Selection Guide for Quality Lighting, Form 9200, 20th edition, The General Electric Company, 1990.

Snyder, Stuart D., *Building Interiors, Plants, and Automation*, Prentice Hall, New York, 1990.

White, Mary Grant, *Pots and Pot Gardens,* Abelard-Schuman, London, 1969.

Whiton, Sherrill, *Interior Design and Decoration,* J. B. Lippincott Company, Philadelphia, 1974.

World Book Encyclopedia, Volume 15, "Pliny the Elder", World Book, Inc., Chicago, 1985.

APPENDIX G

NASA STUDY: INTERIOR LANDSCAPE PLANTS FOR INDOOR AIR POLLUTION ABATEMENT

Final Report - September 1989 by B.C. Wolverton, Ph.D., Principal Investigator

Anne Johnson, M.S., and Keith Bounds, M.S., Sverdrup Technology

National Aeronautics and Space Administration
John C. Stennis Space Center, Stennis Space Center, MS 39529

ABBREVIATIONS AND ACRONYMS

Term	Definition
ALCA	Associated Landscape Contractors of America
EPA	Environmental Protection Agency
GC	gas chromatograph
HP	Hewlett-Packard
NASA	National Aeronautics and Space Administration
PCA	plate count agar
TCE	trichloroethylene
UF	urea formaldehyde
UFFI	urea-formaldehyde foam insulation
cfu/g	colony forming units per gram
cm	centimeter
cm2	square centimeter
g	gram
h	hour
in.	inch
m	meter
mL	milliliter
min	minute
m3	cubic meter
p/m	parts per million
s	second
yr	year
μL	microliter
°C	degrees Celsius

INTERIOR LANDSCAPE PLANTS FOR INDOOR AIR POLLUTLON ABATEMENT

Introduction

During the late 1970's, when the energy crunch was being felt at both the gas pump and in heating and cooling costs, buildings were being designed to maximize energy efficiency to help alleviate spiraling energy costs. Two of the design changes that improved energy efficiency included superinsulation and reduced fresh air exchange. However, upon the occupation of these buildings, the workers began to complain of various health problems such as itchy eyes, skin rashes, drowsiness, respiratory and sinus congestion, headaches, and other allergy-related symptoms. It was determined that the airtight sealing of buildings contributed significantly to the workers' health problems. Similarly, synthetic building materials, which are known to emit or "off-gas" various organic compounds, have been linked to numerous health complaints. The office equipment and furnishings placed in these buildings are also a contributing factor because of the types of materials used in their manufacture and design.

Man himself should be considered another source of indoor air pollution, especially when living in a closed, poorly ventilated area. This becomes very apparent when a large number of people are present in a confined place such as an airplane for an extended period of time.

All of these factors collectively contribute to a phenomenon called "sick building syndrome." One world health organization recently estimated that approximately 30 percent of all new or remodeled buildings have varying degrees of indoor air pollution. Problems of this type have been reported in the United States and Canada as well as in most other highly developed nations of the western world.

Two major problems with indoor air pollution are the identification of the trace chemicals and their correlation with diseaselike symptoms. Energy-efficient buildings that are filled with modern furnishings and high-tech equipment off-gas hundreds of volatile organics which possibly interact with each other. Even at concentrations below present detection limits, some of these chemicals and reactive by-products may adversely affect inhabitants of these buildings. The problems of indoor air pollution have been studied and documented by many investigators over the past ten years. (1-27) Dr. Tony Pickering of the Wythenshawe Hospital near Manchester, England, has studied sick building syndrome extensively and has learned that symptoms are minimal in naturally ventilated buildings which contained the highest levels of microorganisms. On the other hand, the highest levels of symptoms are found in mechanically ventilated buildings containing low levels of microorganisms. The results of his analyses indicate that it is unlikely that symptoms associated with sick building syndrome can be attributed to microorganisms.

Now that most environmental scientists and government agencies agree that indoor air pollution is a realistic threat to human health, how can the problem be solved?

A PROMISING, ECONOMICAL SOLUTION TO INDOOR AIR POLLUTION

The first and most obvious step in reducing indoor air pollution is to reduce off-gassing from building materials and furnishings before they are allowed to be installed. The National Aeronautics Space Administration (NASA) identified indoor air pollution problems associated with sealed space habitats over 16 years ago. (1) Although a final solution to the trace contamination problems in these sealed environments has not been found, NASA does screen for off-gassing all new materials that are to be used in future space structures.

Another promising approach to further reducing trace levels of air pollutants inside future space habitats is the use of higher plants and their associated soil microorganisms. (28-29) Since man's existence on Earth depends upon a life support system involving an intricate relationship with plants and their associated microorganisms, it should be obvious that when he attempts to isolate himself in tightly sealed buildings away from this ecological system, problems will arise. Even without the existence of hundreds of synthetic organic chemicals off-gassing into tightly sealed environments, man's own waste products would cause indoor air pollution problems.

The answer to these problems is obvious. If man is to move into closed environments, on Earth or in space, he must take along nature's life support system. This is not easily achieved, however. At John C. Stennis Space Center, NASA has been attempting to solve this ecological puzzle for over 15 years. Professor Josef Gitelson of the USSR and his team of scientists and engineers have also been working with closed ecological systems for many years in Krasnoyarsk, Siberia. (30) Only recently, however, have critical parts of this complex puzzle begun to come together. Although maintaining the balance of the complete ecological cycle involves treating and recycling sewage, toxic chemicals, and other industrial water and air pollutants, only indoor air is addressed here.

In this study the leaves, roots, soil, and associated microorganisms of plants have been evaluated as a possible means of reducing indoor air pollutants. Additionally, a novel approach of using plant systems for removing high concentrations of indoor air pollutants such as cigarette smoke, organic solvents, and possibly radon has been designed from this work. This air filter design combines plants with an activated carbon filter as shown in Figure 1. The rationale for this design, which evolved from wastewater treatment studies, is based on moving large volumes of contaminated air through an activated carbon bed where smoke, organic chemicals, pathogenic microorganisms (if present), and possibly radon are absorbed by the carbon filter. Plant roots and their associated microorganisms then destroy the pathogenic viruses, bacteria, and the organic chemicals, eventually converting all of these air pollutants into new plant tissue. (31-37) It is believed that the decayed radon products would be

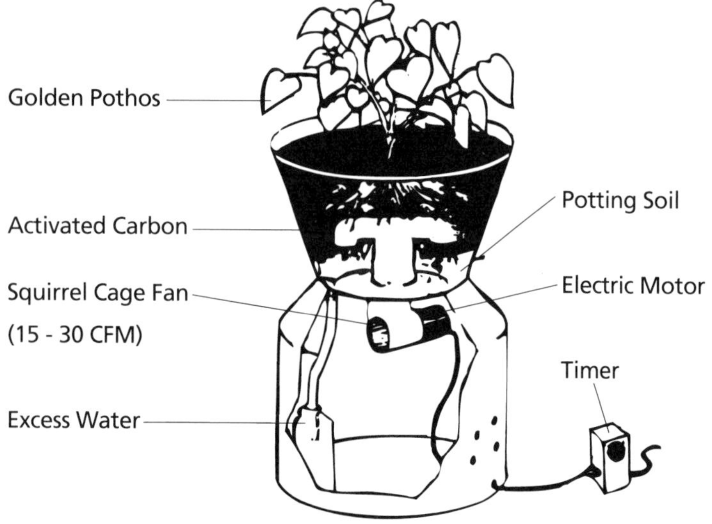

Figure 1. Indoor air purification system combining houseplants and activated carbon.

taken up by the plant roots and retained in the plant tissue. Experiments are currently being conducted to test this hypothesis for NASA at the Department of Energy Oak Ridge National Laboratories in Oak Ridge, Tennessee.

As NASA looks toward the possibility of scaling people inside a Space Station, or moon base, along with large numbers of plants the ecology of such a closed environment (interactions between man, plants, microorganisms, soil, etc.) must be further evaluated. See Figure 2. As plant studies continue at Stennis Space Center, emphasis is being placed not only on identifying trace chemical contamination, but also on identifying any volatile organic metabolites that may be off-gassed by plants themselves.

This joint effort between NASA and the Associated Landscape Contractors of America (ALCA) covers two years of data on the potential use of houseplants as a tool in solving indoor air pollution problems on Earth, and has gone a long way toward reminding man of his dependence on plants for his continued existence and well-being on our planet.

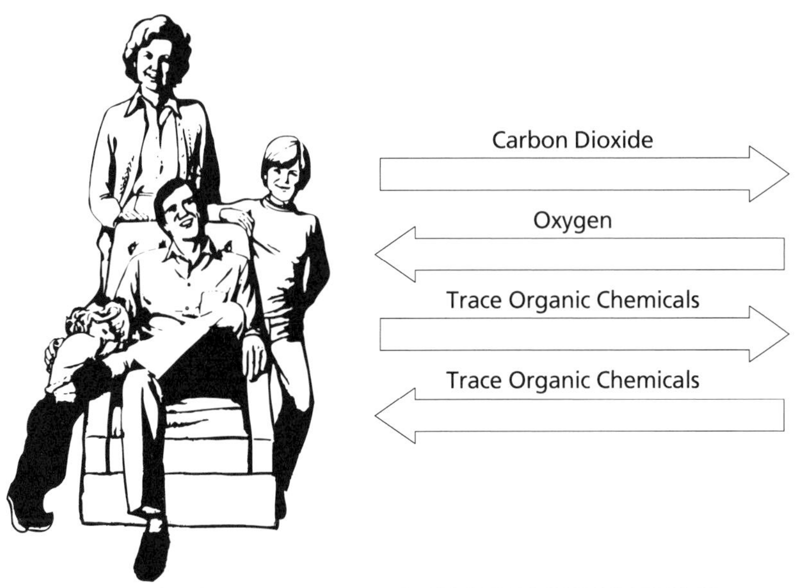

Figure 2. Man's interaction with his environment—plants, soil, microorganisms, and water.
By means of respiration alone, man releases over 100 volatile chemicals into the atmosphere, plants also discharge chemicals such as hydrocarbons, aldehydes, alcohols, ketones, and esters into the atmosphere. Plants, and the microbial-rich soil in which they grow, can remove from the atmosphere air pollutants produced by other plants, man and industry.

CHEMICALS USED IN THE PLANT SCREENING TESTS

Benzene

Benzene is a very commonly used solvent and is also present in many basic items including gasoline, inks, oils, paints plastics, and rubber. In addition, it is used in the manufacture of detergents, explosives, pharmaceuticals, and dyes.

Benzene has long been known to irritate the skin and eyes. Furthermore it has been shown to be mutagenic to bacterial cell cultures and has shown embryotoxic activity and carcinogenicity in some tests. Evidence also exists that benzene may be a contributing factor to chromosomal aberrations and leukemia in humans. Repeated skin contact with benzene causes drying, inflammation, blistering, and dermatitis. Acute inhalation of high levels of benzene has been reported to cause dizziness, weakness, euphoria, headache, nausea, blurred vision, respiratory diseases, tremors, irregular heartbeat, liver and kidney damage, paralysis, and unconsciousness. In animal tests, inhalation of benzene led to cataract formation and diseases of the blood and lymphatic systems. Chronic exposure to even relatively low levels causes headaches, loss of appetite, drowsiness, nervousness, psychological disturbances, and diseases of the blood system, including anemia and bone marrow disease.

Trichloroethylene

Trichloroethylene (TCE) is a commercial product with a wide variety of industrial uses. Over 90 percent of the TCE produced is used in the metal degreasing and dry-cleaning industries, but it is also used in printing inks, paints, lacquers, varnishes, and adhesives. In 1975, the National Cancer Institute reported that an unusually high incidence of hepatocellular carcinomas was observed in mice given TCE by gastric intubation. The Institute considers this chemical a potent liver carcinogen.

Formaldehyde

Formaldehyde is a ubiquitous chemical found in virtually all indoor environments. The major sources, which have been reported and publicized, include urea-formaldehyde foam insulation (UFFI) and particle board or pressed-wood products. Consumer paper products, including grocery bags, waxed papers, facial tissues, and paper towels, are treated with urea-formaldehyde (UF) resins. Many common household cleaning agents contain formaldehyde. UF resins are used as stiffeners, wrinkle resisters, water repellants, fire retardants, and adhesive-binders in floor covering, carpet backing, and permanent-press clothes. Other sources of formaldehyde include cigarette smoke and heating and cooking fuels such as natural gas and kerosene.

Formaldehyde irritates the mucous membranes of the eyes, nose, and throat. It is a highly reactive chemical that combines with protein and can cause allergic contact dermatitis. The most widely reported symptoms from exposure to high levels of this chemical include irritation of the upper respiratory tract and eyes and headaches. (2,3) Until recently, the most serious disease attributed to formaldehyde exposure was asthma. *However, the Environmental Protection Agency (EPA) has recently conducted research which indicates that formaldehyde* is strongly suspected of causing a rare type of throat cancer in long-term occupants of mobile homes.

MATERIALS AND METHODS

The following ALCA plants were screened:

Common Name	Scientific Name
Bamboo palm	*Chamaedorea seifritzii*
Chinese evergreen	*Aglaonema modestum*
English ivy	*Hedera helix*
Ficus	*Ficus benjamina*
Gerbera daisy	*Gerbera jomesonii*
Janet Craig	*Dracaena deremensis "Janet Craig"*
Marginata	*Dracaena marginata*
Mass cane/Corn cane	*Dracaena massangeana*
Mother-in-law's tongue	*Sansevieria laurentii*
Peace lily	*Spathiphyllum "Mauna Loa"*
Pot mum	*Chrysanthemum morifolium*
Warneckei	*Dracaena deremensis "Warneckei"*

All plants tested were obtained from nurseries in our local area. They were kept in their original pots and potting soil, just as they were received from the nursery, and were maintained in a greenhouse between tests. Stern's Miracle-Gro fertilizer was used to keep the plants in a healthy condition for the project.

Chemical contamination tests were conducted in four Plexiglas chambers, which were constructed to the following dimensions:

	Width	Depth	Height
Two chambers measuring	0.76	0.76	0.76
	(30)	(30)	(30)
Two larger chambers measuring	0.76	0.76	1.53
	(30)	(30)	(60.5)

Each dimension is given in meters (m); the equivalent in inches (in.) is given in parentheses.

The tops of the small chambers and side sections of the large chambers were removed to allow entry. Bolts and wing-nuts *ensured complete scaling of the lids and created airtight* chambers for testing. Constant illumination was provided during the testing from a bank of Damar Gro-lights *that encircled the outside of each chamber. Mounted on the inside* of each chamber has a coil of copper tubing through which water at a temperature of 7°C was circulated. This cooling coil prevented the Gro-lights from causing excessive heat buildup inside the chambers and minimized any fogging from plant respiration in the chambers. The chambers also contained two small removable ports, each 0.6 cm (1/4 in.) in diameter, through which contaminants could be introduced and air samples could be obtained. A small fan was used to circulate air within each chamber.

All tests were conducted for a period of 24 h. Experimental testing included sealing a selected plant in the Plexiglas chamber, injecting one of the three chemicals into the chamber in the method described below, and collecting air samples immediately following chemical introduction, at 6 h and, finally, 24 h later. Leak test controls, wherein the same chemicals were injected into an empty, sealed chamber, were conducted periodically throughout the study. In addition, soil controls without plants were tested to determine if the potting soil and associated microorganisms were effective in removing the different chemicals. These control tests were conducted by using pots of the same size containing the same potting soil as the potted plants used in actual testing. Experimental procedure then followed the same order as described above.

Benzene testing at high concentrations was performed by introducing 35 L of benzene into the chamber using a 50-mL microsyringe. The benzene was injected onto a small metal tray attached to the chamber wall just below the introduction port and allowed to evaporate with the help of the fan inside the chamber. A period of 30 min was allowed for complete evaporation of the benzene prior to withdrawing the initial sample.

Sampling was done with a Sensidyne-Gastec air sampling pump and gas detector tubes specific for benzene concentrations ranging between 1 and 100 p/m. In sampling, a 200-mL volume of air from the chamber was drawn through a Gastec tube. Detection of a color change in the benzene-specific indicator reagent present in the tube measured the concentration of benzene.

Introduction and sampling of TCE was performed in a similar manner, except that the indicating reagent in the Gastec tubes was specific for TCE. The levels of TCE that could be detected ranged from 1 to 25 p/m.

Because formaldehyde is a water-soluble chemical and is routinely supplied as a 37.9 percent solution in water, it was necessary to utilize a different method to introduce this chemical into the test chambers. The formaldehyde solution was placed into a gas scrubber apparatus, which was attached to both an air pump and to the chamber sample inlet using pieces of Tygon tubing. Air was bubbled through the formaldehyde solution and introduced into the chamber as a gas. The time necessary to achieve the desired concentrations of formaldehyde in the two chambers was determined experimentally to be 50 s for the small chamber and 120 s for the large chamber. Sampling was performed in the same manner as that used for benzene and TCE using a Sensidyne-Gastec air pump and formaldehyde-specific tubes. The detection range of the formaldehyde-specific tubes was 2 to 20 p/m.

Because the Sensidyne-Gastec equipment was not sensitive enough for testing less than 1 p/m concentrations, a gas chromatographic method was developed for low-concentration analysis of benzene and TCE simultaneously in a single sample. For the low-concentration benzene-TCE studies, two chambers of similar size were used, having volumes of 0.868 and 0.694 m3. Benzene and TCE were introduced into the chambers using a 1-μL volume of an equal volume mixture of benzene and TCE. The sample was injected onto a Kimwipe tissue and allowed to evaporate for a 30-min period before the initial sampling. Sampling was performed by using the air pump to withdraw 200 mL of air through a glass tube containing Tenax adsorbent. The samples were analyzed promptly using a Supelco air desorption unit interfaced to a Hewlett-Packard (HP) Model 5890 gas chromatograph (GC) equipped with an HP Ultra capillary column and flame ionization detector.

GAS CHROMATOGRAPH-MASS SELECTIVE DETECTOR ANALYSIS FOR TRACE METABOLITES

After chemical injection, 500-mL air samples were collected from the chambers onto 1 8-cm (7-in.) by 0.6-cm (1/1-in.) outside diameter stainless steel tubes packed with Tenax adsorbent, using the Sensidyne-Gastec air pump. Trace chemical contaminants were desorbed from the Tenax tubes using a Tekmar Model 5000 automatic desorber into a HP 5890 GC equipped with a 30-m, 0.32-mm inside diameter, Restek Rtx–volatiles capillary column. The GC oven was initially cooled to 0°C using carbon dioxide, and then followed a temperature program beginning at 0°C, with a 30-s hold at 0°C, and a rise in temperature of 8 °C/min. The program ended when the temperature reached 200°C, for a total run time of 25.5 min. After separation on the GC, the sample entered an HP 5970 mass selective detector. Analysis of the sample was conducted using a scanning range of 35 to 400 atomic mass units.

MICROBIOLOGICAL ANALYSIS

Using both potted plants and potting soil controls, 1-g samples of soil were taken from surface and subsurface regions (approximately 10 cm in depth). Samples were subsequently analyzed by means of the pour plate technique to determine the number of "colony forming units" per gram of sample (cfu/g). Plate count agar (PCA) was utilized as the primary microbiological medium. Plate count data reflect bacteriological counts.

Triplicate samples were taken both before and after exposure of the plants and soil to benzene and TCE. Following incubation at 25°C for 24 h, samples were examined for the presence of bacteria. Due to the inherently slower growth rate of fungi and actinomycetes, these microorganisms cannot be detected until three to five days of incubation have elapsed. After plate count data were recorded, both bacterial and fungal samples were isolated. Stock cultures were maintained on PCA and Sabouraud's dextrose agar, respectively. Bacterial isolates were then subjected to a series of biochemical tests in order to aid in preliminary identification. Fungal isolates were examined by light microscopy to search for the presence of asexual and sexual spores.

ACTIVATED CARBON HOUSEPLANT AIR FILTER SYSTEM

Air filters designed as shown in Figure 1 were tested in one of the large Plexiglas chambers for simultaneous removal of benzene and TCE. Benzene and TCE in 500-L volumes were injected onto a Kimwipe tissue taped inside the chamber and were allowed to evaporate for 5 min. Complete volatilization occurred and 100-mL air samples were drawn, using a Tenax tube and air pump. Analysis followed on the Supelco desorber and HP GC that have been previously described. Samples were drawn initially and at 15-min intervals for a minimum of 2 h, or until all trace chemicals were removed.

RESULTS AND DISCUSSION

The ability of houseplants or potting soil to remove benzene, TCE, and formaldehyde from sealed experimental chambers is demonstrated in Tables 1 through 8. The screening of plants shown in Tables 1 through 3 was accomplished during the first year of studies, while data shown in Tables 1 through 8 were collected during the second and final year of this project.

Plants in Tables 1 through 4 were exposed to high concentrations of chemicals, in the 1 to 20 p/m range. Although these exposures gave a good indication of which plants might be particularly suited to the removal of one or more of these chemicals, they are far above the levels commonly found in indoor atmospheres. During the final year of this project, investigations were conducted using low concentrations of benzene and TCE (less than 1 p/m) and more sophisticated analytical methods. Results from these studies are shown in Tables 5 through 8.

Table 1. Trichloroethylene (TCE) Removed from a Sealed Experimental Chamber by Houseplants During a 24-h Exposure Period

	Total Plant Leaf Surface Area (cm^2)	Total Micrograms Removed per Plant
Gerbera daisy (Gerbera jamesonii)	4,581	38,938
English ivy (Hedera helix)	981	7,161
Marginata (Dracaena marginata)	7,581	27,292
Peace lily (Spathiphyllum "Mauna Loa")	7,960	27,064
Mother-in-law's tongue (Sansevieria laurentii)	3,474	9,727
Warneckei (Dracaena deremensis "Warneckei")	7,242	13,760
Bamboo palm (Chamaedorea seifritzii)	10,325	16,520
Mass cane (Dracaena massangeana)	7,215	10,101
Janet Craig (Dracaena deremensis "Janet Craig")	15,275	18,330

Table 2. Benzene Removed from a Sealed Experimental Chamber by Houseplants During a 24-h Exposure Period

	Total Plant Leaf Surface Area (cm^2)	Total Micrograms Removed per Plant
Gerbera daisy (Gerbera jamesonii)	4,581	107,653
Pot mum (Chrysanthemum morifolium)	4,227	76,931
English ivy (Hedera helix)	1,336	13,894
Mother-in-law's tongue (Sansevieria laurentii)	2,871	28,710
Warneckei (Dracaena deremensis "Warneckei")	7,242	39,107
Peace lily (Spathiphyllum "Mauna Loa")	7,960	41,392
Chinese evergreen (Aglaonema "Silver Queen")	3,085	14,500
Marginata (Dracaena marginata)	7,581	30,324
Bamboo palm (Chamaedorea seifritzii)	10,325	34,073
Janet Craig (Dracaena deremensis "Janet Craig")	15,275	25,968

Table 3. Formaldehyde Removed from a Sealed Experimental Chamber by Houseplants and Soil During a 24-h Exposure Period

	Total Plant Leaf Surface Area (cm^2)	Total Micrograms Removed per Plant
Banana (Musa oriana)	1000	11,700
Mother-in-law's tongue (Sansevieria laurentii)	2,871	31,294
English ivy (Hedera helix)	985	9,653
Bamboo palm (Chamaedorea seifritzii)	14,205	76,707
Heart leaf philodendron (Philodendron oxycardium)	1,696	8,480
Elephant Ear Philodendron (Philodendron domesticum)	2,323	9,989
Green spider plant (Chlorophytum elatum)	2,471	10,378
Golden pothos (Scindapsus aureus)	2,723	8,986
Janet Craig (Dracaena deremensis "Janet Craig")	15,275	48,880
Marginata (Dracaena marginata)	7,581	20,469
Peace lily (Spathiphyllum "Mauna Loa")	8,509	16,167
Lacy tree philodendron (Philodendron selloum)	2,373	8,656
Chinese evergreen (Aglaonema modestum)	1,894	4,382
Aloe vera	713	1,555

Table 4. Chemicals Removed by Household Plants from a Sealed Experimental Chamber During a 24-h Exposure Period

	Formaldehyde			Benzene			Trichloroethylene		
	Initial (p/m)	Final (p/m)	Percent Removed	Initial (p/m)	Final (p/m)	Percent Removed	Initial (p/m)	Final (p/m)	Percent Removed
Mass cane	20	6	70	14	11	21.4	16	14	12.5
Pot mum	18	7	61	58	27	53	17	10	41.2
Gerber daisy	16	8	50	65	21	67.7	20	13	35
Warneckei.	8	4	50	27	13	52	20	18	10
Ficus	19	10	47.4	20	14	30	19	17	10.5
Leak control	18	17.5	2.8	20	19	5	20	18	10

Note: Plants were maintained in a commercial type greenhouse until ready for testing. Each test, 24 h in duration, was conducted in a sealed chamber with temperature and light intensity of 30°C +1 and 125 footcandles +5, respectively.

Table 5. Benzene Removal from a Sealed Experimental Chamber by Houseplants During a 24-h Exposure Period

	Initial (p/m)	Final (p/m)	Percent Removed
English ivy	0.235	0.024	89.8
Janet Craig	0.432	0.097	77.6
Golden pothos	0.127	0.034	73.2
Peace lily	0.166	0.034	79.5
Chinese evergreen	0.204	0.107	47.6
Marginata	0.176	0.037	79.0
Mother-in-law's tongue	0.156	0.074	52.6
Warneckei	0.182	0.055	70.0
Leak test control	0.171	0.162	5.3
Soil control	0.119	0.095	20.1

Table 6. Trichloroethylene (TCE) Removal from a Sealed Experimental Chamber by Houseplants During a 24-h Exposure Period

	Initial (p/m)	Final (p/m)	Percent Removed
English ivy	0.174	0.155	109
Janet Craig	0.321	0 265	17.5
Golden pothos	0.207	0.188	9.2
Peace lily	0.126	0.097	23 0
Warneckei	0.114	0.091	20.2
Marginata	0136	0118	13.2
Mother-in-law's tongue	0.269	0.233	13.4
Leak test control	0.121	0.120	< 1.0
Soil control	0.141	0.128	9.2

During the first-year studies, the only controls used were chambers free of plants to test for loss of chemicals from chamber leakage and pots with fresh potting soil without plants. It was then assumed that after correcting for controls, the removal of chemicals from the sealed chambers could be attributed to the plant leaves. Because of the low photosynthetic and metabolic rates expected from these plants at light levels of 125 to 150 footcandles, the high chemical removal rates attributed to these low-light-requiring houseplants were puzzling.

In an effort to determine the exact mechanism(s) involved in chemical removal from the plant-soil system, plants were tested with foliage and then the same pots and soil were tested again after removing all foliage. Controls using full plant foliage with pca gravel covering the soil were also tested (Table 7). A microbiologist was brought into these studies to determine the microbial profile found in the potting soils.

Early tests demonstrated that potting soil, after all foliage had been removed, was more effective in removing benzene than pots containing full foliage and soil. However, further studies and careful observation determined that this phenomenon occurred only when large amounts of foliage covered the potting soil surface, reducing contact between the soil and the air inside the chamber. Thus, some of the lower leaves were removed, allowing maximum contact between the soil-root zone and the chamber air containing toxic chemicals. Results of these new studies are shown in Tables 7 and 8.

Table 7. Benzene Removal from a Sealed Experimental Chamber by Houseplants in Potting Soil and the Same Potting Soil After Removing all Plant Foliage During 24-h Exposure Periods

	Initial (p/m)	Final (p/m)	Percent Removed
Marginata			
Full foliage	0.343	0.144	58.0
Foliage removed	0.348	0.175	49.7
Fresh potting soil control	0.206	0.164	20.4
Leak test, empty chamber control	0.215	0.199	
Marginata			
Full foliage	0.176	0.037	79.0
Full foliage and soil covered with pea gravel	0.205	0.069	66.3
Janet Craig			
Full foliage	0.369	0.077	79.1
Foliage removed	0.321	0.176	45.2
Golden pothos			
Full foliage	0.122	0.040	67.2
Foliage removed	0.175	0.062	64.6
Fresh potting soil control	0.099	0.091	8.1
Leak test, empty chamber control	0.262	0.254	3.1

Table 8. Benzene Removal and Soil Bacterial Counts of a Chinese Evergreen Plant After Being Exposed for Several 24-h Periods to Benzene in a Sealed Experimental Chamber

	Percent Removed	Soil Bacterial Counts (cfu/g)
Initial exposure	47.6	3.1×10^4
After six weeks of intermittent exposure	85.8	5.1×10^4

Although the bacterial counts correlated with increased chemical removal in some of the studies as shown in Table 8, this finding was not consistent. Therefore, other yet unidentified biological factors may also be important. Data from this two-year study indicate that when the same plants and potting soil are constantly exposed to air containing such toxic chemicals as benzene, their capacity to continuously clean the air improves as shown in Table 8. This is not surprising, since it is a well-established fact that microorganisms have the ability to genetically adapt, thereby increasing their ability to utilize toxic chemicals as a food source when continuously exposed to such chemicals. This phenomenon is currently used to remove toxic chemicals from wastewater. (31-37)

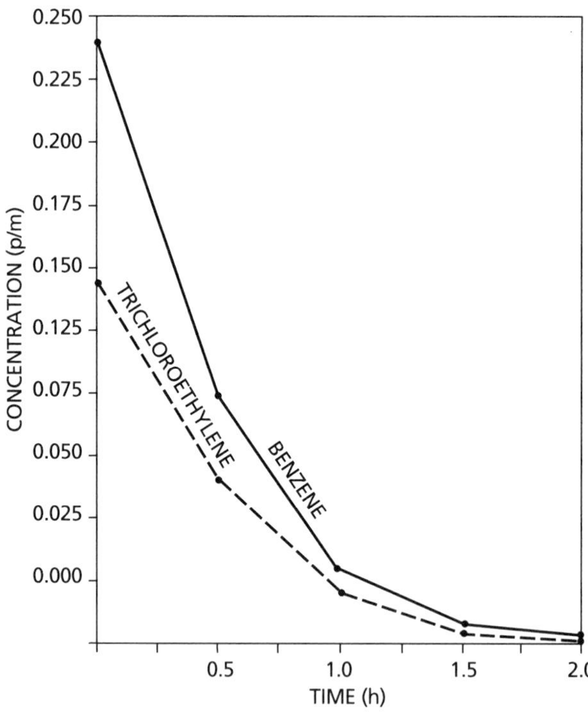

Figure 3. Removal of low concentrations of benzene and trichloroethylene from the air inside sealed experimental chambers using golden pothos in an 8-in. activated carbon filter system.

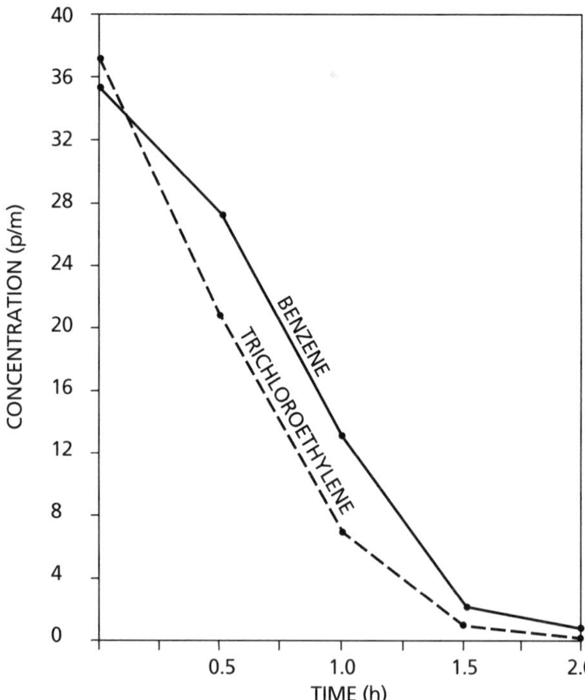

Figure 4. Removal of high concentrations of benzene and trichloroethylene from the air inside sealed experimental chambers using golden pothos in an 8-in. activated carbon filter system.

Bacterial isolates found in the soil in which mother-in-law's tongue had been growing for a long period were Alcigenes, Bacillus, Curtobacterium, Flavobacterium, Micrococcus, Myxococcus, and Pseudomonas. Arthobacter, Bacillus, and Leuconostoc were found in the marginata root soil. Bacteria such as Bacillus, Flavobacterium. Leuconostoc, and Micrococcus were also found in the Chinese evergreen potting soil. The peace lily potting soil contained Aurobacterium, Bacillus, Curtobacterium, Micrococcus, Pseudomonas, and Streptomyces. These are common soil microorganisms and most are known to be capable of biodegrading toxic chemicals when activated by plant root growth.

Results of the activated carbon-houseplant studies are shown in Figures 3 and 4. Although this research effort was not part of the NASA-ALCA two-year study, it is an essential component in the development of an indoor air pollution control system with plants to remove high concentrations of pollutants such as cigarette smoke and organic solvents. This biological system also utilizes plant roots and their associated microorganisms to purify indoor air; it differs from the potted plant study reported here in that a fan is used to rapidly move large volumes of air through an activated carbon filter. This filter absorbs air pollutants and holds them until the plant roots and microorganisms can utilize them as a food source; therefore, biogenerating the carbon.

To assure that no disease-causing microorganisms were released into the room from the carbon-plant filter, exhaust air from the filters was analyzed for microorganisms. To date, no pathogenic microorganisms have been found in the filter exhaust air.

It is common knowledge that plants give off trace levels of organic chemicals under certain conditions, so metabolic off-gassing studies were conducted by screening several of the ALCA plants. These low-light-requiring plants were normally maintained at relatively low metabolic rates; therefore, one would not expect significant off-gassing of ethylene, terpenes, or any other metabolite. Gas chromatograph-mass selective detector studies using Tenax adsorption tubes to analyze the air inside the sealed experimental chamber indicated that the levels of plant metabolites were negligible.

As temperature and light levels are increased, it is expected that indoor pollution removal rates will increase along with some plant metabolite off-gassing. Increased oxygen production and carbon dioxide removal should also increase the rate of leaf participation in the removal rates of trace volatile organic chemicals.

Studies of the beneficial or detrimental effects on man of volatile plant metabolites in a closed system have been limited. However, available data do not demonstrate that harmful effects can be expected in complete ecological closure involving man, plants, and some microorganisms. NASA studies at Stennis Space Center, private studies by Biosphere 2 in Arizona, and USSR studies in Siberia are beginning to present a clearer picture of what man can expect to experience when sealed inside facilities with plants and soil as his major means of life support.

SUMMARY

Low-light-requiring houseplants, along with activated carbon plant filters, have demonstrated the potential for improving indoor air quality by removing trace organic pollutants from the air in energy-efficient buildings. This plant system is one of the most promising means of alleviating the sick building syndrome associated with many new, energy efficient buildings. The plant-root-soil zone appears to be the most effective area for removing volatile organic chemicals. Therefore, maximizing air exposure to the plant root-soil area should be considered when placing plants in buildings for best air filtration.

Activated carbon filters containing fans have the capacity for rapidly filtering large volumes of polluted air and should be considered an integral part of any plan using houseplants for solving indoor air pollution problems.

ACKNOWLEDGMENTS

The authors wish to recognize the technical contribution of Willard L. Douglas, Ph.D., and the editorial contribution of Yvonne Travis to the preparation of this report.

REFERENCES

1. National Aeronautics and Space Administration. 1974. *Proceedings of the Skylab Life Sciences Symposium, August* 27-29, 1974. NASA TM-X-58 154. Johnson Space Center. I61-68.

2. Gammage, R.B. and S.V. Kaye, eds. 1984. Indoor Air and Human Health. *Proceedings of the Seventh Life Sciences Symposium,* October 29-31, 1981. Chelsea, Mich.: Lewis Publishers, Inc.

3. Walsh, C., S. Dudney, and E.D. Copenhauer. 1984. Indoor Air Quality. Boca Raton. Fla.: CRC Press, Inc.

4. Wallace, L., S. Brombert, E. Pellizzari, T. Hartwell, H. Zelon, and L. Sheldon. 1981. Plan and preliminary results of the U.S. Environmental Protection Agency's indoor air monitoring program (1982). In *Indoor Air*. Stockholm: Swedish Council for Building Research. 1:173-78.

5. Pellizzari, E.D., M.D. Erickson, M.T. Giguere, T. Hartwell, S.R. Williams, C.M. Sparacino, H. Zelon, and R.D. Waddell. 1980. Preliminary Study of Toxic Chemicals in Environmental Human Samples: Work Plan, vols. I and 2, Phase 1. Washington: U.S. EPA.

6. Pellizzari, E.D., M.D. Erickson, C.M. Sparacino, T. Hartwell, H. Zelon, M. Rosenweig, and C. Leininger. 1981. Total Exposure Assessment Methodology (TEAM) Study, Phase II: Work Plan. Washington: U.S. EPA.

7. Wallace, L., R. Zweidinger, M. Erickson, S. Cooper, D. Wittaker, and E. Pellizzari. 1982. Monitoring individual exposure: measurements of volatile organic compounds in breathing-zone air, drinking water, and exhaled breath. *Env. Inr.* 8:269-82.

8. Pellizzari, E.D., T. Hanwell, C. Leininger, H. Zelon, S. Williams, J. Breen, and L. Wallace. 1983. Human exposure to vapor-phase halogenated hydrocarbons: fixed site vs. personal exposure. *Proceedings from Symposium on Ambient, Source, and Exposure Monitoring Systems Lab.*, EPA 600/99-83-007. Washington: U.S. EPA.

9. Wallace, L., E. Pellizzari, T. Hanwell, M. Rosenweig, M. Erickson, C. Sparacino, and H. Zelon. 1984. Personal exposure to volatile organic compounds: I. direct measurement in breathing-zone air, drinking water, food and exhaled breath. *Env. Res.* 35:193-211.

10. Pellizzari, E., T. Hartwell, C. Sparacino, C. Shelson, R. Whitmore, C. Leininger, and H. Zelon. 1984. Total Exposure Assessment Methodology (TEAM) Study: First Season. Northern New Jersey—Interim Report. Contract No. 68-02-3679. Washington: U.S. EPA.

11. Hartwell, T., R.L. Perritt, H.X. Zelon, R.W. Whitmore, E.D. Pellizzari, and L. Wallace. 1984. Comparison of indoor and outdoor levels of air volatiles in New Jersey. In *Indoor Air.* Stockholm: Swedish Council for Building Research. 4:81-86.

12. Pellizzari, E., C. Sparacino, L. Sheldon, C. Leininger, H. Zelon, T. Hartwell, and L. Wallace. 1981. In *Indoor Air.* Stockholm: Swedish Council for Building Research. 4:221-26.

13. Wallace, L., E. Pellizzari, T. Hanwell, H. Zelon, C. Sparacino, and R. Whitmore, 1988. Analysis of exhaled breath of 355 urban residents for volatile organic compounds. In *Indoor Air.* Stockholm: Swedish Council for Building Research. 4:15-20.

14. Hartwell, T., H.X. Zelon, C.C. Leininger, C.A. Clayton, J.H. Crowder, and E.D. Pellizzari. Comparative statistical analysis for volatile halocarbons in indoor and outdoor air. In *Indoor Air.* Stockholm: Swedish Council for Building Research. 4:57-62.

15. Molhave, L., and J. Moller. 1979 The atmospheric environment in modern Danish dwellings: measurements in 39 flats. In *Indoor Air.* Copenhagen: Danish Building Research Institute. 171-186.

16. Lebret, E.H., J. Van de Wiel, H.P. Box, D. Noij, and S.M. Boleij. 1984. Volatile hydrocarbons in Dutch homes. In *Indoor Air.* Stockholm: Swedish Council for Building Research. 4:169-74.

17. Seifert, B., and H.J. Abraham. 1982. Indoor air concentrations of benzene and some other aromatic hydrocarbons. *Ecotoxicol. Environ. Safety* 6:190-92.

18. De Bortoli, M., H. Knoppel, E. Pecchio, A. Peil, L. Rogora, H. Schauenberg, H. Schlitt, and H. Vissers. 1984. Integrating "real life" measurements of organic pollution in indoor and outdoor air of homes in northern Italy. In *Indoor Air.* Stockholm: Swedish Council for Building Research. 4:21-26.

19. Gammage, R.B., D.A. White, and K.C. Gupta. 1984. Residential measurements of high volatility organics and their sources. In *Indoor Air.* Stockholm: Swedish Council for Building Research. 4:157-62.

20. Monteith, D.K., T.H. Stock, and W.E. Seifert, Jr. 1984. Sources and characterization of organic air contaminants inside manufactured housing. In *Indoor Air.* Stockholm: Swedish Council for Building Research. 4:285-90.

21. National Research Council, Committee on Toxicology. 1980. Formaldehyde—an assessment of its health effects. Washington: National Academy of Sciences.

22. National Research Council, Committee on Aldehydes. 1981. Formaldehyde and other aldehydes. Washington: National Academy Press.

23. National Research Council, Committee on Indoor Pollutants. 1981. Indoor pollutants. Washington: National Academy Press.

24. Nero, A.V., Jr. 1988. Controlling indoor air pollution. *Scientific American* 258(5):42-48.

25. Marklein, M.B. 1989. Taking a healthy day from work, Contaminants in our Office May Be Making You Sick . *Washington Business Journal Magazine.* April, 29-33.

26. Sheldon, L.S., R.W. Handy, T. Hartwell, R.W. Whitmore, H.S. Zelon, and E.D. Pellizari. 1988. Indoor Air Quality in Public Buildings, vol. 1. EPA 600/6-88-009a. Washington: Office of Acid Deposition, Monitoring and Quality Assurance.

27. Sheldon, L., H. Zelon, J. Sickles, C. Eaton, and T. Hartwell. 1988. Indoor Air Quality in Public Buildings, vol. 2. EPA 600/6-88-009b, Research Triangle Park, N.C.: Office of Research and Development.

28. Wolverton, B.C., R.C. McDonald. and E.A. Watkins, Jr. 1984. Foliage plants for removing indoor air pollutants from energy efficient homes. *Econ. Bol.* 38.

29. Wolverton, B.C., R.C. McDonald, and H.H. Mesick. 1985. Foliage plants for the indoor removal of the primary combustion gases carbon dioxide and nitrogen dioxide. J. *Miss. Acad. Sci.* 30:1-8.

30. Wolverton, C. 1987. Artificial marshes for wastewater treatment. In *Aquaria plants for wastewater treatment and resource recovery.* K.R. Reddy and W.H. Smith, eds., 141-52. Orlando, Fla.: Magnolia Publishing.

31. Wolverton, B.C. 1987. Natural systems for wastewater treatment and water reuse for space and earthly applications. In *Proceedings of American Water Works Association Research Foundation, Water Reuse Symposium IV,* August 2-7, 1987, 729-741. Denver, CO.

32. Wolverton, B.C. 1987. Aquatic plants for wastewater treatment: an overview. In *Aquatic plants for wastewater treatment and resource recovery. K.R.* Reddy and W.H. Smith, eds., 3-15. Orlando, Fla: Magnolia Publishing.

33. Wolverton, B.C., and B.K. Bounds. 1988. Aquatic plants for pH adjustment and removal of toxic chemicals and dissolved minerals from water supplies. J. *Miss. Acad. Sci.,* 33:71 -80.

34. Wolverton, B.C., and R.C. McDonald-McCaleb. 1986. Biotransformation of priority pollutants using biofilms and vascular plants. J. *Miss. Acad. Sci.,* 31:79-89.

35. Wolverton, B.C., and R.C. McDonald. 1981. Natural processes for treatment of organic chemical waste. *The Environ. Prof.* 3:99-104.

36. McCaleb, R.C., and B.K. Bounds. 1987. Biological activated carbon. In: *Proceedings of American Water Works Association Research Foundation, Water Reuse Symposium* IV, August 2-8, 1987, 1301-16. Denver, CO.

37. Gitelson, J.I., B.G. Kovrov, G.M. Lisovskig, Yu. N. Okladnikov, M.S. Rerberg, F. Ya Sidko, and I.A. Terskvo. 1975. *Problems of Space Biology. Vol.* 28, *Experimental Ecological Systems Including Man, 1-312.* Navka Press, Moscow.

NOTES

NOMENCLATURE

Hortus Third (first edition, 1976) is the primary source used in this text for horticultural reference. Correlations of common and botanical names refer to *Hortus Third* whenever applicable, as does the spelling of common and botanical names. As such, the genera of all plants are capitalized; while species are usually presented in lower case (e.g., *Aglaonema commutatum*). Exceptions to this are as indicated in *Hortus Third*. Common names of families or genera are presented in lowercase; while common names of species are capitalized (e.g., fern, Table Fern). This may create contradictions to accepted practice in the interior landscape industry, for many nurseryworkers growing plant materials for interior use routinely label products listed in Hortus Third under other names which have become widely used, and, of course, many new species have been introduced since the publication of *Hortus Third*.

ABBREVIATIONS

ASTM = American Society for Testing and Materials
CF = cubic foot
cm = centimeter
fc = footcandle
ft = foot
hp = horsepower
in = inch
IPM = integrated pest management
kg/CM = kilograms per cubic meter
lbs/CF = pounds per cubic foot
LF = linear foot
m = meter
mm = millimeter
ppp. = plants per pot
SF = square foot
SM = square meter
spp. = species

METRIC EQUIVALENTS

1 centimeter	=	0.3937 inch
1 foot	=	0.3048 meter
1 inch	=	2.54 centimeters
1 meter	=	3.2808 feet
1 square centimeter	=	0.1550 square inches
1 square inch	=	6.4516 square centimeters
1 square meter	=	10.7639 square feet

DIMENSIONS

Dimensions are listed in inches and feet. Corresponding metric dimensions are also provided, in centimeters and meters, respectively in parentheses. Example: 6 in (15.2 cm). All conversions are typically to the nearest tenth of a centimeter or meter.

All linear dimensions can be calculated with these two basic conversion factors:

1" = 2.54 cm

1' = 0.3048 m

To convert centimeters to inches, or meters to feet, use the reciprocals of these conversions:

$1 \text{ cm} = \frac{1}{2.54}$ in, or $0.3937 \pm$ in

$1 \text{ m} = \frac{1}{0.3048}$ ft, or $3.2808 \pm$ ft

INDEX

A

B

E

F

N

O

P

T

U

V

W

Y

Z

PROJECT CREDITS

Figs. 1-1, C9-1 through C9-6, 9-4 through 9-9
Project: Ford Foundation, New York City, New York
Interior Landscape Designer: Office of Dan Kiley, Charlotte, Vermont Interior Landscape Contractor: The Everett Conklin Companies, Montvale, New Jersey

Figs. 2-3, C8-6
Project: Mine Safety and Appliance Corporate Headquarters, Pittsburgh, Pennsylvania
Interior Landscape Designer: Joseph A. Hajnes & Associates, Pittsburgh, Pennsylvania Interior Landscape Contractor: Plantscape, Inc., Pittsburgh, Pennsylvania

Figs. 2-4a, C8-1
Project: Opryland Hotel, Nashville, Tennessee
Interior Landscape Designer: Schumm, Werle & Maxian, Nashville, Tennessee
Interior Landscape Contractor: Rentokil Tropical Plants, Riverwoods, Illinois

Figs. 2-5, 2-44
Project: Household Finance Corporation Headquarters
Interior Landscape Designer: Wehler, Peterson & Associates, Chicago, Illinois
Interior Landscape Contractor: Rentokil Tropical Plants, Riverwoods, Illinois

Fig. 2-6
Project: Schaumberg Corporate Center, Schaumberg, Illinois
Interior Landscape Designer: Jacobs, Ryan Associates, Chicago, Illinois
Interior Landscape Contractor: Rentokil Tropical Plants, Riverwoods, Illinois

Fig. 2-7 and Back Cover
Project: Battery Park City, New York City, New York
Interior Landscape Designer: M. Paul Friedberg & Associates, New York City, New York
Interior Landscape Contractor: Parker Interior Plantscape, Scotch Plains, New Jersey

Figs. 2-8, 8-17
Project: CIGNA Corporation, Bloomfield, Connecticut
Interior Landscape Designer: The Architects Collaborative, Cambridge, Massachusetts
Interior Landscape Contractor: John Mini Indoor Landscapes, City Island, New York

Figs. 2-20, C8-8
Project: International Mineral and Chemical, Northbrook, Illinois
Interior Landscape Designer: Joe Karr & Associates, Chicago, Illinois
Interior Landscape Contractor: Rentokil Tropical Plants, Riverwoods, Illinois

Figs. 2-28, 8-10 through 8-12, 8-14, C9-7 through C9-14, 9-12, 9-13, 9-15 and Front Cover
Project: Copley Place Shopping Galleries, Boston, Massachusetts
Interior Landscape Designer: The Architects Collaborative, Cambridge, Massachusetts
Interior Landscape Contractor: Rentokil Tropical Plants, Riverwoods, Illinois

Fig. 2-40
Project: Chemical Bank's Chem Court, New York City, New York
Interior Landscape Designer: Haines, Lundberg, & Waehler, New York City, New York Interior Landscape Contractor: John Mini Indoor Landscapes, City Island, New York

Fig. 2-65
Project: Guest Quarters Suite Hotel, Santa Monica, California
Interior Landscape Designer: Earl R. Flansburgh + Associates, Boston, Massachusetts
Interior Landscape Contractor: Associated Plantscapers, Irvine, California

Figs. 8-16, C8-7
Project: Parkway North Center, Deerfield, Illinois
Interior Landscape Designer: Johnson, Johnson & Roy, Ann Arbor, Michigan
Interior Landscape Contractor: Rentokil Tropical Plants, Riverwoods, Illinois

Fig. 8-21
Project: Private Residence, Hidden Hills, California
Interior Landscape Designer: Stephen McCurdy, Inglewood, California
Interior Landscape Contractor: Landscape Images, Inglewood, California

Figs. 8-24, C8-10, C8-11
Project: Longwood Gardens, Kennett Square, Pennsylvania
Interior Landscape Designer and Contractor: Longwood Gardens

Figs. 8-25, 8-27
Project: Tropical Rain Forest, Franklin Park Zoo, Boston, Massachusetts
Interior Landscape Designer: Jerry Johnson Productions, Newton, Massachusetts
Interior Landscape Contractor: City Gardens, Newton, Massachusetts

Fig. C2-16
Project: The Landmark Condominiums, Braintree, Massachusetts
Interior Landscape Designer: Nelson Hammer, ASLA, Needham, Massachusetts
Interior Landscape Contractor: City Gardens, Newton, Massachusetts

Figs. C8-2, C8-3
Project: Hyatt Regency Hotel, Greenwich, Connecticut
Interior Landscape Designer: The Berkshire Design Group, Northampton, Massachusetts
Interior Landscape Contractor: Decora, Greenwich, Connecticut

Figs. C8-4, C8-5
Project: Embassy Suites Hotel, Deerfield, Illinois
Interior Landscape Designer: James Martin & Associates, Vernon Hill, Illinois
Interior Landscape Contractor: Rentokil Tropical Plants, Riverwoods, Illinois

Fig. C8-9
Project: John Deere West, Moline, Illinois
Interior Landscape Designer: Sasaki Associates, Watertown, Massachusetts
Interior Landscape Contractor: Rentokil Tropical Plants, Riverwoods, Illinois

Fig. C8-12 and Back Cover
Project: Tropics North, Montreal, Canada
Interior Landscape Designer: Proctor & Redfern, Tampa, Florida
Interior Landscape Contractor: Landscape Technologies, Clearwater, Florida

Fig. C8-13
Project: Enid A. Haupt Conservatory, New York Botanical Garden, Bronx, New York
Interior Landscape Designer and Contractor: New York Botanical Garden

Figs. C8-14, 8-28, 8-29
Project: Isabella Stewart Gardner Museum, Boston, Massachusetts
Interior Landscape Designer and Contractor: The Gardner Museum

Fig. C8-15
Project: Fulton County Government Center, Atlanta, Georgia
Interior Landscape Designer: M. Paul Friedberg & Partners, New York, New York
Interior Landscape Contractor: IPS, Marietta, Georgia

Figs. C9-15 through C9-17, 9-17 through 9-19
Project: Hyatt Regency Grand Cypress, Orlando, Florida
Interior Landscape Designer: Edward D. Stone, Jr. and Associates, Fort Lauderdale, Florida
Interior Landscape Contractor: Plantscape House, Orlando, Florida

Figs. C9-18 through C9-21, 9-23 through 9-27
Project: Private Residence, Mexico City
Interior Landscape Designer and Contractor: Muray Arquitectos, S.A., Mexico City, Mexico

Figs. C9-22 through C9-25, 9-34 through 9-37, 9-39
Project: John Hancock Child Care Center, Boston, Massachusetts
Interior Landscape Designer: Earl R. Flansburgh + Associates, Boston, Massachusetts
Interior Landscape Contractor: City Gardens, Newton, Massachusetts

Figs. CE-1, CE-2
Project: Corporate Executive Dining Area, Mexico City, Mexico
Interior Landscape Designer and Contractor: Muray Arquitectos, S.A., Mexico City, Mexico

Figs. CE-3, CE-4
Project: London Standard Chartered Bank, London, England
Interior Landscape Designer: Daniel Urban Kiley & Peter Ker Walker, Landscape Architects, Charlotte, Vermont
Interior Landscape Contractor: Rochford Nurseries, Broxbourne, England

Fig. CE-5
Project: Kuwait Fund for the Advancement of Science, Kuwait City, Kuwait
Interior Landscape Designer: The Architects Collaborative, Cambridge, Massachusetts

PHOTOGRAPHIC CREDITS

Specific credit has been noted for all photographs not provided by the author, with this caveat: I wish to gratefully acknowledge the assistance of the Associated Landscape Contractors of America; Roger Cheever of City Gardens; and Richard L. Gaines, AIA, author of Interior Plantscaping, Building Design for Foliage Plants, for the use of several photographs, copies of which have been assimilated into my personal collection over the years, which I unfortunately cannot specifically credit.